THE MENTAL GROWTH OF THE
PRE-SCHOOL CHILD

THE MENTAL GROWTH
OF THE
PRE-SCHOOL CHILD

A Psychological Outline of Normal
Development from Birth to the Sixth Year,
Including
A SYSTEM OF DEVELOPMENTAL DIAGNOSIS

BY

ARNOLD GESELL, Ph.D., M.D.
PROFESSOR OF CHILD HYGIENE
DIRECTOR OF YALE PSYCHO-CLINIC, YALE UNIVERSITY

*Illustrated with two hundred
Action Photographs*

New York
THE MACMILLAN COMPANY
1926

PRINTED IN THE UNITED STATES OF AMERICA BY
THE BERWICK & SMITH CO.

PREFACE

The scope of this volume is indicated by the subtitle. The basic data furnish an outline of the psychology of infancy, by bringing into systematic view cross-section behavior pictures of the ascending stages of development. The emphasis throughout is on the normal aspects of behavior. The application of norms of development to problems of developmental diagnosis and supervision is treated in the concluding sections.

The investigation on which this book is based was begun some six years ago and has put the writer under an increasing sense of indebtedness to many persons who have lent their assistance. The study is one which has required a considerable degree of coöperation. We have been particularly fortunate in the amount and kind of coöperation which we have received from numerous mothers—to say nothing of the several hundred children, whose contribution we hope is not altogether lost in the pages of this book.

The nurses of the Visiting Nurse Association of New Haven have been very helpful. We are also indebted, for various services, to the physicians of the pediatric division of the New Haven Dispensary.

I wish particularly to mention my obligation to the graduate students and clinical assistants of the Yale Psycho-Clinic who were most closely identified with the investigation. Mrs. Margaret Cobb Rogers served as clinical and research assistant from 1919 to 1921 and did much of the work involved in gathering and organizing the data relating to the age groups from 6 months to 18 months. Her successor, Miss Elizabeth E. Lord, has rendered equally unstinted assistance and made a thorough study of our four-year-old group of children. Mr. Leonard Muntz, Miss Sara M. Holbrook, and Miss Isabel Kearny wrote their essays for the degree of Master

v

of Arts at the Yale Graduate School in the field of pre-school psychology. Mr. Muntz made a study of "Individual Differences among Two-Year-Old Children"; Miss Holbrook made "A Psychological Study of a Group of Three-Year-Old Children"; and Miss Kearny wrote on "The Mental and Educational Status of a Group of Kindergarten Children." These studies, which were made under the direction of our clinic, have been consulted in the preparation of our data. Miss Elizabeth Lord and Miss Ruth Washburn, who has more recently become an assistant in the clinic, have both participated in the practical testing out of our diagnostic procedures on the problem and research cases which have come to the clinic. During the past year over one third of these clinical cases were of pre-school age.

The main body of this volume is devoted to a descriptive and normative treatment of data derived from a first-hand study of normal children. This part of the study has been supplied with illustrations and is so concrete that it may, perhaps, be of interest to the general reader, as well as to the parent or to the special worker who is directly concerned with the mental health and development of early childhood.

Much of the investigation described in the text was conducted incidentally to the regular activities of the Yale Psycho-Clinic. There have been some compensations in this, because our methods have been constantly put to the test of practical clinical application. They have had sufficient trial in actual clinical experience to warrant the belief that they will be useful to others.

The applied phases of the volume, we trust, will be serviceable to pediatricians, general medical practitioners, and mental examiners who are called upon to make responsible estimates of the developmental status of young children. The diagnostic norms and procedures have been presented in such a manner that they can scarcely be misapplied. The text lays ample emphasis upon the importance of trained observation and of clinical judgment.

The subject of Chapter 2, "The Significance of Pre-School Development," has been treated at greater length in the author's previous volume on "The Pre-School Child: from the Standpoint of Public Hygiene and Education." A portion of Chapter 27 was printed in *The Scientific Monthly* of April and May, 1922. Otherwise the subject matter of the present volume has not been hitherto published.

Current tendencies in child hygiene and education are bringing the pre-school years into a new perspective. There are scientific as well as practical reasons for giving special consideration to this foundational period of childhood. Our aim in the present volume is to give a systematic view of the entire pre-school period of development. We are conscious of the preliminary character and of the limitations of our data; but we probably have not over-emphasized the basic importance of the pre-school years of development.

ARNOLD GESELL

YALE UNIVERSITY
New Haven, Connecticut

TABLE OF CONTENTS

ix

0378532

TABLE OF CONTENTS

PART ONE

INTRODUCTION

Mental Growth of the Pre-School Child

CHAPTER 1

INTRODUCTORY SUMMARY

The mental development of the pre-school child, when treated in an objective manner, becomes a subject with both familiar and scientific aspects. Our task is to bring the familiar and the scientific into closer relation.

We have attempted a systematic survey of the ordinary and normal behavior of infancy and early childhood. In making this survey it has been our purpose to formulate the findings with sufficient concreteness to make them suitable for at least partial application. The characteristics of infancy are so changing and so fugitive that orderly information becomes a practical necessity.

The plan of this book is evident from the section headings of the table of contents. There are four parts. Parts I, II, and III are mainly descriptive and interpretative. They lie in the general field of genetic and comparative psychology. Part IV deals with practical applications in developmental diagnosis and supervision. The bulk of the text deals in one form or other with the norms and evidences of mental development.

Since this book considers the principles as well as the problems of developmental diagnosis, with special reference to the pre-school period of childhood, our discussion has required a rather formidable array of chapters. A summary glance at the whole field covered, it is hoped, will assist the reader to understand the arrangement and relations of these chapters.

For perspective we must grant, at the outset, that the pre-school period exceeds all other epochs in developmental importance. This period occupies approximately the first seventy months of the scriptural allotment of seventy years—only one clock hour, reckoning the entire span of human life as a day. But during that hour the major portion of the total stream of development flows under the bridge. This statement holds true even if, with Huxley, we make life and development coextensive terms. In a biological sense, at least, the first period of development must outrank all others in the wealth of phenomena displayed.

This basic biological fact is a reason why any systematic treatment of the first five or six years of life must present a far-flung outline. Chapters multiply because the range of development is so extensive. Even with simplification we must recognize in the first year of life at least three developmental intervals and devote attention to the stages of maturity presented at four months, six months, and nine months. Including the neonatal period, this volume gives separate consideration to ten successive stages of development.

The criterion used in selecting these stages, and the general developmental significance of the whole pre-school sequence, are discussed in the chapter on *Development and Duration* (Chapter 3). An attempt is made, in this chapter, to give some expression to the relative dynamic value which the first sexennium appears to have when compared with other periods of equal length. The argument has bearing on the clinical importance of the pre-school phase of development.

Another introductory chapter (Chapter 2) deals with the social significance of the pre-school period. Recent public health, educational, and sociological developments are pointed out to show that this field is assuming a new importance from the standpoint of public welfare. If society is gradually extending its supervisory solicitude to cover the developmental welfare of children of pre-school age, increasing diagnostic demands will be made upon physicians.

Children of school age have in general received a larger measure of legislative and social protection than pre-school children. The scientific development of general and applied child psychology has shown a similar emphasis on the school age. The methods of investigation which have been used in the study of infancy and early childhood are treated historically, but sketchily, in Chapter 4.

The main purpose of the present volume is to report the normative data gathered in the investigation related in Chapters 5 and 6. This study was begun in a restricted way in 1919, but soon came to embrace the ten age groups above referred to. Fifty normal (representative) children were examined at 4, 6, 9, 12, 18, 24, 36, 48, and 60 months of age. Over five hundred children (counting retests as new cases) were included in the investigation.

A psychological examination and an analytic survey of the child's home behavior were made in each case. The results were codified into a set of "developmental schedules," containing in all as many as 150 normative items. These items were assembled and classified in a syllabus, reproduced in Chapter 7. The reader is requested to regard this classification as one made chiefly for editorial and clinical convenience. No attempt was made by statistical methods to consolidate the items into a delimited and inflexible psychometric scale. Our purpose has been to devise an adjustable clinical instrument, suitable to the practical demands and difficulties peculiar to the examination of infants and children of tender age.

The procedure for the application of the various diagnostic items is described in Chapters 8–12, under the headings of *Motor Development, Language Development, Adaptive Behavior, Personal-Social Behavior*.

In spite of the confessedly preliminary and approximate character of the normative data, we venture to call the combined schedules, materials, and methods, a system of developmental diagnosis. The procedure and devices as presented are the outgrowth of clinical experience with children of pre-school age, and have been tested out practically in the Yale Psycho-Clinic.

Chapter 12 assembles a large number of action photographs, taken in the clinical laboratory by a Graflex, and some of them by a cinema camera. These pictures show our subjects in characteristic behavior situations, and are classified in such a way that they may be put to normative and comparative uses.

Part Three is entitled *Comparative Studies of Development*. This section is intended to furnish a concrete background for the section on Clinical Methods and Applications. We wish to stress the importance of the comparative approach in both genetic and clinical psychology. Chapters 13, 14, and 15 emphasize the continuity of behavior development. Chapters 16–25 report the results of a comparative survey of nine developmental levels. In this study we made observations of eight pairs of children, selected to bring adjacent levels of development into immediate comparison. The comparisons provide a cumulative synopsis of pre-school development and also illustrate the application of various diagnostic tests.

The possibilities and the desirability of comparative research are discussed in Chapter 26. Chapters 27, 28, and 29 contain comparative studies of developmental correspondence in twins, of precocity, and of retardation. The chapter on *Retardation and Inferiority* is supported with photographs and case studies, and is made as concrete as possible in order to illustrate the value of the comparative approach in clinical procedure. The significance of this approach is set forth in the chapter on *Normative and Clinical Psychology* (Chapter 30).

Part Four is mainly devoted to details of both general and specific clinical procedure in the field of developmental diagnosis. The use of the developmental schedules and normative summaries, and the parental interview in this procedure, are indicated. Methods of recording and estimating personality traits are considered in

Chapter 35. The importance of supplementing objective measurements with clinical judgment is emphasized throughout. It should be repeated in this summary that our schedules and procedures for developmental diagnosis do not operate automatically. They are presented in such a way that they readily provide or permit approximate estimates of developmental status in terms of age level; they also facilitate concrete, descriptive, analytic records of development; but any responsible diagnosis should rest upon the trained judgment of the examiner.

The concluding chapters suggest the broader social applications of developmental diagnosis. Child guidance, child placement, and child adoption all call for certain clinical safeguards and diagnostic technique. Child adoption presents peculiar problems, which are discussed in Chapter 36.

The applications of developmental diagnosis are not, however, limited to special social situations like child placement, or to abnormal and subnormal children. Developmental hygiene always is a relative concept. Norms and standards of development concern children of every age, condition, or status. The chapter on *Developmental Supervision* (Chapter 37) considers the feasibility of gradually extending a consecutive, supervising type of developmental diagnosis to normal children of pre-school age. The current tendency of the mental hygiene and child health movements and even the present organization of child health work make such a policy of Developmental Supervision far from visionary.

If the field of developmental diagnosis is to undergo considerable scientific and professional cultivation, it will inevitably take a larger place in medical training and practice. This subject is briefly considered in the final chapter.

Applied psychology is destined to extend its activities more and more into the domain of infancy; but artificial distinctions between mind and body will probably diminish with time; and the concept of development which unifies both will gradually be adopted. Development thus construed retains its place as a fundamental subject of medical science and becomes a basic discipline of Pediatrics, as well as of Psychology.

The interpretation of "the mind" in terms of behavior will inevitably bring the psychology of infancy into closer relations with neurology, physiology, and medicine. In the present volume we conceive *behavior* as the functional index of developmental maturity. A man may be as old as his arteries, but an infant is as old as his behavior. In the very nature of things an infant can do neither more nor less than the maturation and organization of his behavior patterns permit. An interpretation of developmental status in relation to chronological age and personal-social environment is the diagnostic basis for safeguarding the mental welfare of the pre-school child. Developmental diagnosis is essential to the mental hygiene of infancy.

CHAPTER 2

The Significance of Pre-School Development

Development is always dynamic and never discontinuous. It is, therefore, impossible to separate one period of development sharply and completely from any other period of development. The foetal period is continuous with the neonatal, the neonatal with the pre-school, and this in turn with the school period, pubescence, adolescence, and adulthood. Indeed the biologist goes still further. He does not even separate senescence from immaturity. Some of the most penetrating studies of growth and development have emphasized the fact that senescence and rejuvenescence are relative terms and that both processes may go on at the same time in one individual. As Child puts it, "The age changes in the organism are merely one aspect of *Werden und Vergehen*. The coming and passing away which make up the history of the universe."

Even though development be recognized as a "physiologically continuous process," there are none the less biological and practical considerations which make the pre-school period of human development one of distinctive importance. The total period of maturation may be regarded as extending from birth to the middle twenties. This span may be further subdivided into four periods of approximately six years each. The first permanent molar divides the first two sexennia; the second molars come at the teens or at the beginning of the third sexennium. The wisdom teeth linger until about the age of twenty-four.

Now the front line of developmental advance is not a straight one and there is, of course, no localized point of time or space where maturity abruptly begins. Organs and systems do not develop at a uniform rate. It has even been suggested that sixteen

9

years ordinarily marks the end of the period of intelligence development. The pre-school period of development, however, holds an unambiguous and undisputed preëminence in the dynamic series. *It comes first.* This priority confers upon it a dominating influence. It is the most consequential period of development for the simple but decisive reason that it does come first. Science has confirmed the judgment of common sense in this matter. The earliest periods of development are always the periods of most rapid, most intense, and most fundamental growth.

The basic lines of both physical and mental organization are laid down during the formative pre-school years. How could it be otherwise? When a shipbuilder builds a ship, he lays down the timber first, the trimming and rigging come second—often after launching. What counts first, last, and most in the ship are her planking, her beam, her keel. How she will mind the rudder, how she will take the waves, and how she will weather the sea are fundamentally influenced by what happened when she was on the stocks. In a more profound way still, the pre-school years are fundamental to all the development that follows. This is when the individual is on the stocks. It is, therefore, not surprising to find that a general survey of the pre-school epoch of childhood proves that this period has a peculiar significance both from scientific and from practical points of view. We may briefly indicate the practical considerations from the medical, from the mental hygiene, and from the administrative standpoints.*

Medical Significance. One third of all the deaths of the nation occur below six years. There are ten times as many deaths during the half decade of pre-school life as during the following full decade of school life. Even physical accidents like being scalded, burned, injured, and run over by automobiles, bear with special weight on the pre-school age. The susceptibility to infection is generally

---

*For extended discussion on this subject see the author's volume on "The Pre-School Child: From the Standpoint of Public Hygiene and Education." Houghton Mifflin Company, Boston, 1923.

greater, the younger the child. Over eighty per cent of all cases of diphtheria and of all deaths from diphtheria occur below the age of five. Malnutrition, likewise, is more prevalent among pre-school than among school children. Rickets, a disorder of nutrition, is almost as common as dental caries and is essentially a pre-school disease. Approximately fifteen per cent of 3,000 pre-school children clinically examined in Gary, Indiana, showed bony effects of rachitic origin. With few exceptions the typical physical defects of school children, like malnutrition and nose and throat conditions, are more prevalent among pre-school children.

This disproportion of mortality and morbidity in the pre-school period is not a result of chance. The concentration of development in this period carries with it an increase of developmental hazards and this increase of hazards carries in its train death, disability, and distortion and makes the period as a whole a relatively critical one in the physical development of the child.

Mental Hygiene Significance. What is true of general physical development is true of mental and nervous development. The brain grows at a tremendous rate during the pre-school age, reaching almost its mature bulk before the age of six. The human cerebral cortex, according to Donaldson, attains it full thickness at about fifteen months of age and he remarks: "All this shows that the important events in the postnatal growth of the nervous system occur early in life, and this in turn emphasizes the paramount importance of favorable conditions during the first three years of childhood."

The mind develops with corresponding velocity. The infant learns to see, to hear, handle, walk, comprehend, and talk. He acquires an uncountable number of habits fundamental to the complex art of living. Never again will his mind, his character, his spirit advance as rapidly as in this formative pre-school period of growth. Never again will we have an equal chance to lay the foundations of mental health. From the standpoint of mental hygiene the pre-school period, therefore, appears to have no less significance than it has for physical vigor and survival.

Normal mental growth is not a matter of complete predestination, even in infants. Defects, handicaps, deviations, many of them preventable, occur. Practically every case of mental deficiency is present and recognizable during the pre-school years. Three fourths of all the deaf, a considerable proportion of all the blind, one third of all the crippled, and over three fourths of all the speech defective come to their handicap during the pre-school period. Numerous cases of mental abnormality, of perversion, of faulty habit formation, and of conduct disorder have their roots in the pre-school years. Our kindergartens and nurseries must reckon with many problem children, manifesting serious errors or defects in behavior development. One fourth of all our school beginners fail of promotion at the end of the first year in public school. Retardation, abnormal prematuration, normal precocity, superiority, and normality all tend to reveal themselves well before the child cuts his sixth-year molar.

Social and Administrative Significance. For all the reasons suggested above our practical outlook upon the pre-school period is undergoing rapid and significant changes. These changes have already begun to crystallize themselves into new social legislation and new public and semi-public provisions for children of pre-school age. The World War has stimulated these changes and the whole field is now in an extraordinary state of ferment and formativeness.

The social status of the pre-school child is undergoing nothing less than a revolutionary change comparable to that which in an earlier generation altered the status of the school child and the youthful wage earner.

The Fisher Education Act, passed by the English Parliament in 1918, contains this significant passage:

"The powers of Local Education authorities . . . . shall include power to make arrangements for supplying or aiding the supply of nursery schools (which expression shall include nursery classes) for children over two and under five years of age, or such later age as may be approved by the Board of Education, whose attendance at such a school is necessary or desirable for their healthy physical and mental development . . . "

Partly under the stimulus of this law, nursery schools have multiplied in England. They are also being established in this country. The nursery school, however, is still in the experimental and demonstration stage of its development. It does not have the established place in our traditions and public school administration which the kindergarten holds.

The kindergarten is in a sense the most official agency of pre-school child welfare which we possess. The first kindergarten was established in this country in 1855 and has had such a notable development that one child out of ten children of kindergarten age is now reached by this important institution. With the cumulative emphasis which will be placed upon systematic parental guidance and upon the educational welfare of pre-school children, the kindergarten because of its strategic position is destined to wield increasing influence.

The Federal Children's Bureau since its establishment in 1912 has emphasized constantly the importance of hygienic and welfare measures relating to the pre-school period. The Sheppard-Towner Act of 1921, for the promotion of the welfare and hygiene of maternity and infancy, has crystallized some of its recommendations. The Smith-Hughes Act recently has provided grants of federal aid for vocational training in Home Economics, including training for parenthood. Within the last decade practically every state in the Union has established a separate department of child hygiene, New York leading in 1914. These departments, as well as the large voluntary national organizations like the American Child Health Association, have systematically emphasized the importance of continuous protection of the developmental welfare of pre-school children.

In 1892 the first Infant Welfare Center recorded in history was established in Paris by Dr. Budin. This simple social invention proved to be one of basic importance and has been adopted in every civilized country in the world. Infant welfare and child health centers are multiplying at a rapid rate. Such devices promise in time to be almost as pervading and far reaching as present provisions for public elementary education.

Even a sketchy summary is sufficient to convince one that the hygiene of the pre-school child is gradually coming under systematic social control. How this control is to be worked out administratively is a question which does not concern us in this chapter. It is evident, however, that our administrative procedure can be sound only if it is based upon more adequate knowledge of the pre-school period of child life.

CHAPTER 3

DEVELOPMENT AND DURATION

This chapter deals to some extent with theoretical questions relating to the measurement of development. The discussion is, however, inserted here because of its practical bearing on the preceding chapter. The dominating developmental significance of the pre-school period is due to certain interesting relations between development and duration.

Development is conditioned in a basic and almost curious manner by the factor of time. Only in mythology does a fully formed, fully fledged creature spring from the forehead of a god. In nature time is necessary for the production of an organism. Little as we know about the phenomena of development, it appears that the relation between time units, developmental life cycles, and periodicities is of a lawful character.

The difference in longevity between various species bears some lawful relation to biochemical laws which themselves were probably established through evolutionary processes. Abderhalden compiled a table in which he arranged the following species in order: man, horse, cow, goat, pig, sheep, cat, dog, rabbit. In another column he arranged the number of days required for each species of animal indicated to double its weight after birth. The figures range in descending order from 180 in man to 7 in the rabbit and these diminishing differences were in turn correlated with differences in the constitution of the mother's milk. The rabbit's milk contained a protein percentage of 10.4, the human a percentage of 1.6. The evolutionary prolongation of infancy likewise denotes an important correlation between the time factor and developmental mechanics.

15

There are very fundamental interdependencies between development and duration which further investigation will clarify. Observable differences between individuals of the same race, between different races, and between normal and abnormal individuals have indicated the existence of important developmental laws.

The chief reason why it has been impossible thus far to formulate these laws with precision lies in the fact that we really have no absolute units for the measurement of development. Development is such a complicated and dynamically conditioned phenomenon that it does not lend itself to any simple forms of linear measurement. The growth of an organism, to be sure, expresses itself in an increase of length or height and an augmentation of bulk. Such increases can be measured by absolute units and comparative interpretation of growth curves has, therefore, given us some clue as to the rate of growth. Very suggestive biological interpretations of these studies of growth have been made by various biologists, notably by Charles S. Minot.

Minot emphasizes particularly the marked decline in the growth power which takes place in the earliest periods of development. Assuming the germ to weigh .0006 gramme and the child at birth 3200 grammes, he calculates that the percentage of increment is 5,400,000. Assuming the weight of a man of twenty years to be 130 pounds, the increase after birth would be as 1 is to 16. Even in the first year of life the swift decline in the rate of growth asserts itself. In the neonatal month the percentage increment is 23 per cent; in the twelfth month it has fallen to 2.8 per cent. On the basis of this and other evidence Minot formulates two laws of age as follows: (a) The rate of growth depends on the degree of senescence. (b) Senescence is at its maximum in the very young stages and the rate of senescence diminishes with age.

These laws formulate what might be called the paradoxical aspect of development. If we view the quantitative aspect of developmental potency in a different time perspective, the positive developmental significance of the earliest stages will be equally emphasized. The problem is, How can these phenomena be brought into a proper time perspective? How can we focus upon the quantitative aspect at all if there is no available absolute unit of measurement? This problem is profoundly perplexing. Psychologists, in spite of voluminous applications of tests and measurements and in spite of a very high refinement of statistical technique, have come to no agreement as to a proper method of measurement of mental development. Even the shape of the curve of mental growth is in dispute. Does it proceed in a straight line or is it logarithmic in character? When psychometric methods are employed for the measurement of intelligence shall we determine mental capacity and mental progress by number of points scored per minute or number of minutes consumed to earn a point? The mere statement of these questions reveals some of the fundamental difficulties in the solution of the problem.

Intelligence has proved to be the most objective and measurable aspect of mental phenomena. In the following chapter we shall discuss some of the methods which have been used by way of measurement. The point scale and the mental-age index and the intelligence quotient have been proposed, but the whole subject is in such an early stage of cultivation that we are on no fully assured ground with respect to the final validity of these measures and the relations between them. These psychometric approaches, however, have been very useful in defining problems and in suggesting working hypotheses.

We revert to the question which we proposed above: How can we formulate the phenomena of mental development in accurate coherence with the factor of time? If we attempt to state the increments of development in terms of absolute time units, we shall come to the untenable conclusion that one year of development at any age is equal to one year of development at any other age. There is a principle of relativity in operation which can be

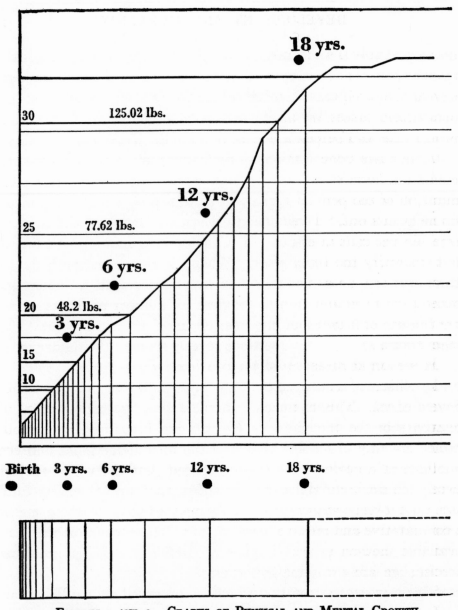

FIGURES 1 AND 2.   GRAPHS OF PHYSICAL AND MENTAL GROWTH

The upper figure is adapted from Minot's graph, showing the physical growth of man from birth to maturity, with vertical lines added to mark the duration of the periods required for each 10% addition to the weight. (See Minot: *Age, Growth, and Death*, Putnam's, N Y)

The lower figure illustrates the arrangement of developmental intervals discussed on page 21 of the present volume Beginning at 3 months these intervals are so placed as to yield the following sequence of developmental quotients: ¾, ⅔, ¾, ¾, ⅔, ¾, ⅔, ¾, ⅔, ¾, ⅔, ⅔. There is an analogous concentration of mental growth in infancy. The older the child gets, the longer it takes to develop a proportionate amount.

18

uncovered only if we succeed in formulating development in relative rather than absolute units. Even in the phenomena of physical development we cannot perceive the changes of stature in proper perspective unless we block out these changes on a basis which brings time and percentage increments into relation.

Minot has done this for us in a curve showing the growth of man from birth to maturity with vertical lines added to mark the duration of the periods for each ten per cent addition to weight. As he points out, "These lines are very close together at the start. One ten per cent after another follows in a short interval of time, but gradually the time, as indicated by the space between two of these vertical lines, increases. . . . . Our diagram is merely another form of graphic representation of the fact that the older we are the longer it takes us to grow a definite proportional amount." (See Figure 1).

If we could measure mental stature by pounds or inches we could construct a similar chart to portray the course of "mental" development. This is manifestly impossible, but the concept of relativity or the percentage increment concept seems to be applicable. By way of hypothesis, at least, we may use the intelligence quotient as a device for treating differences in rate of growth between different individuals. The advantage of this device is the fact that it deals with ratios and approaches the whole problem in a comparative and relative manner. We are not assuming that any available method of deriving the I. Q. is absolutely accurate or precise; we are provisionally accepting the formula as having a usefulness in expressing the effects of duration upon development.

Let us, therefore, agree to express the ideal course of mental development by a series of mental or developmental ages which vary directly and proportionately with duration as expressed by chronological ages. The nine-months-old child has a developmental age of nine months. The eighteen-months-old child has a developmental age of eighteen months; the five-year-old child a developmental age of five years. Let us assume further that retardations in development can be expressed by fractions; the denominator denoting chronological age and the numerator, developmental age or biological maturity.

Recognizing that there are no absolute units available to apply as measures, let us approach the problem circuitously, from a comparative angle, using the developmental quotient as a point of reference. From a comparative standpoint we are certain that "more" development is compressed in early than in late stages of the life cycle. Figures in regard to physical growth confirm this common-sense observation. This compression is apparently graduated; so that in a broad way we may venture the formula that the "current volume" of development varies inversely with duration. How can we give mathematical or graphic expression to this relation? By means of a series of developmental ratios.

Let us illustrate this in terms of the practical problem with which this volume is concerned, namely with the developmental diagnosis of children of pre-school age. Our system of diagnosis comprehends the span from three months to six years. Now we have found in accordance with ordinary psycho-clinical experience with school children that to express in psychometric terms borderline degrees of retardation we must use quotients which range, say, from 65 to 75.

Accordingly if we are to devise a schedule of diagnostic norms applicable to children of pre-school age, including infants, we must at least have a sliding scale or "comparometer," which will enable us to formulate, normatively, subnormal states of development in ratios which lie between 65 and 75. We have had due regard for this fact in constructing our series of normative developmental schedules, nine in number. Disregarding the neonatal schedule, which is descriptive rather than normative, we begin with a four-months' schedule, which permits estimates of three or four month levels of maturity, and end with a schedule applicable to five and six year levels. In conformity with the recognized compression of development in the early period of life, the series of normative schedules was arranged as follows: (1) Three to four months. (2) Six months. (3) Nine months. (4) One year. (5) One and one-half years. (6) Two years. (7) Three years. (8) Four years. (9) Five to six years.

This interspacing serves a practical clinical purpose. It bridges the span of pre-school maturation with a series of developmental intervals, so ordered that there is a consecutive series of ratios of three fourths* or two thirds from three months to six years of age. Expressed in months this series progresses as follows: 3 (mos.): 4: 6: 9: 12: 18: 24: 36: 48: 72 mos. (=6 yrs.) Now if this series had been continued into the school years up to approximate maturity (*i. e.* eighteen years), we should have the following order of intervals expressed in years: 6 (yrs.): 8: 12: 18.

When we compare the pre-six with the post-six series of ratios we are confronted with an arresting discrepancy. It takes nine developmental ratio intervals to bridge the span from three months to six years. It takes only three corresponding ratio intervals to bridge the span from six years to eighteen years.

It is at best hazardous to formulate development in precise quantitative terms. We shall not ascribe any absolute importance to the exact figures derived in the above comparison. If there were no Pythagorean or statistical fallacies lurking in the premises we might, however, venture a developmental syllogism somewhat as follows:

(a) The pre-school period of development from three months to six years yields nine consecutive developmental ratios as follows: ¾, ⅔, ⅔, ¾, ⅔, ¾, ⅔, ¾, ⅔.

(b) The school period from six years to eighteen years yields three comparable consecutive developmental ratios as follows: ¾, ⅔, ⅔.

*There would have been a theoretical advantage in making all of the intervals exactly a three-fourths value; but this would have introduced artificial time fractionations and was an unnecessary refinement in our system.

(c) It therefore follows, broadly and relatively conceived, that the proportion of development attained during the first sexennium of life is treble that attained in the two succeeding sexennia.

Startling as this conclusion is, it finds a certain confirmation in clinical facts and in empirical impressions. Take a bird's-eye view of the whole drama of development, and is it not true that more action, more unravelling, more "denouement" appear in the first scenes than in the later? Or to change the figure, does not the movement of development compare with that of an automobile charging a long, steep hill? The rate of advance is greatest at the bottom or the early part of the incline.

Developmental hazards and correlated deviations are more numerous in the pre-school than the school period. Growth is so rapid in the former period that we can almost "see" the child grow, and significant weekly increments of mental development may be recorded, when later they would be beyond the scope of the acutest observation. Follow-up examinations during infancy tend to crowd the appointment calendar. These periodic examinations "mature" in brief intervals of two or three months, whereas in later school life it would take as many years to leave an equal impress on the topography of development. We can follow up or check up the development of a young child with much more frequency and expedition than we can that of an old child. This fact is not without practical importance from the standpoint of developmental supervision and it places a certain premium upon early developmental diagnosis. It must be reckoned with in the construction of diagnostic scales and procedures.

If we attempt by graph to indicate the periodic placement of ascending developmental intervals we get a diagram which bears a certain analogy to Minot's chart of physical growth, which likewise places the apex near age eighteen. (See Figure 2.) It will be noted that in both charts the vertical lines tend to crowd each other near the birth line. If pushed too near the zero point the geometric arrangement of developmental ratios becomes fantastic; but the graph itself is not misleading. The older the child the longer it takes him to achieve a definite proportional developmental increment. The graph also accords with the incontestable clinical observation that one month of constitutional retardation in early infancy may be predictive of a whole year of retardation after the first birthday. In developmental economy the value of a month i. determined by its placement in the life cycle.

CHAPTER 4

The Scientific Study of Development

The conception of development is an old one. It must have figured in various ways in the mental processes even of primitive man. It has appeared and reappeared in many forms in the history of human thought both in philosophy and in science. The opposition between the immutable ideas of Plato and the flux and flow doctrine of Heraclitus is a fundamental one which reasserted itself in conflicting schools of medieval thought and which is revived in altered guise in present-day discussions of philosophical biology.

Development may be defined as the succession of steps by which any living being has acquired the morphological and dynamic characters which distinguish it. It is scarcely necessary to incorporate the adjective psychological or physiological in this definition for we may subsume it under the broad term dynamic.

Embryology is the fundamental science of development. Broadly conceived, Embryology considers the entire developmental history of the individual from conception till death. A summary of the history of Embryology would, therefore, furnish a suggestive background for a review of modern studies of mental development. Such a summary history would show how fundamentally the growth of the science of Embryology has been affected by the doctrine of evolution. It would also show what an enormous amount of patient painstaking descriptive work lies at the basis of modern Embryology.

Genetic psychology, relatively speaking, has only begun to amass the detailed observational data necessary for a scientific substructure, and genetic psychology has scarcely begun to use systematically the comparative method which has been so productive in the field of Embryology. The knowledge of the development of the human embryo was in a very fragmentary state until Wilhelm His, in 1885, published his systematic work. This fundamental contribution rested, in no small measure, upon an extraordinary number of micro-cross-section views of the embryo which were assembled into contiguous series both transverse and longitudinally. By relating these sections serially and comparatively he built up an outline of morphogenesis.

Must not genetic psychology build its foundations in a similar manner? Speculation has played too large a part in the literature of this subject. The modern biologist takes the view that development is as tangible and concrete and legitimate a subject for scientific study as is the process of glandular secretion. He attacks the problem in the same manner, beginning always with observed descriptive data. The fascinating field of Developmental Mechanics, the study of morphogenesis, becomes a branch of experimental physiology. Here the scientist deals, sometimes very daringly, with all the controllable factors of growth. He studies the effects of gravity, heat, light, chemicals, mutilation, and transposition and juxtaposition of parts in relation to anatomical growth. Recently he has begun to work experimentally with the effects of biochemical stimuli and hormones. This aspect of the physiology of development which pertains to postnatal as well as prenatal life is full of promise as well as marvel. Osler rightly calls the discovery of the effects of thyroid secretion upon growth one of the most brilliant gems in the crown of modern physiology.

The highly dynamic nature of the phenomena of development no longer serves as a barrier to scientific scrutiny or as an excuse for purely speculative interpretation. Science may be no more successful here than elsewhere in solving an ultimate riddle; still the intricate phenomena of mental development can be made to yield to constructive scientific analysis and formulation. Whatever else development may be, it is at least a series of moments.

Just as the embryologist gets his basic conceptions of morphogenesis by building up indefatigably, step by step, detailed sectional views of growing organisms or of a growing organ, so may genetic psychology build up a continuing series of sections corresponding to the stages and the moments of development. Even the cinema film is a series of static pictures. When reproduced in close succession, this series restores the original motion. The analogy does not altogether break down in the domain of mental development.

Mental development is dynamic and elusive but it is essentially no more elusive than physical development and, just as the science of embryology is clarifying the phenomena of physical growth through countless sectional studies, so may genetic psychology attain an insight into the obscure developmental mechanics of the growth of behavior. Genetic psychology has depended too much upon philosophical approaches to the problems of origin, unfoldment, and recapitulation.

The securest basis for a developmental psychology is a vast amount of descriptive data which will delineate what the generic human individual is in the ascending stages of maturity. Interpretation of the behavior of this individual will be simpler and certainly less speculative if rested upon such foundation. Statistical method will elucidate these observed data but will not contribute the data themselves. These can come only through incessantly observing and recording. First of all developmental psychology is descriptive; second, it is comparative and finally interpretative.

We shall not attempt in this chapter to take even an "airplane flight" over the history of genetic psychology, but shall content ourselves with a few references to the development of scientific methods in this field. Four such methods may be readily distinguished in the voluminous literature: 1, the Observational Biographical Method; 2, the Questionnaire Method; 3, the Experimental Method; and 4, the Psychometric Method.

I.   THE OBSERVATIONAL BIOGRAPHICAL METHOD

Historically this is the oldest method and also the most widely used. From the close of the eighteenth century to the present day it has had its exponents. In the following chronological list are found some of the names which are associated with this type of child psychology: Pestalozzi, 1774; Tiedemann, 1787; Perez, 1787; Froebel, 1826; Mme. Necker de Saussure, 1828; Sigismund, 1856; Darwin, 1877; Preyer, 1880; Shinn, 1893; Moore, 1896; Major, 1906; Dearborn, 1910.

This list, though very incomplete, is motley enough and reflects a diversity of approach and interest in the study of child development. Pestalozzi, who heads the list, was a picturesque educational reformer, whose diary of his little son, Jacobli, is full of quaint and pious entries but with many suggestions of the modern attitude. Froebel's and Madam Necker de Saussure's writings are highly colored by mystical and philosophical conceptions. Darwin's *Biographical Sketch of an Infant* reflects the naturalist's keenness of perception. Preyer wrote as a physician and physiologist. Miss Shinn's work is a model of careful observation and her *Biography of a Baby* has literary charm. Dearborn's *Moto-Sensory Development* is in the nature of a day-book inventory but is full of factual items.

It is very difficult to generalize in regard to the merits or results obtained through the use of the individual biographical method of study. Much of this literature is tedious to read and leaves too much to the interpretation and critical ability of the student. Many of the studies reveal *a priori* philosophical interpretations of development. "Did the baby start out ready equipped with ideas of space, personal identity, time, causation, such as we find so ineradicable in our own minds? . . . The hope of answering such questions," as Miss Shinn said, "was the first stimulus to the study of infants."

It is the individual, personal character of much of this child-study material which has made it relatively ineffective from the standpoint of application. Although the literature abounds in observations of importance it has left us scarcely the outline of a systematic psychology of childhood.

Brief mention should be made of autobiographical studies. In these, the mature mind attempts by a process of more or less systematic retrospection to restore early impressions. G. Stanley Hall in his monograph on early memories (*Pedagogical Seminary*, 1899) makes detailed effort at such psychological reconstruction. There have been other efforts of similar character by Henri, Colegrove, Potmin, and Loti. Non-psychological writers of reminiscences frequently have interesting though scant details respecting their pre-school memories. It is possible that a critical study of a large amount of data of this character may throw some light on pre-school psychology, but the limitations of this method are obvious.

Certain applications of psychoanalysis may be briefly mentioned in this same connection, because these applications are in a sense autobiographical and have a reference to early childhood. Those case studies which show a continuity between adult behavior and psychogenetic factors in early childhood are interesting for the light that they shed on both normal and abnormal psychology. As a method of research, however, this type of biographical analysis has decided limitations.

2.   THE QUESTIONNAIRE METHOD

This method deserves mention because historically it played an important part in the development of the child-study movement and because in spite of all its errors and misuse it netted a considerable amount of psychological data. The questionnaire method was used productively by Sir Francis Galton. It was for a time a major device in the hands of G. Stanley Hall and his school. These questionnaire studies address themselves to special phases of child life like fears, anger, the collecting instinct, crying, sense of humor, etc.

The defects and limitations of this method are too obvious to need discussion. The method itself, however, cannot be dismissed as being altogether sterile and unscientific. Indeed when properly controlled it becomes an economical device for preliminary exploration.

Instead of being abandoned altogether the questionnaire method might be safeguarded and readapted and judiciously exploited as a technique. One of the most important sources of information in regard to the social behavior of young children is the mother, and a controlled analytic verbal use of the questionnaire offers here definite advantages in building up a knowledge of prevailing characteristics in children. The science of psychology is not yet so refined and organized that we can afford to abandon the natural-history approach to our problems. Just as the natural-history method has a recognized place in zoölogy, so do comparable methods have a value in the field of child psychology.

The natural-history approach might be described as an interpretative study of child behavior in its natural or accustomed settings. Direct observation of this kind reinforced by systematic exploitation of the psychological questionnaire may be made to yield data of clinical usefulness.

3. THE EXPERIMENTAL METHOD

It is customary to define an experiment as a controlled observation which can be duplicated. Now in the very nature of things almost every specific bit of behavior in infancy is so complicated by variable and inaccessible factors that perfect, complete duplication can scarcely be hoped for except under very special conditions. However, there are certain types of technique and modes of laboratory approach which deserve the term experimental and which can be readily distinguished from casual and from natural-history modes of observation.

This experimental procedure finds its best exemplification in the field of animal psychology; it has also been anticipated in many forms of physiological research which have proved to have a direct bearing on the study of infant behavior. The recent behaviorist movement in psychology has received its impetus from these two fields of investigation. For an excellent summary of the relation of behaviorism to child psychology, the reader is referred to a compact chapter in Florence Mateer's monograph on Child Behavior.

Watson, in 1914, wrote both from the standpoint of a behaviorist and of a comparative psychologist when he said: "Should human psychologists fail to look with favor upon our overtures and refuse to modify their position, the behaviorists will be driven to use human beings as subjects and employ methods of investigation which are exactly comparable to those now employed in animal work."

Yerkes expressed a similar point of view in the same year, saying that human behavior "must be studied by methods similar to, if not actually identical with, those emphasized by the student of infra-human behavior." Watson, himself, has made experimental studies most notably in regard to the hereditary responses and emotional reactions of hospital infants in the first half year of life. Yerkes, Hunter, and Hamilton have used young human subjects to compare their behavior with that of various animals in identical situations. These situations involved multiple choice, quadruple choice, delayed reactions, associative learning, etc.

A more fundamental and more strictly physiological type of experimental study is that represented by the method of the conditioned reflex. This method was the principal one used by Ivan P. Pavlov as early as the nineties, in the work of The Physiological Department of the Institute of Experimental Medicine of St. Petersburg.

The typical conditioned reflex is a cerebral reflex based on habit formation, or associative learning. A reaction produced by a stimulus which has been substituted for the natural stimulus is a conditioned reflex. The salivary glands "learn" to secrete not only on the taste of the food but upon the sound of a whistle which has been associated with the taste of the food. Pavlov's experiments were mainly upon animal subjects and secretory processes. Bechterew studied motor reflexes in a similar manner. Krasnagorski (1907) applied the method to normal infants.

Florence Mateer (1918) made a critical and experimental study of young children by the same method. She used a group of unselected normal cases and several defectives for comparison. The ages ranged from twelve months to seven years. Her procedure was simple, her results very suggestive. A piece of chocolate served as the ordinary adequate stimulus (for opening the mouth to eat); a bandage over the eyes served as the substituted stimulus. The bandage was always applied ten seconds after the child was fed with the chocolate. At the twentieth second the bandage was removed; three minutes were allowed to elapse and the previous stimulation was repeated. The reflex was counted as established if the child opened his mouth twice by way of anticipation of the chocolate, during the ten-second interval. Unlearning and inhibition were studied in the same manner. The results of the investigation indicate individual differences of an apparently lawful character.

Even this brief sketch is sufficient to indicate the potential clinical value of the method of the conditioned reflex and comparable methods. The conditioned reflex is significant for developmental diagnosis, because it must correlate in some basic manner with the maturity and the caliber of the cerebrum. Although the method itself is not ready for practical application, it is clear that that precise neuro-physiological researches of an experimental and of a quantitative character are applicable to infancy.

Early infancy invites objective physiological methods of study, and may permit of observations of great refinement. The acquisition of oculo-motor control, for example, might be studied with highly precise technique aiming at quantitative standardization. The results might prove to have a significant correlation with the maturity of the central nervous system. It would not, at least, be surprising if clinical contact with the problem of individual differences could be established in neonatal infancy by means of a behaviorist or physiological technique.

4. THE PSYCHOMETRIC METHOD

The psychometric method may be described as a method of measuring or grading behavior by means of standardized test procedures. It may, therefore, be regarded as a special phase of the experimental method. It derives its practical significance from the fact that it is based not on the study of the individual so much as upon the study of related groups of individuals. Miss Mateer suggests that we owe to Kussmaul, writing in 1859, the first application of the extensive method of child psychology. In his study of new-born infants he did not limit himself to one or two individual cases but made generalized statements based upon observations of a number of cases. This kind of generalization is the basis of the psychometric method.

In 1880 G. Stanley Hall made a survey of the contents of children's minds on entering school. He made use of a large number of Boston kindergarten children in this study, which is reckoned as a landmark in the beginning of the child-study movement in America. The literature of this movement, both here and abroad, soon included similar studies of an extensive character. Even the statistical method began to come into play and the data were presented with percentage classifications.

Curiously enough, however, it remained for one psychologist, namely, Alfred Binet, in Paris, to make a simple but unique application of the quantitative method. He, in common with many contemporary psychologists, had first confined himself to individual studies, but in 1890 he made a comparative study of discriminative number and length judgment in his two daughters, age 32 and 52 months,—a study which was perhaps the germ of his later work.

Binet himself, however, attributes the Measuring Scale of Intelligence to "the desire to serve the interesting cause of the education of subnormals." In 1904, he was appointed by the Minister of Public Instruction to serve on a commission charged with the study of measures to be taken for insuring proper instruction to defective school children. The necessity of establishing a scientific diagnosis of inferior states of intelligence engaged the attention of this French psychologist. He noted the confusion of prevailing methods of diagnosis which existed at that time. He noted the limitations of anatomical, medical classifications. He noted also the defects of the pedagogical method which would estimate intelligence on the basis of acquired knowledge. He came to the broad conclusion that the classification of inferior states of intelligence is a problem of clinical classification to be made by means of psychology. He recognized, however, the limitations of purely descriptive psychological observation. He granted the usefulness and the objectivity of M. Blin's elaborate questionnaire schema, but he did not find in this collection of questions any solid basis for the gradation of intelligence. In his own words, "This brings us very naturally to the exposition of a plan of our work. It will be seen that our directing idea is different from that of M. Blin although our system of measurement, like his, is essentially psychological."

What was this difference? It consisted essentially in a quantitative standardization of psychological characteristics in terms of age level. To quote again Binet's own words, "The fundamental idea of this method is the establishment of what we shall call a Measuring Scale of Intelligence. This scale is composed of a series of tests of increasing difficulty, starting from the lowest intellectual level which can be observed and ending with that of normal intelligence. Each group in the series corresponds to a different mental level (or mental age)." When thus stated in the author's unpretentious language the method of age gradation appears to be utterly obvious and simple. Nevertheless the distinction of formulating and virtually originating this method belongs uniquely to Binet. Even Wm. Stern, the foremost child psychologist of Germany, calls him the highly esteemed creator of the method of age gradation. Other psychologists agreed with Binet that "quantitative differences are of no value unless they are measured, even if measured but crudely"; but these psychologists were relying upon special tests and series of tests and objective measurements to solve the problem. None of them grasped and exploited the age level concept as Binet did.

Whatever defects and limitations the age-grade idea as a psychological method may have, it proved itself to be a stimulating conception which set into operation a vast amount of psychological activity and publication. Hundreds of articles and monographs and volumes have been written on psychological measurement, which trace their inception in no small measure to the fruitful work of the French psychologist. In a certain sense even the vast psychological enterprise in which the American military authorities tested and measured the mentality of some 1,700,000 soldiers may be traced back to the same source. The group method of mental testing is a special variation of the Binet individual measuring scale. The standardization and even the formulation of the results of the war-time psychology have made use of the mental age principle.

The revisions and modifications of the Binet Measuring Scale of Intelligence, most widely in use in this country, do not depart far from this central principle. The Point Scale of Yerkes and Bridges, although it scores by points, recognizes the fundamental importance of the age factor in mental classification. The Kuhlmann revision of the Binet-Simon Scale extends the scale below the three-year level, but the standardization of the tests is limited to kindergarten and school-age groups. The Stanford revision of the Binet Measuring Scale does not extend below the three-year level and is incompletely standardized at that level, being based upon an observation of ten three-year-old children.

Terman has not only improved and extended the Binet Measuring Scale but has added to the mental-age formula that of the Intelligence Quotient or "I. Q." A similar quotient or index had also been suggested by Stern and Kuhlmann. The I. Q. now has a more prominent place in psychological literature than the older expressions of mental age and mental level. It has become a kind of legal tender in educational measurement and applied psychology.

The I. Q., as is well known, expresses a ratio between mental age and chronological age. The numerator of this fraction designates mental age as ascertained by the Stanford-Binet Measuring Scale. The denominator represents life age in years and months. The quotient is a numerical index which permits a serial arrangement of grades of intelligence from zero I. Q. up to two hundred I. Q., assuming that two hundred is about the upper limit of genius. The convenience of such a graduated scale is apparent, and many psychologists have recognized the appropriateness of such an index.

The clinical and practical validity of the I. Q. determination is a question which we need not discuss in the present connection. We may, however, note here that the denominator of the intelligence fraction has a mathematical precision of which the numerator cannot boast. For this reason alone the exactitude of the I. Q. must be critically qualified. The practical and hypothetical application of the I. Q. concept must be cautiously made. Binet himself clung consistently to the mental-age concept, which is less complicated, and he was careful to qualify even this concept. As early as 1905 he made the following cautious statement, which still has a certain pertinence in view of the discussions which have arisen about the

I. Q. Speaking of the Measuring Scale of Intelligence, Binet said: "This scale, properly speaking, does not permit the measuring of intelligence, because intellectual qualities are not superposable and, therefore, cannot be measured as linear surfaces are measured but are on the contrary a classification or hierarchy among devious intelligences; and for the necessities of practice this classification is equivalent to a measure."

We may recur to this point of view in a succeeding chapter. Purely from a historical standpoint, it must be granted that if the I. Q. has in any way obscured and confused old problems it has had none the less a stimulating effect upon research in applied psychology.

PART TWO

NORMS OF DEVELOPMENT

CHAPTER 5

A NORMATIVE INVESTIGATION OF PRE-SCHOOL DEVELOPMENT

A somewhat informal narrative will be the most convenient manner of placing before the reader the methods used in our investigation of pre-school norms of development. When the Yale Psycho-Clinic was established in 1911 it was chiefly interested in the problem of exceptional school children. During the early years of this clinical service, nearly all the clients were of school age. The Clinic, however, was located in the New Haven Dispensary in close working proximity to the medical clinics of the School of Medicine and children of pre-school age were from time to time referred from the pediatric and other departments. Weekly baby welfare conferences were conducted across the hall; and this brought us into occasional contact, and not infrequent auditory communication, with normal infants. We readily developed a special interest in the pre-school period of childhood. An increasing number of children of pre-school age were referred to the clinic until in the past year one-third of all the cases seen in the regular clinical service belonged to the pre-school age group.

Although the investigation was not planned in detail as a single project, we began in 1919 to bring normal infants into the clinic for observational study. In 1920, with the assistance of L. Muntz, a systematic study was made of the two-year-old group. A brief account of the method used in this part of the investigation will illustrate in general the method of approach used throughout the study.

With the two-year-old group no effort was made to have the children brought to the clinic, and it was decided to visit each child in his home. This was no small undertaking, because it was definitely decided that only babies in their twenty-fourth month should be considered in the study. We were unwilling to allow even one month of deviation from the actual birthday at this age level, and all the children were therefore examined on the very day of their second birthday or within two weeks thereof.

How could these two-year old children be located? The records in the local department of vital statistics were consulted. Fortunately for the research the records contained all the desired information; the name, address, date of birth, sex, place of father's birth, nationality, and color. From the office records a working list of names and addresses was selected. If one will read between the lines, the following summary will give some idea of the work involved simply in the selection of a representative group of fifty two-year-old children:

1. Cases examined 50
2. Families moved 36
3. Not at home   28
4. Cases postponed to a later date 20
·5. Cases to call back (child asleep, etc.) .... ·... 30
6. Refusals 4
7. Dead.......... · 14
    Total visits 182

Although the method of home visitation requires expenditure of time and patience it is in the end both productive and economical. Once rapport is established with the mother and the child the investigation can be pursued under relatively favorable conditions. It will be noted that there were no unusual difficulties in establishing contact with the homes. No doubt the householder was frequently surprised to find that a representative of Yale University came knocking at the front door with precise knowledge of the birthday of a son or daughter, but the nature of the mission was easily explained and as easily understood. In the two-year-old group there were only four definite refusals. These were highly exceptional. The rule was active coöperation, even though it was frankly stated that the chief purpose of the visit was to find out more about the characteristics of two-year-old children. We have very frequently found that parents are ready to make their contribution to a research enterprise that concerns children.

The method of investigation followed with the three-year-old, four-year-old, and five-year-old age groups was substantially the same. A proportion of the children in these age groups were seen in our clinic but always in the company of the mother and under very natural circumstances. Since these age levels were studied after the two-year-old investigation, a proportion of the two-year-old cases was included in the subsequent series. The interest of the parents in cases of reëxamination did not decline but on the contrary increased. Some of the mothers developed an annual expectation of a psychological visitor at springtime. One Italian mother long ago placed an advance order for our book!

In the case of the three-year-old group a working list of 129 names was prepared. The tabular summary may be compared with the previous one.

1.	Examined	50
2.	Moved	14
3.	Sick	5
4.	Refused	2
5.	Sleeping	3
6.	Mentally deficient	1
7.	Failed to come to Clinic	13
8.	Did not need to use	10
9.	Unable to find	31
	Total	129

We neglected to keep a faithful record of the total number of hours expended in the selection of subjects and in the visitations and examinations. At each level we confined ourselves to children who were within two weeks of their chronological ages. Only a few negligible exceptions were made to this rule except in the five-year-old group, where the latitude was extended to one month. Whatever imperfections our method of selection may have in other directions, with respect to this factor of central importance it is reliable.

In the age groups below the two-year-old level, children were seen both at home and at the clinic and child welfare stations, but again always in the presence of mother and under natural circumstances.

Our method of approach throughout the investigation is best described as being of the clinical and natural-history type. No effort was made to place the subjects under rigidly uniform experimental or laboratory conditions. The psychological examination of the subject was supplemented with an analytic interview with the parent. Our first objective was to define specific behavior items both characteristic and distinctive of the various age levels. The interview and the developmental examination were jointly used to determine and to multiply such concrete behavior items. We did not pursue the investigation in conformance with a detailed preconceived plan. We did not, for example, subdivide the fields of behavior into motor, language, adaptive, and personal-social behavior categories. The orderly systematization suggested by the syllabus of normative items reproduced in a succeeding chapter is largely editorial and must be so interpreted. We did not conduct our investigation in accordance with this schema. Indeed the syllabus has been drawn up only recently to facilitate the analysis and record of developmental examinations and reëxaminations.

It will be asked how we were able to avoid selective factors in our normative groups of children. No doubt we have not escaped the influence of such factors altogether. However, we made a deliberate effort to secure what might be called a representative, unselective sample of the pre-public-school population of the community. Our subjects were pre-school children, but the nine normative groups may be considered equivalent to the similar samplings of the public-school population. Children from foreign-language homes were not altogether excluded nor were children from the homes of professional classes, but in no group was there an over-weighting in these selections. In only one group was a departure made in this respect: in the case of two-year-old children, the investigation was strictly confined to American homes. This may make the language norms for this group somewhat higher than for the other groups, but there is a real advantage in the special selection made in this instance because the results of this study furnished us with some concrete data concerning the language norms appropriate to this age. It is not intended, however, that children from foreign-language homes should suffer from the application of these language standards in the developmental examination.

Although many of the children in the sub-two-year-old groups were enrolled at baby welfare stations, it should not be inferred that they came from the lower economic strata. We gave preference to those stations which were largely attended by mothers and babies coming from the so-called middle-class homes.

The homes of the children of the three-year-old group were rated according to the Whittier Scale and a range from eight to twenty-five was found with a median of nineteen and one-half.

The two-year-old homes were broadly classified on the basis of social status into middle high group (32 per cent), middle group (38 per cent), and middle low group (30 per cent).

Definitely feeble-minded and markedly retarded children were excluded from the normative series. Undue selection in the other direction was likewise avoided. The number of boys and girls in each group was similar but no effort was made to make the sex division absolutely even. In the case of each study the findings were carefully tabulated and percentage frequencies were calculated.

In the lower age groups the successes of the children were translated into points with the percentage frequency determining the points assigned, and the cases were then seriated into a rank order with the highest score at the head and the lowest score at the end. By means of a simple formula the index of consistency between the total score (which determined the rank order) and each specific test item was determined. The tendency toward consistency displayed by these calculations was reassuring. There were, however, not a few instances in which the index of consistency was low. If we had adopted this mathematical index as a basis for constructing the developmental schedule we should have excluded items that are very useful in developing the estimate of a child's developmental status. An item with a low coefficient of consistency may still have considerable clinical value because it brings personality factors into play. And it should be said at the outset that our objective has not been to construct a measuring scale of intelligence in a strict sense of the term, or even a measuring scale of native endowment. Our aim has been of a broader, clinical character. We have assembled in the developmental schedules all items which have a normative and descriptive value because of the frequency with which they occur in the given age groups.

It is not presumed that these normative items always bear a significant relation to so-called general intelligence. They, however, always have some significance with respect to developmental status. They are frequency values which show prevailing or predominating tendencies and as such they serve a purpose for clinical orientation, for orderly observation, and interpretation of both capacity and personality.

The syllabus printed in Chapter 7 will give a summary view of the ground covered in the normative investigation and of the items finally included in the diagnostic schedules.

CHAPTER 6

Psychological Materials and Apparatus

In this chapter are listed all the materials and psychological apparatus used in the system of developmental diagnosis. Most of this material is easily purchasable and much of it can be readily duplicated. The paraphernalia are not expensive and can be put into a filing drawer which fits into a box that serves both as container and as carrying kit if a handle is attached. A box of light-weight wood is desirable but not indispensable; instead, one may purchase a pasteboard filing case from a stationer and convert it into a combined container and performance box as described below and indicated in the accompanying illustration. (See Figure 3.) A cloth-bound pasteboard filing case is more durable than one of ordinary cardboard. The drawer which slides into the box is very useful for keeping the material both at ready disposal and, when necessary, concealed from the child's view.

A very large proportion of the developmental items require no apparatus, and many of them no materials beyond paper, crayon, cup, saucer, box, and blocks.

1. White enamel saucer, diameter 15 cm.
2. White enamel cup with handle, 9.5 cm. in diameter at top, 6 cm. deep.
3. Teaspoon, standard size, aluminum.
4. Ten wooden cubes, 2.5 cm. square, painted bright red.
5. Pencil, standard size, full length.
6. Small nickel bell, wooden handle of type used in kindergartens.
7. Wooden embroidery ring, diameter outer edge 11 cm., painted bright red. Piece of white string 25 cm. in length attached.
8. Several sheets of paper, letter size and half letter size.
9. Wooden rod, length 10 cm., diameter 1 cm., painted bright red.

10. Red lumber crayon, Faber.
11. White sugar pellets (Admiralo, Gardiner Lenas Co.) flat on one side, convex on other, diameter 8 mm.
12. Small rubber ball painted in bright colors.
13. Glass bottle, 7 cm., diameter of opening 1.2 cm.
14. Rubber doll, small, whistle at back, height 12 cm.
15. Form board made of half inch board 36 x 16 cm., stained dark green on top. Three holes cut equidistant from each other and from edges of board from left to right as follows: Circle, diameter 8.7 cm. Equilateral triangle, each side 9.3 cm. Square, each side 7.5 cm. Three black wooden forms to fit above holes, each 2 cm. thick. Circle, diameter 8.5 cm. Equilateral triangle, each side 9 cm. Square, each side 7.3 cm.
16. Performance box: wooden box, painted bright red, length 38 cm., width 24.7 cm., height 17.6 cm., open only at one end. (Ends 24.7 x 17.6 cm.) Top of box is 38 x 25 cm. 8 cm. from closed end of box is rectangular hole 2.5 x 7.6 cm., short side of rectangle parallel to long side of box. 18 cm. from closed end of box is a round hole, diameter 2 cm. 27.5 cm. from closed end of box is a rectangular hole 3.2 x 2 cm., long side of hole parallel to long side of top of box. Measurements for placements of holes are made from closed end of box to side of hole nearest it. The geometric center of all holes is on a line which bisects the top lengthwise. Use with performance box, wooden rod No. 9 and black square wooden form described in No. 15.
17. Eight white cards 8 x 5 in. with following figures outlined in black, center of card:
    Card 1. Circle, diameter 8 cm.
    Card 2. Cross; lines at rectangles. Length of lines 7.5 cm.
    Card 3. Cross; lines oblique. Length of lines 7.5 cm.
    Card 4. 7 cm. square.
    Card 5. Equilateral triangle, 9.5 cm.
    Card 6. Diamond, length of sides 5.5 cm.
    Card 7. Hexagon, length of sides 5 5. cm. Sides parallel to long side of card 5 cm. apart.
    Card 8. Rectangle, 10 x 6.5 cm., with the two diagonals and lines drawn perpendicular to centres of sides.
    See Figure 6 for designs.

18. White card 5¾ x 5¼ in. divided by black lines into four equal rectangles. Drawings of cup, shoe, dog, and house (Figure 4) in rectangles.

19. White card 5¾ x 5¼ in. divided as above into six equal rectangles. Drawings of flag, star, basket, clock, leaf, book (Figure 5).

20. White card 8 x 5 in., six circular drawings symmetrically placed, representing stages in drawing of watch (Figure 9).

21. Two gray cards each 14 x 5½ in. (Smaller size of 4¼ in. x 11 in. may be substituted.) Cards properly placed make picture of little girl knitting (Figure 10).

21a. Same cards bisected.

22. Puzzle box used in test A34 is 2½ by 3½ by 1½ inches. An opening at the top 1½ inches square allows a bright-colored ball to project slightly. The box is fastened by a cord attached at one end. At its free end a loop passes through a ring at the centre of the bottom of the box and a small wooden stick is slipped through the loop. In order to get the ball, three steps are necessary: (1) the bar must be slipped from the loop, (2) the loop must be pulled through this ring, and (3) the cover must be lifted from the box. The cover is the same depth as the box. (See Figure 3.)

23. Ten brightly colored cardboard forms, and four sheets of cardboard on which is indicated by lines where the forms should be placed. Three forms can be placed on each sheet. Figure 15 illustrates forms and spaces into which they should be fitted, corresponding numbers indicating relative positions. Five cardboard sheets, size 8½ x 11 in., on which are drawn incomplete outlines of ten forms similar to the forms of the Seguin formboard. Corresponding to these outlines are ten brightly colored cardboard forms. The square is 2¾ x 2¾ in. and the rectangle 2¼ x 4½ in. in size. The other forms are in proportion.

24. Card 8 x 5 in., picture of domestic scene (Figure 7).

24a. Same picture card, cut diagonally.

25. White card 8 x 5 in. In centre of card a two-inch square is drawn, subdivided into four one-inch squares, the whole square colored red with a crayon.

26. Green cardboard, 12 x 8 in. White circle 2¼ in. in diameter

painted in centre. Cardboard fish 2½ in. long, round hole
for eye, held in swimming position by means of a slit in one
end of a small cork. Steel rod 1 cm. in diameter, 9 in. long.

27. Paper sheet, half letter size, with incomplete drawing of man
(Figure 11).

28. Three pairs of pictures—one humorous and one non–humorous
in each pair—on cards 11 x 8½ in. (Figure 16a, b, c, d.)

28a. On green sheet half letter size, picture of boy seated blowing
bubbles (Figure 12).

29. Free construction box containing 1 long timber, holes in end,
4 in.; 2 long timbers, holes in end, 3½ in.; 4 long timbers, six
holes in side, 3½ in.; 4 short timbers, 3 holes, 1¾ in.; 10
round rods 4½ in., 1 round rod 1½ in. which fit into holes;
4 square colored rods; placques: 20 triangular, 12 diamond,
6 checkers (3 black, 3 white), one large bead. Distractions:
small flag, shoe, penny.

30. Green sheet, letter size, with first three Porteus maze tests reproduced on it (diamond, cross, garden maze).   (Figure 13.)

31. Picture of man on shying horse (Figure 8).

32. Picture of man fishing up shoe (Figure 16d).

33. Maze 9 x 12 in. with fourteen blind alleys (Figure 14).

In addition to the above, certain material of the Binet intelligence scale may be used, as described in Terman: *The Measurement
of Intelligence* (Houghton Mifflin Company, Boston).

34. Five objects—door key for common lock, closed pocket knife,
watch, penny, pencil.

35. Vocabulary list—first twelve words from each list.

36. White card with two black lines in center, one line 2¼ in., one
1¾ in.

37. Two black one-inch cubes, weighted. One weighs 3 grams, one
15 grams.

38. Card with four figures drawn on it—some feature on part of
the body omitted from each figure.

39. Card with ten geometric forms drawn on it. Same forms, drawn
individually on ten small cards.

40. Two cardboard rectangles 3 x 2 in. One rectangle is bisected
diagonally.

41. Picture card Dutch scene.
42. Card with four bright-colored rectangles symmetrically placed. First rectangle colored red, second yellow, third blue, and fourth green.
43. Card showing three pairs of women's faces, one of each pair of faces pretty, the other ugly.

It is taken for granted that adequate hygienic safeguards will be observed in the care and use of all test materials which are applied with infants, such as the cubes, cup, spoon and rod.

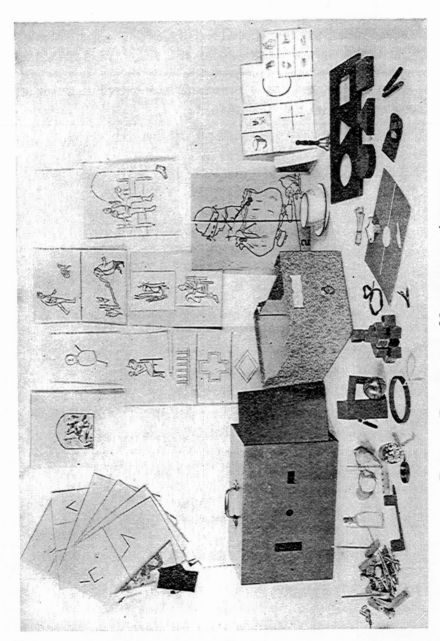

FIGURE 3. PSYCHOLOGICAL MATERIALS AND APPARATUS

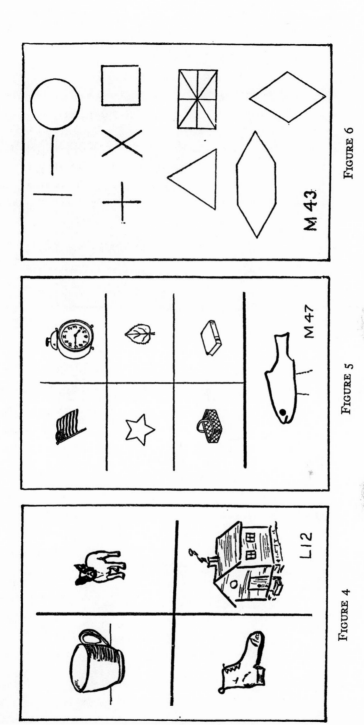

Figure 6

M 43

Figure 5

M 47

Figure 4

LI2

51

FIGURE 8

FIGURE 7

52

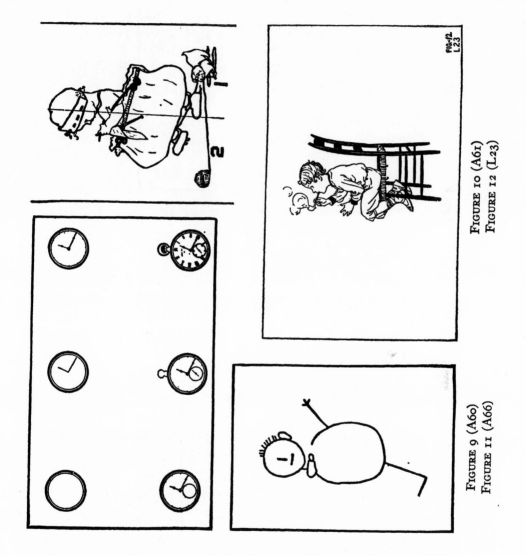

FIGURE 9 (A60)
FIGURE 11 (A66)

FIGURE 10 (A61)
FIGURE 12 (L23)

53

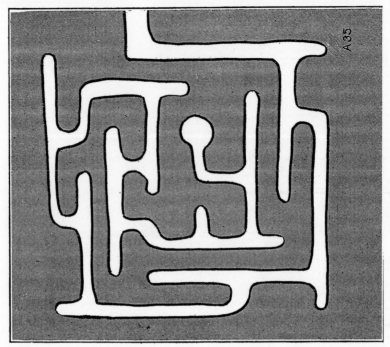

FIGURE 14

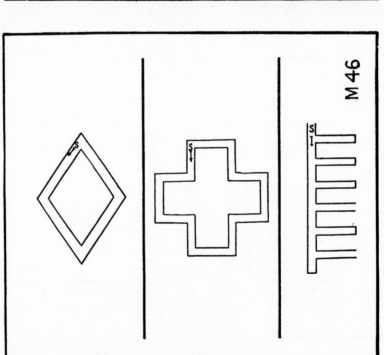

FIGURE 13

54

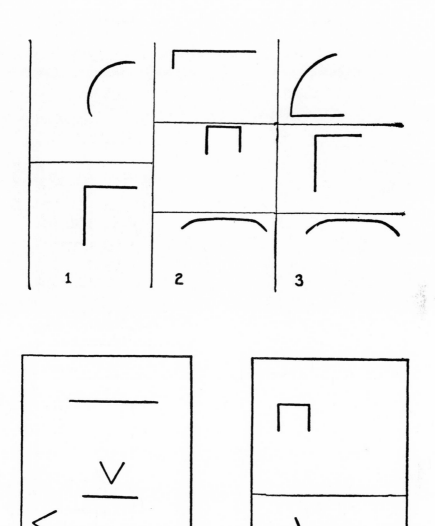

FIGURE 15

55

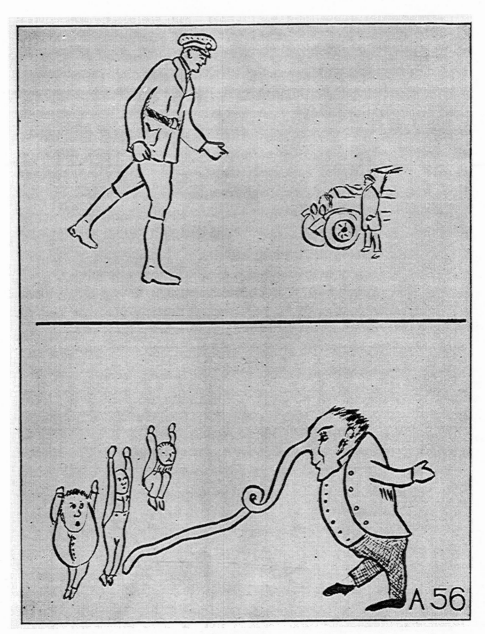

FIGURE 16A

56

FIGURE 16B

57

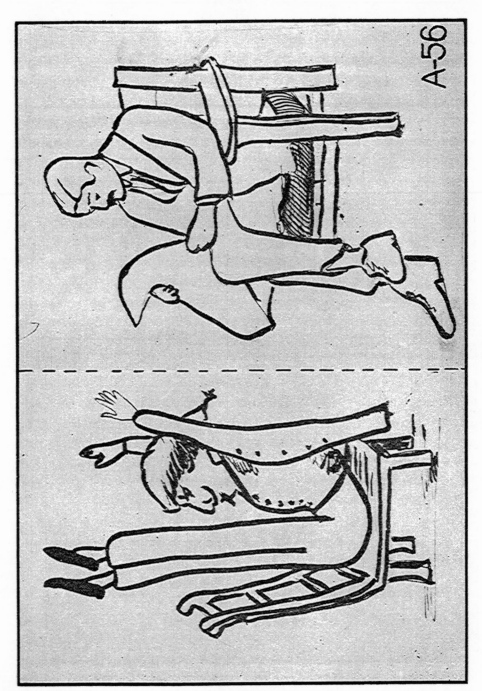

A-56

FIGURE 16C

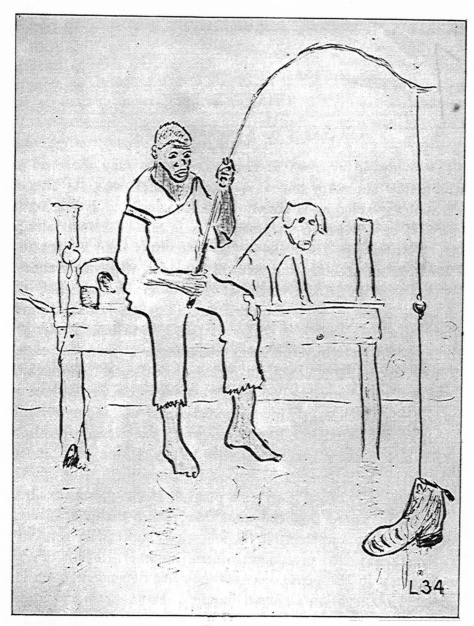

FIGURE 16D

59

CHAPTER 7

SYLLABUS OF NORMATIVE ITEMS

The following syllabus of normative items may serve as an introductory summary and as a table of reference. As already indicated the syllabus is simply a codification and is not to be construed or applied in an artificial manner. The schedules in Chapter 31 arrange the items in the order for actual application.

The syllabus specifies four fields of behavior, without, of course, implying any actual cleavages between them; and classifies the normative items in these four groups. The classification follows natural psychological lines so far as this is possible. Under the heading MOTOR are included items which relate to muscular capacity and coördination. LANGUAGE includes vocalization, speech, and auditory comprehension. To the PERSONAL-SOCIAL group are assigned items which largely involve social experience and personality traits. In the ADAPTIVE-BEHAVIOR group are placed remaining items which concern general capacity to exploit the environment or to make adjustments to imposed situations. Although the term is extremely broad it serves a purpose in the present context.

It will be noted that the term *item* rather than *test* is used. Many of the items, as shown in the following chapters, are tests with strictly standardized procedure; others, however, do not deserve the term *test* in this sense, because they are dependent upon less controlled observation or upon inquiry. From a clinical standpoint, however, they may be quite significant. They contribute either to description or to estimation; usually to both.

The order in which the items are to be applied in making a developmental examination is indicated in the schedules printed in Chapter 31.

Letter ratings are assigned to each item, based upon the frequency with which the item was found in the cases studied. Letter ratings rather than numerical expressions were used to avoid the disadvantages of over-precise formulation. The items are designated by key letters and key numerals.

The initial letters *M, L, A, P,* indicate general fields of behaviour: M, Motor; L, Language; A, Adaptive; P, Personal-Social behavior.

Each item is numbered. The first digit indicates the subdivision in the general field and the second digit indicates the specific item in this subdivision:

Thus, M24; M—Motor, 2—locomotion, 4—pushes with feet.

Ratings are always given in month and letter values. A+ represents a frequency of 1% to 19%; A equals 20% to 49%; B+ equals 50% to 64%; B equals 65% to 84%; C equals 85% to 100%.

Thus M24 is given a 4C rating; *i.e.,* pushing with feet is found at 4 months in 85% to 100% of the cases.

(M) MOTOR

M1. POSTURAL CONTROL

10. Resists head pressure 4C
11. Holds head erect 4B   6C
12. Lifts head prone 4C   head and chest 4B   6C
13. Back resistant 4C
14. Tries to sit 4C   Sits with support 4A+   slight 6B+   alone 6A+
    9C
15. Stands with help 9A   12C   alone 12A   18C

M2. LOCOMOTION

20. Reaction when prone: crawling 4C   creeps or hitches 6A+   9B
    12C   can climb stairs 12B+   18C
21. Rolls side to back 4C
22. Rolls back to stomach 4A+   6B
23. Motor reaction in bath: kicks 4C+   splashes with hands 4A   6C
24. Pushes with feet 4C

25. Makes stepping movements 9B
26. Walks with help 9A+   12B   alone 12A   18C

M3. PREHENSION

30. Resists rod withdrawal 4C
31. Clasps cube, 4C   Thumb opposition partial 4C   complete 4A   6C
32. Hand reacts to table 4B   6C   Picks up cube 4A+   6B   Secures
      pellet: whole hand 6A   fine prehension 6A+   9B
33. Puts hand to mouth 4C   inhibits 12B
34. Inhibits one hand 6A
      Manipulates one hand 6A   9C
      Preferential use one hand 6A+   9B+   12B
35. Holds two cubes 6B   9C   drops one for third   6B+   9B accepts
      third 9A   12B   accepts fourth 18B
36 Releases objects: throws objects to floor 6A   puts cube into cup
      (imitation) 12A   throws ball into box 18B

M4. DRAWING AND HAND CONTROL

40. Makes a scribble spontaneously 12A   18B   imitatively 12B   9A+
41. Makes a stroke 18B
      Differentiates stroke and scribble 18A
42. Imitates vertical 18A   24B   36C   circle 24A   36C
      horizontal 24A+   36B   cross 24A+   36B+
43. Copies circle 24A+   36B   48C   cross 36A   48B   square 48A
      60C   triangle 48A+   60B   Prism 60B   Hexagon 60A
44. Copies diamond in ink 60A+
45. Aligns card 36B
46. Coördinated tracing: Diamond 36A+   48B   Cross 48B+   60C
47. Steadiness Fish test A.   3=60B   48B   B.   4=60B+
48. Draws a man 48A   60B

(L) LANGUAGE

L1. VOCABULARY

10. Vocalizes 4B   Says "mama," "dada," or equivalent syllables 6A+
      9B
11. Says one other word 9A   two 9A+   three   12C   four 12B   five
      12A+   18B
12. Names one picture 18A   two 18A+   five to seven 24B   eight to
      nine 24A   36B

13. Names five familiar objects 24B+
14. Two or more words together 18A+   Speaks sentences 24B
15. Uses pronouns, plurals, past 24A+   36B
16. Defines by use 48A   60A
17. Word Test Series. 3-8. 60B 8-12. 60A 96B

L2. WORD COMPREHENSION

20. Adjusts to words 9B+
21. Points to one or two pictures 18A   three or more 18A+   five to seven 24B   seven plus 24B+
22. Obeys two prepositions 24B   three 24B+   36B   four or five 24-A+   36A
23. Obeys four prepositions 48C   48B+

L3. CONVERSATION

30. Names one object in picture 18A+
31. Names three objects in picture 24A   36C   4=36A
32. Uses one or more descriptive words 36A+   48B
33. Describes picture 60A+
34. Interprets humor 60B   60B+
35. Tells what he has drawn 48B   made 48B+
36. Gives differences 60A

L4. REPRODUCTION

40. Repeats things said 12A+   18A
41. Repeats 3 syllables 24A
42. Repeats 6 syllables 36C
43. Repeats 12 syllables 48B+
44. Repeats 4 digits 48B+   60B
45. Repeats 5 digits 48A+   60A
46. Non-infantile articulation 48A   60B

(A) ADAPTIVE BEHAVIOR

A1. EYE-HAND COÖRDINATION

10. Moving persons 4C—   plate 4B
11. Winks at sound 4C—   at hand 4B   at pencil 4A+   6B
12. Reacts to paper 4C   defensive hand movement 4A
13. Regards spoon 4B+   cube 4A   6B   pellet 6B+
14. Picks up spoon from table 4A+   6C

15. Dangling ring: reacts 4C closes in 4A clasps 6B above head 6B+
    pulls down 9B uses string 12B
16. Reaches for spoon 4A+ 6B 9C

A2. IMITATION

20. Spoon in cup 9A 12B
21. Rings bell 9A 12B
22. Hits doll 12A 18B
23. Block building: piles two 12B 12B+ three 12A 18C four 18A
    24B more 24A
24. Builds bridge 24A 36B
25. Builds gate: from model 48A 60B imitation 48B+
26. Recall block stairway 48A+ 60B+
27. Folds paper once 18A+ 24B twice 24A+ 36B+ diagonally
    36A 48B

A3. RECOVERY OF OBJECTS

30. Fallen spoon: conscious of disappearance 6B looks for 6A 9C
31. Cup covered cube test: lifts inverted cup 9C secures cube 9A 12C
32. Unwraps cube 9A+ 12B+ 18C
33. Removes pellet from bottle 2 imitation 18
34. Removes ball from box 36B
35. Garden maze 60B

A4. COMPREHENSION

40. Cube in cup. Commission 9A+ 12C
41. Cube in plate or cup 18B+ 12A+ cup, plate, box 18A 24B
42. Performs three commissions 36A 48B+ 60B
43. Comprehends *IV* "one" 36B two 36B+ 48B
44. Comprehends "lost" 48A 60B crosses street 48A 60B
45. Comprehends *VI* 48A+ 60B+

A5. DISCRIMINATIVE PERFORMANCE

50. Puts rod in box 12B
51. Puts square in box 18A 24B
52. Form board: Circle 18B+ shown 18B adaptation 18A
    Triangle 18A+ shown 18A
    Solves three: no error 24B+ in one minute 24B 36C
    Adapts three: no error 24A+ in one minute 24B+ 36B
53. Discriminates lines 36B

54. Aesthetic comparison 36A   48A   60B
55. Weights 36A   48B+   60B
56. Selects humorous 48B   60C
57. Matches forms   4=   36B   7=   36A   48B
58. Four blocks design 36A   48B

A6.   APPERCEPTION AND COMPLETION
60. Names watch: 4th, 18A+   24B   3d, 24A   36B+   2d, 24A+
     36B+
61. Solves picture completion 24A+   36B
62. Solves picture adaptation 24A+   36A
63. Form completion A (2 of 5) 36A   48B, (3 of 5)   48B+, (4 of
     5) 48A;   Form completion B   3=   60C;   4–5=   60B;   6=
     60B+;   7= 60A;   8= 60A+
64. Patience picture completion 48B
65. Patience card 48A   60B
66. Names incomplete man 48B
67. Man completion 3= 48B   5= 48A
68. Missing parts 48A+   60B+

A7.   NUMBER CONCEPT
70. Puts in "just one" 24A   36B; two 36B+   48B; three   48A+
71. Counts four 36A   48B+; ten 48A; thirteen 48A+   60A
72. Draws one 48C   two 48B   three or four 48A+   60B+
73. Problems: a) 48A   b) 48A+
74. Number of fingers 60B+

(P)   PERSONAL AND SOCIAL BEHAVIOR

P1.   REACTION TO PERSONS
10. Adapts to nursing 4C
11. Selective attention to face 4B   expresses recognition 6B   of stran-
     gers 6B+   9C
12. Anticipatory motor adjustment 4C
13. Reacts to mirror images 6A   9B   12C
14. Salutations: Waves "bye-bye" 9B+   Says "Bye-bye" or "Hello"
     9A+   says "Thank you" 18B
15. Shows affection 18A   24B
16. Forbidden acts: Inhibits acts when forbidden 12B   habitually 18B
17. Tells experiences 24B   tells stories 36B

P2.   PERSONAL HABITS

20. Puts on shoes: Tries 12B   succeeds 24A   laces 48B   ties 60A
21. Uses spoon 12A   well 18B, 24C   uses knife 48B+
22. Bowel control 12A   18B   asks to go 18A   24C
23. Bladder control 12A+   18A   24B
24. Buttons clothes 48B
25. Washes self 36A, 48B, 60B   brushes teeth 48B
26. Orderliness: Puts away toys 36B   orderliness in box 60B

P3.   INITIATIVE AND INDEPENDENCE

30. Asks for things at table: pointing 12A   18C   by name 18A   24B
31. Persistence in reaching 6A   9B
32. Knows where he wants to go 18B
33. Tries to turn knob 18B   24C   opens door 36B
34. Climbs for objects 18A   moves chair to attain end 24C
35. Goes on simple errands 18B+   outside 36A   48B
36. Trusted with breakables 36B
37. Resists suggestion 48B   4 times 60A   3 times 60B
38. Crosses street alone 36B+

P4.   PLAY RESPONSE

40. Enjoys bath 4C   laughs aloud 4B   frolics when played with 6B+
41. Plays with hands 4C   scratches 4B   with objects 4B+   pats table
    6B   9C   bangs spoon 6B   casts objects for noise 6A   12C
    exploits paper 6B   6A   9B   puts cube in cup 9A+   12A
42. Reacts to music 4C   turns head to voice 4C   to bell 4B+   6B
    coos 6A, 9B+, 12B   smiling, laughing 6B+   dances 9B   re-
    quests tunes 24B   recognition 36B
43. Plays pat-a-cake or peek 9B+   12C   with mirror image 9A   12B
44. Looks at pictures 18B+   likes stories with pictures 18A   24B   36C
45. Dramatic play: Imitative 18A   24B   pretence 36B   constructive
    48C
46. Dramatic drawing 48A   60B
47. Constructive play: Plays with cup, spoon, plate 6B   6A   9B   12C
    Uses building material constructively 48B   48A   60B

P5.   ACQUIRED INFORMATION

50. Asks questions of elders 36B
51. Points to parts of body 18B   two 18A   24B   distinguishes right
    and left 60B+

52. Verbal facility: counting 18A+   repeats part of alphabet 18A+
    recognition of letters or rhymes 36A
53. Tells name 24B   full 24A   sex 24A   36B+   age 60B
54. Knows money is for purchase 48C   names coins   48A+   60A
55. Distinguishes forenoon and afternoon 60B+
56. Uses color names 24A   names one color 24A+   36B+   two colors
    48B+   four colors 48A   60B

CHAPTER 8

Norms of Motor Development

Postural Control

M 10. Resists Head Pressure

RATING: 4C

Procedure: The examiner takes the baby's head between the palms, and gently exerts pressure to right and left and then forward and backward. There is a perceptible difference in the amount of resistance felt in the transverse and median directions. If the resistance is very slight or absent, no credit is given.

Comment: This item has potential clinical value. Lack of postural tonicity is an early symptom of developmental deficiency. Tonicity is not altogether conditioned by physical vigor and nutritional status. It depends upon dynamogenic factors and upon the maturity of the neuro-muscular system. There are interesting individual differences in the reaction of infants to this test which are worth noting. They would be still more significant if they could be registered with some accuracy by a dynamometric device.

M 11. Holds Head Erect

RATINGS: 4B 6C

Procedure: The examiner depends chiefly upon ordinary observation to determine whether the head posture is normal. At four months a marked tendency for the head to deviate from an erect posture should be given a minus rating. A definite tendency for the head to wobble when the body is gently shaken back and forth in a transverse direction should also be rated as minus. The child may also be held at various angles to note whether compensatory head postures are assumed.

Comment: When the wobbling is manifestly due to fatigue or debility, clinical allowance must be made. Normally, however, we may expect the four-months-old child to maintain fairly continuous erect posture of the head. To what extent rickets and abnormal size of head affect this reaction can only be determined by investigation. Fundamentally this postural control depends upon the maturity rather than the health of the nervous system.

M 12. Lifts Head in Prone Position

RATINGS: 4C Head and chest 4B 6C

Procedure: A pad is placed upon the table or floor and the examiner places the child in a prone position, being careful to place the hands and arms so that they will not be strained. The examiner then notes whether the head lies prone or whether the child lifts it up.

Comment: There are perceptible differences with respect to the alertness and intensity of this reaction. It is noteworthy that head wobbling is more evident in this position than in normal attitudes. Relative size of head and presence of rickets may seriously affect the reaction in this test and diminish its normative significance. However, it contributes to our total impression of any four-months-old baby under careful examination.

The head may lie prone or even drop forward, so that the examiner with his hand helps to make the head-lifting adjustment.

The child may lift the head a short distance or he may even raise both head and the upper chest well above the table surface. At four months the latter reaction is entitled to a B rating. At six months it is so prevalent that it receives only a C rating. Absence of the reaction at that level gives the item special significance.

M 13. Back Resistant

RATING: 4C

Procedure: The examiner lifts the child into his own lap and notes the rigidity of the spine. Although the four-months-old baby ordinarily has very little ability to sit up, he normally exhibits postural tone which keeps his back somewhat rigid while he is being handled.

Comment: Again, this test has little significance ordinarily, but in cases of abnormal retardation the examiner will detect an absence of the postural tonicity above mentioned. If the examiner suspects retardation it is important that he hold and handle the infant sufficiently to gain a tactile impression of the child's motor reactiveness. The "tension-feel" reported in this way may be quite informing.

M 14. Tries to Sit Up

RATINGS: 4C 4A+ 6B+ 6A+ 9C

Procedure: A four-months old child is placed in a dorsal position to note whether he makes any effort to sit up by lifting his head or shoulders. In the absence of evidence, the mother's testimony should be secured. A rating of 4C is given if he makes such an effort. A rating of 4A+ if he sits up with very slight support from pillows or blanket. His powers of sitting equilibrium can be verified by the examiner by placing the child on the table top in varying positions which will bring his balancing coördination into play. If he sits with slight support at six months, the rating is 6B+. If he sits altogether alone for some seconds, it is 6A+. At nine months the ability to sit alone is almost universal among normal children, and the rating falls to C.

Comment: This is a relatively objective test, even though precision of estimate is impossible. The broader clinical differences just noted can be ascertained and they are particularly interesting

at the four- and six-months-old levels because they are indicative
of the stage of neuro-muscular development. To what extent
nutritional factors, like rickets, obscure or distort the significance
of the reactions can, of course, be determined only by careful research. Our data are not sufficient to tell us the frequency with
which children at six months and nine months can raise themselves
unaided to a sitting posture when lying on a hard table surface.
This is a well defined response, and although it must be modified
somewhat by the freedom of movement which has been permitted
to the child, norms for it should be determined.

M 15. Stands

RATINGS: 9A 12C 12A 18C

Procedure: The baby is held (under the arms) in a suspended
position so that the feet just touch the floor. If he stands with help,
he receives a rating of A at nine months, and a rating of C at twelve
months. If he stands alone, he receives a rating of A at twelve
months and a rating of C at eighteen months.

Comment: This test is not subject to much error in observation.
The prevalent factor of rickets, however, undoubtedly distorts its
normative significance as a symptom of motor development. The
ability of the body to support its weight by standing while the
examiner holds the hands is one which may be tested as low as
four months, for one child in our group of fifty was able to stand
with ease for a considerable time simply by being held by the hands.
Moreover, this particular child showed great desire to assume this
very position and manifested marked pleasure in it. This suggests
that the development of standing ability ought to be determined
for the six months level. We have made numerous observations
on the spontaneous posture of the legs when four- and six-months
babies are held up in the air to give the legs free play. Over half of
the four-months babies kept their legs in a flexed or semi-flexed

position. Extension of the legs into a straight position may be related to the nascency of standing, but our observations are not clear enough to warrant a frequency norm.

LOCOMOTION

M 20. Reactions when Prone

RATINGS: Crawl, 4C; creep, 6A+ 9B 12C; Climb, 12B+ 18C

Procedure: Place the child in a prone position on the floor or table (a big table is convenient) and note his locomotor reactions. Supplement observation with interview inquiry.

Comment: Some kind of squirming, wriggling progression is all but universal at four months. Any marked lack of reactiveness, if not due to physical debility, is suggestive of retarded neural development. Creeping shows a consistent letter rating differentiation at three successive levels. Since retardation in walking is one of the outstanding symptoms of developmental defect, it is well to have a perception for all these earlier locomotive responses which antedate walking.

To what extent constraint from clothing and crib inhibit the attainment of locomotive abilities is difficult to estimate. Undoubtedly there are ultrasolicitous and ultrainattentive mothers who do not permit the baby sufficient opportunity to display these abilities.

Hitching is of many varieties, some fortuitously and picturesquely conditioned. One retarded twelve-months baby whose developmental status was six months, propelled herself forward while lying on her back by a regressive pushing by the heels. She would go a considerable distance by this method, but she could not sit up.

M 21. Rolls from Side to Back

RATING: 4C

Procedure: Place the child on his side and note whether he attempts to roll onto his back. In the failure of a reaction, the testimony of the mother may usually be relied upon.

Comment: Nearly all four-months-old children have given evidence of this capacity. Sometimes the failure may be due to the fact that an inexperienced or overbusy mother has not given the baby any freedom of exercise or movement. Discount should be made in those cases, but where a child has been given the freedom of a floor or bed, we may ordinarily assume that at four months he can roll from his side to the back, or *vice versa.*

M 22. Rolls from Back to Stomach

RATINGS: 4A+ 6B

Procedure: The examiner must usually rely upon the observation of the mother with respect to this item. A small percentage of four-months-old children are able to roll completely over from back to stomach or stomach to back.

Comment: This item is interesting because a predominating percentage of six-months-old children are able to perform this motor feat. The rating at six months, therefore, is B. It follows that complete absence of this ability at nine months may have presumptive value in diagnosis.

M 23. Motor Reactions in Bath

RATINGS: Kicks, 4C Splashes with hands, 4A 6C

Procedure: Interview with questioning to determine if possible precisely when the splashing began.

Comment: We do not imply that these reactions have any recapitulatory relation to aquatic locomotion, by including them here! They throw a little light, however, on the general motor maturity of the infant. This rather than the playful aspect of the responses is important. Splashing with the hand is a very specific and clear-cut bit of behavior, which emerges rather acutely. Four months appears to be definitely the nascent period for it. Well established hand splashing at four months appears, therefore, to be a sign of somewhat advanced motor development. At six months this ability is so nearly universal as to have little discriminating value. But absence of this item (always assuming normal opportunity) at that time is noteworthy.

M 24. Pushes with Feet

RATING: 4C

Procedure: The child is held as in M15 but his feet are now allowed to touch the examiner's lap. The examiner notes whether there is a definite upward pushing reaction in response to the stimulus. This pushing reaction may also be observed to advantage sometimes when the child's feet are allowed to touch the floor or table.

Comment: This pushing reaction is very strongly developed at the age of six months and is milder but not infrequent at four months. It is possible that its absence may in certain cases at least be associated with relatively slow development. In more than one of our subnormal cases, marked limberness of the legs is evident at six and nine months.

M 25. Makes Stepping Movements

RATING: 9B

Procedure: The child is held as described in M 24, but his feet are allowed to touch the floor only lightly. The purpose is to see whether this stimulus initiates a rhythmic stepping response of any kind.

Comment: This reaction may be merely a playful one comparable to patting the table, or to splashing. It may, however, be genetically related to walking. It is very characteristic of the nine-months level.

M 26. Walks

RATINGS: With help, 9A+ 12B Alone, 12A 18C

Procedure: The examiner can usually determine for himself whether a child shows any disposition or capacity to walk, either alone or by support of both hands. As early as nine months this ability may be tested, because a small proportion of advanced children walk with help at that time. The rating at nine months for walking with help is A+; at twelve months it falls to B. Ability to walk alone earns a credit of A at twelve months and a credit of C at eighteen months.

Comment: Although the age of walking bears some broad correlation with the development of intelligence, the examiner must be ready to make clinical discounts for individual cases at all times, largely because the very common disease of rickets inflicts delay.

PREHENSION

M 30. Resists Rod Withdrawal

RATING: 4C

Procedure: A small red rod is placed in the palm of the child's hand, the fingers being pried open if necessary. The examiner then attempts to pull the rod from the child's grasp and notes the strength of resistance.

Comment: Success in this test is uniformly expected in normal children at four months. Failure may be related to defective development. Even in the neonatal period a reflex type of clasp is present. The individual differences in the strength of resistance and the aggressiveness of the response may be noted.

Reflexes are always conditioned by the prevailing physiological state of the nervous system, and variations may be expected even in a simple reflex response during a short period of time in the same individual.

M 31. Clasps Cube

RATINGS: 4C   complete 4A   6C

Procedure: One of the red cubes is placed in the palm of the child's hand to note whether there is a reflex closure. Credit score is given if the cube is held for a few moments or longer.

While the child is handling the cube (or rod or spoon in connection with other tests) note whether the thumb frees itself from the curled-up position which is characteristic of an earlier age. If at any time the thumb partially straightens and coöperates in the manipulation or prehension reactions, the response is recorded as partial thumb opposition and a credit is given for the four-months level. Complete thumb opposition at four months would be entitled to an A rating. At six months, we give credit only when there is consistent unmistakable thumb opposition in similar manipulation.

Comment: The length of time during which a four-months-old baby can retain hold of a cube seems to depend upon variable and rather fortuitous factors. If the child is relatively quiescent, or if the impulse to random activity finds outlet in eye, facial, or leg movements, he may retain hold of the cube for a minute or more. The test, however, is inserted to disclose cases where the reflex clasp is very weak or lacking altogether.

Here, as elsewhere, further investigation might enable us to work out a more detailed procedure and a more objective standardization with regard to thumb opposition. There are unquestionably ascertainable individual differences at the age of four months with respect to the mobility and freedom of the thumb. These differences may be correlated with more fundamental developmental differences. Thumb opposition reappears as a factor in an important nine-months-old test (M 32). Between the gross manual scoop at six months and the pincer-like prehension of a pellet at nine months there are interesting gradations.

M 32. Hands React to Table Edge

RATINGS: 4B 6C

Procedure: The child is taken up by the examiner or by the mother and held in sitting position so that his hands are within favorable range of the edge of the table or of the performance box. Care should be taken to remove, so far as possible, distracting stimuli and to keep the child in a comfortable but favorable posture. It may be necessary actually to bring the hands up to the table edge and to place them on the edge in order to initiate the response. The test is passed if the child shows even very simple fingering or manipulation. The test is scored a failure if the child is altogether passive and if the hands remain inert.

Comment: The test is a very interesting and useful one. It does not, of course, yield to very precise standardization, but it does permit the detection of individual differences in reactiveness among four-months-old children. These differences pertain chiefly to the vigor and complexity of the manual attack upon the table. Four-months infants advanced in development will make incipient or mild exploratory movements and even the patting or banging movements, which are so characteristic of the six-months level. The test merits further study and elucidation.

M 32. Picks Up Cube

RATINGS: 4A+ 6B

Procedure: While the child is seated at the table as just described, place a red cube within easy access. In the case of a four-months infant wave the cube before his eyes and bring the cube to the surface with a little force to attract attention if possible. In the case of six-months infants simply place the cube in position. It is permissible to make the adjustment as easy as possible for a four-months infants, but credit is only given when there is a definite picking or reaching; a reflex, accidental clasp does not count.

Comment: This item is especially interesting and probably significant of more than average ability in a child just four months of age. In the case of six-months subjects it reveals differences in directness, deftness, and motor control.

M 32. Secures Pellet

RATINGS: Whole hand, 6A   Fine prehension, 6A+   9B

Procedure: A white pellet is placed on its convex surface before the child, within easy reach; his motor adaptation to the pellet is particularly noted. At six months a very small percentage of the children pick the pellet with a pincer movement of thumb and forefinger. The rating at six months, therefore, is A+ for fine prehension. It is 6A for a coarse whole-hand reaction. At nine months, however, a deft direct thumb and finger prehension is highly characteristic and the rating becomes B.

Comment: This test proved to be very interesting and probably has considerable clinical usefulness. It makes a rather sharp cleavage between the six- and nine-months levels. The reaction cannot be greatly distorted by extraneous factors and perceptible differences in skill can be noted. It is also probable that general nutritional conditions, including rickets, are not likely to affect this reaction seriously. We have in mind one very frail, seriously underweight, six-months-old child, prematurely born, who had so little energy that she did not even kick her feet, but was able at six months to trace a reed border in her crib with her forefinger. It it quite possible that this child could have picked up a pellet even at six months, in spite of her general appearance of motor disability.

The six-months infant ordinarily disregards or does not perceive the pellet; and if he secures the pellet, it is by a coarse, infrahuman kind of palmar scoop.

Although this test establishes a cleavage between the six- and nine-months levels, there is a gradation of responses between the simian scoop and the precise pincer prehension. Our observations suggest that defective infants achieve this coördination more slowly than normal infants; and that the intermediate or partially achieved type of response lingers longer and is more readily observed in the latter. (See Figures 120–129.)

A shot rolling about freely in an enamel saucer offers a somewhat more difficult problem than the pellet; but the attention frequently goes to the saucer instead of the pellet, and a better procedure must be found.

M 33. Hand to Mouth Reaction

RATINGS: 4C 12B

Procedure: Incidental to the general examination on the four-months schedule, the examiner tries to note whether the child can put his hand to the mouth. During an examination of a four-months-old child it frequently happens that this reaction does not come into play, and the testimony of the mother may then be used. On the twelve-months schedule, the examiner notes whether in the cube tests and similar situations the hand to mouth reaction is prevailingly inhibited.

Comment: The test has little normative significance at four months, but an absence of this reaction at this age would suggest serious retardation in development.

In general the hand-to-mouth reaction is very dominant at six months, is on the wane at nine months, and relatively inhibited at twelve months. If it is pronounced at twelve months and there are no associated symptoms of retardation, it may express a personality factor of some kind which needs investigation. That the intensity of the reaction is also affected by dentition seems possible.

M 34. Uses One Hand

RATINGS: Inhibits one hand, 6A   Manipulates with one hand, 6A
9C Prefers right (or left) hand, 6A+,   9B+   12B

Procedure: We attempt to determine unidextrality in connection with the persistent reaching test.   A red rod is held definitely in the median plane and the child is encouraged to make repeated efforts to grasp it.   Usually the hands go down before a renewal of effort.   The attempt is made to determine whether the child shows preference for one hand in these renewals of efforts or whether at six months he suppresses one hand in his reaching.   At nine months the examiner notes whether the child uses one hand independently in his manipulations.

Comment: The margin of error in judgment is a large one, but there is a small proportion of cases in which unidextrality unmistakably asserts itself as early as six months.   Our ratings indicate that there is a progressive increase from six months to twelve months with respect to this trait.   At six months both hands and the head and the mouth may participate in the reaching response.   There is a tendency to reach with the head when the hands do not attain the object.

M 35. Holds Two Cubes

RATINGS: 6B   9C

Procedure: A red cube is placed in a palm of each hand or is held so that the child may secure each of the two cubes by reaching. The purpose of the test is simply to ascertain whether the child accepts and retains temporary hold of both cubes, one in either hand.   He is entitled to a rating of B at the age of six months and of C at the age of nine months.

Comment: Why there should be the percentage difference at these adjacent levels in this particular reaction is not clear.   Probably the excess of random activity at the age of six months favors the prompt dropping of one of the cubes. In any event, the ability to hold definitely two cubes is a symptom, so far as it goes, of advancing maturity and inhibition.

M 35. Accepts Additional Cube

RATINGS: Drops one for third, 6B+ 9B Accepts third cube, 9A 12B Accepts fourth 18B

Procedure: While the child is retaining hold of two cubes, a third one is speedily proferred him within easy reach and the examiner assists, so far as he can, in facilitating the acquisition of the third cube without actually placing it into the hand of the child. At six months he gets B+ credit if he drops one or both cubes to get a third. At nine months he gets a B credit for this reaction, but an A credit if he takes the third cube without dropping either of the other two. At twelve months he gets a B rating for this accomplishment, and at eighteen months he will accept a fourth or even a fifth cube without losing hold of those he first possessed.

Comment: In most cases this test is easily scorable on the basis of objective evidence, although there are many variations in the response including seizure of the third cube by mouth. We have not carried the test into the two-year level, but the responses at eighteen months suggest the possibility of doing so with advantage. Even at eighteen months it is well to offer not only a fourth, but a fifth and sixth cube to note how the child solves the situation. The response must have some significance for intelligence because it is distinctly an adaptive form of behavior. It reflects not only degree of motor capacity but range of attention.

M 36. Throws Objects to Floor

RATING: 6A

Procedure: Interview or incidental observation.

Comment: There are conditioning factors which reduce the

normative value of this item; but if casting or brushing aside objects is definitely acquired at six months it denotes favorable motor development.

M 36. Puts Cube into Cup

RATING: 12A

Procedure: The examiner places a cube into a cup and by word and gestures asks the child (repeatedly if necessary) to do the same.

Comment: The ability to relinquish hold of an object is a more complicated motor adjustment than we ordinarily suppose. Even twelve-months children have some difficulty in doing this voluntarily in simple situations. Complicating factors sometimes defeat the object of this test, but it is worth trying.

M 36. Tosses Ball into Box

RATING: 18B

Procedure: The open end of the performance box is presented to the child and he is asked to toss a ball into it. The child stands up.

Comment: The red ball has considerable interest for the child and his willingness, as well as his ability, to relax his hold comes into play. This may make the results of the test ambiguous, but the test may then become significant in another direction.

DRAWING

M 40. Scribbles

RATINGS: Imitative 9A+   12B   Spontaneous 12A   18B

Procedure: The child is given a sheet of paper and large red crayon. The examiner demonstrates scribbling on the same sheet of paper and promptly gives the crayon to the child, with the command and gesture to imitate him. On the basis of our percentages, imitative scribbling merits a rating of A at nine months and B at twelve months. At the twelve- and eighteen-months level the child may be given an opportunity to scribble spontaneously. If he can do so, a rating of A is given at the age of twelve months and B at eighteen months.

Comment: The general significance of drawing as an index of development will be discussed in a subsequent chapter. Drawing should be systematically utilized as a developmental test, if for no other reason than the fact that it leaves its own objective record. The record frequently needs qualifying and interpretative comment, but to a considerable extent it tells its own story. The story becomes reinforced when drawings accumulate as a result of successive examinations.

We make liberal use of (green tinted) drawing paper in our clinical work, and give even nine-months-old subjects a chance to make their mark. It may be nothing more than a banging staccato or a faint fugitive scrawl; but it belongs to the record. True scribbling either spontaneous or imitatively induced is characteristic of the twelve-months level. Successive samples of the child's drawings from this scribble to the representative portrayal at five years furnish important guides for diagnostic estimate and should not be omitted from a continuing clinical record.

M 41. Makes a Stroke

RATINGS: 18B Differentiates from circle, 18A Differentiates stroke and scribble, 18A

Procedure: If the child scribbles imitatively, draw a straight vertical line at the side of a piece of paper and tell the child, with appropriate words and gestures to make one like it. Repeat this procedure two or three times to determine whether the child will in imitation make a single stroke, for which he receives a rating of B at eighteen months. If the child makes a stroke, draw a circular figure by drawing circles on top of one another. If an eighteen-months child can adjust to this situation by changing from the stroke to the circular scribble, he receives an A rating.

Comment: This simple but revealing test involves discrimination (what test does not?) and writes its own record. In this sense the test belongs quite as much to the category of adaptive behavior. It must be understood throughout the schedules that we do not wish to confine this or any other test by any rigid limitations of its classification in the syllabus.—Imitative drawing requires a lower type of capacity than drawing from a copy.

M 42. Imitates Drawings

RATINGS: Vertical, 18A   24B   36C   Horizontal, 24A+   36B   Circle, 24A   36C   Cross, 24A+   36B+

Procedure: The examiner makes a bold vertical line upon the piece of paper and then presents it with crayon to the child. If necessary repeat the act several times with encouraging words. Then with similar procedure he is given an opportunity to draw in imitation a horizontal line, two lines which cross each other and a circle. Definite attempt at reproduction is expected for the above ratings.

Comment: Before imitation of drawings is attempted, an opportunity should be given even to the two-year children to reproduce the drawing of a circle from a card. The reproduction of a circle at the verbal instruction to "make one like this" without the aid of demonstration gesture is rarely found among the two-year children and consequently receives the high rating of 24A+. We have ample evidence that the ability to draw a vertical stroke (imitatively) precedes the ability to draw a horizontal one. The chief purpose of the test is to record higher levels of the imitative discrimination, referred to in M41. If the child shows (without undue persuasion) a willingness to attend to a model on a card and a readiness to copy it, he should be tested on the copy rather than the imitation series. Copying from a model implies a higher grade of ability.

M 43. Copies Drawings

RATINGS: Circle, 24A+ 36B 48C Cross, 36A 48B Square, 48A 60C Triangle, 48A+ 60B Prism, 60B Hexagon, 60A

Procedure: Individual cards are presented with the following designs drawn in bold black outline: circle, square, cross, oblique cross, square triangle, prism, hexagon, diamond. After the child has been supplied with a pencil and a separate piece of paper for each drawing, the cards are placed before him, one at a time, with the remark, "Make one for me like this." If there is hesitation, the examiner must encourage by words but not by drawing around the figure in pantomime. "I am sure you can. Try! Let me see you do it just like this." To conform with the accustomed procedure, three trials should be given in the case of the square, and a pen and ink should be provided in the case of the diamond, though no serious errors result from the use of pencil or crayon.

The child is credited with a passing score for the circle if he draws a line looped back on itself and not carried more than half way round again. He is credited with a pass in drawing the crosses, regardless of the angles which the lines make with each other, though it is worth while to note his ability to make a distinction between a right angle cross and oblique cross. The triangle is scored plus on the basis of three lines and three angles. With younger children, the square and diamond should be scored liberally, following the suggestions in Terman's *Measurement of Intelligence*. The examiner may find it profitable to use the cross and the square as learning tests, but the child's ability to copy from the model card should first be tested so that the scoring will not be invalidated. The scoring on the circle should be more liberal at two and three years than at four years. These drawing problems test spontaneous willingness to attend; but judicious urging and encouragement are permissible with young subjects.

M 44. Copies Diamond in Ink

RATING: 60A+

Procedure: The procedure has been covered in M43. Pen and
ink should be used. If crayon is substituted a note should be made
of the fact, as it simplifies the situation. In exceptional cases, however, such substitution is permissible if the examiner wishes data
uniform with the previous series.

Comment: This classical test in itself raises enough problems
for a psychological monograph. The analysis of failures and ap-
proximations to success is particularly interesting. A diamond is
but two triangles conjoined; but ability to copy a triangle does not
always augur ability to copy a diamond.

M 45. Card Alignment

RATING: 36B

Procedure: In connection with the Form Completion Test
(A63), the examiner notes whether the child can accurately bring a
rectangular card and a straight line into alignment. A B rating
is assigned at three years.

Comment: Personality reactions in this test are often worth
noting.

M 46. Coördinated Tracing

RATINGS: Diamond, 36A+   48B   Cross, 48B+   60C

Procedure: The child is presented with a piece of paper on
which two double diamonds, a "path," and a cross path are outlined. On a demonstration form the examiner traces a pathway
around the diamond. He then gives the pencil to the child and
says, "Now you draw a mark around this one but don't touch any
of the lines." A second trial is given if necessary on a second
diamond, and a credit score is granted if on either trial there are

not more than three errors in crossing the guide lines. At the four, and five-year-old levels, a cross form is presented in a similar manner. The ratings are assigned on the following basis: 36A+ and 48B for the diamond; 48B+ and 60C for the cross.

Comment: This test, adapted from Porteus, inevitably makes demands upon intelligence as well as motor coördination; but the procedure should stress the latter objective; and the part of the formula about not touching the lines should be emphasized. The child's attack on the problem as well as the objective results should be noted.

M 47. Steadiness Fish Test

RATINGS: 48B   60B   60B+

Procedure: The materials described in detail elsewhere consist of a cardboard fish, a metal rod, and a piece of blotting paper with a two inch chalk circle in the middle. The examiner says, "Let's go fishing. Here is a pond and here is the fish (placing fish in the middle of the white circle) and here is your fishing pole. Now see if you can catch the fish just like this, using only one hand, just one hand." Two trials with the right hand are given with the fish facing left on the first trial and facing right on the second. Then two trials are given with the left hand with fish facing right and then with the fish facing left. Time is taken on each trial and recorded separately. There will be a tendency to shift from one hand to the other, to turn the fish to a more favorable position or even to hold it while the rod is put in the eye. If the fish is knocked over the examiner promptly replaces it. The examiner must be ready to restrain the hand, each time saying, "Just one hand." If this is not sufficient it may be necessary, after two or three warnings, to hold the hand for a second or two. Stop at the end of sixty seconds.

Credit is given if on one trial with the right hand the child was successful within fifteen seconds, or if successful within thirty seconds with the left hand. Either credit is rated as B at the four-year level. At the five-year level four successes in one minute are rated as B+ and three successes in one minute as B.

Comment: The test is a rough clinical measure of coördination but is still more useful as a fertile provocative for the instantaneous liberation of personality reactions. Rather fundamental reactions to success and failure are possible.

M 48. Draws a Man

RATINGS: 48A   60B

Procedure: While providing the child with a fresh sheet of paper, say in a casual tone, "Can you draw a man?" If the child says "No," suggest that he try and record the response. This reaction helps to distinguish between critical attitude and real inhibition. After the child is through, ask him what he has made. This helps in scoring the figure and brings out personality traits. We assign a rating of 48A if the child draws a conventional figure with eye, mouth, body, arm, and legs; or of a face with the eyes, nose, mouth, and hair; or any drawing which shows that the child has made lines which represent to him a combination of parts of the body. A circle with two straight lines is common at the age of four. Scribbles, even though called a man, should not be credited. A recognizable picture of a man receives a rating of B at five years.

Comment: The discussion of drawing in Chapter 15 will furnish some hints as to clinical interpretation.

CHAPTER 9

NORMS OF LANGUAGE DEVELOPMENT

VOCABULARY

L 10. Vocalizes

RATINGS: 4B 6A+ 9B

Procedure: By interview, supplemented frequently by observation, the examiner can determine whether the four-months-old child is beginning to produce simple sounds like Ah, Eh, Eeh, Ooh, and other vowel combinations. Can also inquire as to inflection, repetition, etc. The evidence that the child definitely vocalizes two or more distinguishable sounds merits a rating of B at four months.

The examiner ascertains whether the child has said "Da-da, Ma-ma," or some unmistakable equivalent. If so, he earns a rating of A+ at six months, and of B at nine months.

Comment: With intelligent mothers the examiner will do well to make detailed inquiries, and to make some brief record of the variety of vocalization which has been observed. Some distinction must probably be made between sputtering types of sound play, and early articulate syllables. Normative data of some significance can probably be derived from more extended and systematic investigation on this point.

L 11. Uses Words

RATINGS: 9A 9A+ 12A+ 12B 12C 18B

Procedure: Through interview the examiner determines the words which the child unmistakably articulates and assigns rating as follows: One word (in addition to *da-da* or *ma-ma*) 9A; two

89

words (in addition to *da-da* or *ma-ma*) 9A+; three words 12C; four words 12B; five words 12A+ and 18B.

Comment: Although there are inevitable variations in regard to the amount of stimulation, there are few babies who are without the opportunity of assimilating a few simple words relating to their personal or physical environment. Inasmuch as it is possible to ascertain these words at the age interval from twelve to eighteen months, it becomes an objective measure of development which may have considerable significance. The vocabulary test has been called the best single test for older children and there is no reason to believe that it is less significant with pre-school children. We have, therefore, attempted to get a rough index of vocabulary throughout the ascending age levels.

L 12. Names Pictures

RATINGS: 18A   18A+   24B   24A   36B

Procedure: Two cards, one with four, one with six pictures of simple objects, are presented and the child is asked to name them. The simple four-picture card is first shown. The examiner points to each picture in turn if necessary and encourages but does not assist. Naming one picture gives a rating of 18A; naming two pictures gives a rating of 18A+; five to seven pictures, 24B; eight to nine pictures, 24A and 36B. Careful inquiry may elicit definite evidence from the mother; but the inquiry must be detailed and critical.

Comment: This is an exacting test, and when passed in a clear-cut manner should be weighted favorably. Rapport is always important; but the item is a test of willingness to attend as well as of ability. Though the reaction is doubtless affected in some way by home experience, the willingness to attend is itself primarily conditioned by adequate maturity. Naming the flag, leaf and star taps the higher range of ability.

L 13. Names Five Objects

RATING: 24B+

Procedure: Use a key, penny, closed knife, watch, and ordinary pencil, and say in turn for each object, "What is this?" If all five are named correctly, a rating of 24B+ is assigned.

Comment: This is at variance with the Stanford scale, which requires that only three objects be named correctly and assigns the test to the three-year level. It is too easy for three years. It may be extended to the eighteen-months level, but is probably less significant there because the experience factor may be more misleading at that time

L 14. Combines Words

RATINGS: 18A+ 24B

Procedure: If the examiner can assure himself by actual observation or by interview that the child combines two words appropriately and significantly, the item is entitled to an A+ credit at eighteen months. Any simple sentence used conversationally to express thought is entitled to a 24B rating.

Comment: This item is significant and should receive ample attention. It is desirable to record sentences and phrases actually used. The examiner should not attempt to force conversation with timid or silent children. He is more likely to be rewarded with remarks if he exercises patience and unconcern.

L 15. Uses Pronouns and Plurals

RATINGS: 24A+ 36B

Procedure: The examiner must depend upon his observation during the examination supplemented by the information of an intelligent mother to tell whether the child uses correctly I, you, me, and plurals and past tense. For children reared in English-speaking homes the rating at the age of two is A+; for three-year-olds, B.

Comment: Because of the conceptual content of plurals and pronouns these words, properly used, are likely to have considerable significance at both the two- and three-year levels. In a sense, this is a form of vocabulary test. Discount must of course be made when a child has not had sufficient language experience at home.

L 16. Defines by Use

RATINGS: 48A 60A

Procedure: Use the words *chair, horse, fork, doll, pencil,* and *table.* Say, "You have seen a chair. You know what a chair is. Tell me what a chair is," and so on with the other words, always in the order in which they are named above. Four out of six words secures ratings of 48A or 60B.

L 17. Word Test Series Vocabulary List

RATINGS: 60B 60A

Procedure: The first 24 words in the Stanford vocabulary list are presented to the five-year-old child. Say to the child, "I want to find out how many words you know. Listen and tell me what is an orange." Any response which indicates familiarity with the meaning of the word is sufficient to earn a plus credit. Liberal interpretation and procedure may be used at the five-year level. The ratings are on the following basis. Knows three to eight words of vocabulary list, 60B; eight to twelve words, 60A. An unusually high rating on the vocabulary test would suggest the applicability of advanced tests to supplement the pre-school schedule.

Comment: The value of the vocabulary test is widely recognized. High ratings usually though not uniformly have a correlation with general mental ability. The reverse, however, is not equally true, particularly in young children. The fact that conversation is highly conditioned by personality factors must always be borne in mind as a clinical precaution.

COMPREHENSION

L 20. Adjusts to Words

RATING: 9B+

Procedure: Comprehension or motor adjustment to certain words can be determined by interview and sometimes by observation. If present at nine months, it merits an estimated rating of B+.

Comment: We have seen a good many instances in which a child acquired, through training or accidental association, an adaptive response to a word stimulus as early as nine months. For example: Stimulus: "Where is the kitty?" Response: Looks. S: "Has the baby a cold?" R: Coughs. S: "How big is the baby?" R: Puts up hands.

L 21. Points to Pictures

RATINGS: 18A 18A+ 24B 24B+

Procedure: The same pictures used in the picture-naming test are presented, but the child is merely asked, with encouraging gesture to point out an object. The examiner should begin with the four picture card, and say first, "Show me the shoe." The ratings are on the following basis: one or two pictures, 18A; three or four, 18A+; five to seven, 24B; seven or more, 24B+.

Comment: While not as exacting as the ordinary vocabulary test, this has a similar significance and where rapport and home background are normal it has considerable clinical import. Simple outline drawings of objects are more readily recognized than complicated pictures of these objects.

L 22. Obeys Prepositions

RATINGS: 24B   24B+   24A+   36B   36A

Procedure: This test consists in placing a ball in response to command, in order to ascertain the child's comprehension of the common prepositions. The examiner gives the child the following commands in order:

  (a) Put the ball on the box.
  (b) Put the ball in the box.
  (c) Put the ball behind the box (or chair).
  (d) Put the ball in front of the box (or chair).
  (e) Put the ball under the chair.

The ratings are on the basis: Two correct, 24B; three, 24B+   36B; four or five, 24A+   36A.

L 23. Obeys Four Prepositions (Drawing)

RATINGS: 48B+   48C

Procedure: The picture of the boy blowing bubbles is presented. The examiner asks, "What is the boy doing?" Explanations are given if necessary and the bubble in the picture is traced so that the child may know it is a *bubble.* Then he is told to draw one bubble under the chair, two bubbles above his head, three bubbles behind the boy, four bubbles in front of the boy. Number of bubbles and location are scored separately. Ninety per cent of the children place the bubbles under and above correctly, which gives a rating of 48C. Fifty-two per cent of the children place the bubbles in all four commands correctly, which gives a credit of 48B+.

Comment: This test appeals to the four-year-old child's interest and provides in a very brief time an objective record of his comprehension and of his discriminative performance. This same item (A72) is used to test number sense.

L 30. Names Object in Picture 1

RATING: 18A+

Procedure: Picture 1 (Figure 7) is presented and examiner says "Tell me what you see in this picture." He may facilitate response by showing one object and giving considerable encouragement. If the child then names at least one object a rating of 18A+ is given.

L 31. Names Objects in Picture 1 or in Picture 2

RATINGS: 24A 36C 36A

Procedure: The procedure is the same as in the foregoing (L 30). The picture of the Dutch home is shown.

Comment: This picture is used in the Stanford-Binet Measuring Scale of Intelligence and it is interesting to note that it is applicable to the two-year level. It is almost too easy for the three-year level but becomes sufficiently exacting if four objects instead of three must be named. In our group of fifty three-year-old children eighteen per cent named six objects, twenty-two per cent named four objects, and ninety-two per cent named three objects.

L 32. Uses Descriptive Words

RATINGS: 36A+ 48B

Procedure: The examiner presents the pictures as described above in L 30 and notes whether spontaneous description enters in any way into the replies of three- and four-year-old children. If one or more descriptive words are used, a rating of A+ is given for a three-year-old child and a rating of B for a four-year-old child.

Comment: The beginnings of description can be found as low as the three-year level. There is frequently anticipation of it at the eighteen-months level. Terman says that "description is rarely encountered before five years." We found that twelve per cent of the children in our normative group of fifty introduced some degree of description and even of interpretation. For example, one child's response was, "Lady. Girl crying. Mama spanked her. Bread. Kitty. Basket."

L 33. Describes Picture

RATING: 60A+

Procedure: The examiner this time presents the same picture but with the question "What is this picture about?" More than half of the responses to this question should be descriptive in character. The Binet standard of scoring is used.

Comment: The Stanford Revision assigns this test to the seven-year level. It is appropriate for high average five-year-old children and secures a rating of 60A+.

L 34. Interprets Humor

RATINGS: 60B+   60B

Procedure: The examiner presents a humorous picture of a man fishing up a shoe and then says, "You like funny things, don't you?" "Is that funny?" The spontaneous answer may be recorded. The examiner then asks, "Why is it funny?" and also records this answer. If the answer contains any element of interpretation a B+ rating is given. If the child makes negative response or no response at all, the humorous picture of the kittens dancing in a circle is presented in a similar manner. A rating of B is given if an interpretative answer is made. The examiner should score liberally in this test and make ample discount for personality inhibitions. On the other hand conversational spontaneity and definite perception of humor should be weighted favorably.

L 40. Repeats Things Said

RATINGS: 12A+ 18A

Procedure: By actual trial or interview information the examiner can determine whether the child is able to repeat simple words on hearing them. The examiner should enlist the coöperation of the mother in this item because the child is frequently conditioned so that he will respond to the word stimulus if it comes from the mother, when, for example, she says, "Say 'Kitty'." Credit should not be given if this ability does not extend beyond one or two words with which he has been familiarized by previous training. Here, as in many other items, positive evidence is more significant than negative evidence.

L 41. Repeats Three or Four Syllables

RATING: 24A

Procedure: Begins by saying, "Can you say 'Mama'? Now say 'Nice Kitty'." Now ask the child to say "See the cat"; next, "I have a dog"; next, "Where is mama?" If the child grasps the idea that repetition and not an answer to the remark is desired and can reproduce the syllables without error except in articulation an A rating is given at two years. Ability to understand the instructions is tested quite as much as reproduction capacity by this item It is too difficult for the average two-year-old child and need not be applied at all if the child is unfamiliar with English.

L 42. Repeats Six Syllables

RATING: 36C

Procedure: The examiner follows the same procedure as in the previous item but uses instead the sentence "I have a little dog."

He speaks distinctly and in a natural voice. The first sentence may be repeated one or two times but the following two sentences must be said only once. "The dog runs after the cat." "In summer the sun is hot." The test is passed if at least one sentence is repeated without one error after a single reading.

L 43. Repeats Twelve Syllables

RATING: 48B+

Procedure: Same as above. Use following sentences: 1. "The boy's name is John. He is a very good boy." 2. "We are going to have a good time in the country." 3. "When the train passes you will hear the whistle blow."

L 44. Repeats Four Digits

RATINGS: 48B+ 60B

Procedure: The examiner says "Listen, I am going to say over some numbers and after I am through I want you to say them exactly as I do. Listen closely and get them just right." Give (a) 4, 7, 3, 9. (b) 2, 8, 5, 4. (c) 7, 2, 6, 1. If necessary the first four digits (Group A), may be repeated to encourage an attempt, but neither of the other series. The reading should be a little faster than one digit per second. Credit is given if one set of the three is correctly reproduced after a single hearing.

L 45. Repeats Five Digits

RATINGS: 48A+ 60A

Procedure: The procedure is the same as above with the following three sets of numbers: (a) 3, 1, 7, 5, 8. (b) 4, 2, 8, 3, 5. (c) 9, 8, 1, 7, 6. Credit is given if one set of digits is correctly reproduced.

L 46. Articulation

RATINGS: 48A   60B

Procedure: In giving Binet's sentences to determine verbal reproduction it is desirable for the examiner to note the articulation of the child. The sentence "In summer the sun is hot" is particularly useful for this purpose. The children can be divided roughly into two groups, those with relatively infantile and those with non-infantile articulation. The latter group secures a rating of A at four years and B at five years.

Comments: Descriptive comments and an actual record of the malarticulation should be made.

CHAPTER 10

Norms of Adaptive Behavior

Eye–Hand Coördination

A 10. Eyes Follow Moving Person

RATING: 4C

Procedure: While the child is seated in the mother's lap the examiner walks back and forth within the child's range of vision. If there is definite evidence that the child notices the examiner and follows him even a little with the eyes, the test is considered passed. If there is a difficulty in securing the child's attention, window shade may be drawn up and down to determine whether the child notices it.

Comment: The purpose of this simple test is to determine whether the child reacts to gross visual stimuli and is developing rudimentary perception. Every child in our series of fifty readily met this test. If the child clearly fails to respond to large moving objects at the age of four months, developmental retardation may be suspected. Specific sensory defect must of course be ruled out.

A 10. Follows Moving Plate

RATING: 4B

Procedure: A white enamel plate is held with its flat surface before the child's eyes at a distance of about two feet. The examiner then moves it slowly from right to left to determine whether the child's eyes follow coördinately. The plate is then moved up and down in the median line of vision to determine whether ocular following movements take place. A 4B rating is given if the response is prompt and definite in either plane.

Comment: This test is not so simple as it appears to be. Apparently there are many conditioning factors which make the response a variable one. There are marked individual differences with respect to the directness, accuracy, and promptness of the response. Lateral control is acquired earlier than vertical. A gross functional nystagmus is sometimes observed, but this probably occurs more frequently in mentally defective children. The examiner must sometimes make persistent trials before the response is evoked. He may find it necessary to distract the child from an interest in the window or some rival stimulus. The dependence of this response upon attendant factors means that failure must not be taken too seriously. However, eighty-three per cent of four-months children passed the test under ordinary clinical conditions. Four children failed to follow in either direction, three failed to follow in the up and down direction. The whole situation is one which requires considerable research before all of the factors can be evaluated.

A 11. Blinks at Sharp Sound

RATING: 4C

Procedure: Hold the enamel saucer with its bowl surface facing the child's eyes at a distance of about four inches. Take the spoon and give the saucer a sharp rap. Note whether the child blinks.

Comment: This test proved very interesting because the response had none of the uncertainty or precariousness which characterizes the two following tests which use a visual stimulus. There was unanimous and prompt blinking on the very first blow of the saucer. Although we have by no means attained uniform control over the visual responses in the tests just outlined, the fact that we have secured a differentiation even with our crude procedure suggests the possibility of making more accurate and significant clinical observations in this field.

A 11. Winks at Threatening Hand

RATING: 4B

Procedure: While the child is held seated in the mother's lap the examiner brings the open hand, by a feint, within a few inches of the child's eyes to determine whether the child will wink reflexly. This feint is repeated several times if necessary and the test is passed if the child unmistakably winks twice in response to the threat.

Comment: Several of the comments made with reference to A10 apply here. The visual mechanism of the four-months baby seems to be in a relatively unstable state of organization and to be highly conditioned by unknown factors. A baby who does not wink at the beginning of the examination, without any apparent alteration in the surrounding conditions, may respond to the test at the close of the examination. Failure must, therefore, not be interpreted as being of serious import. However, 84 per cent of our group passed the test. At six months 100 per cent of the children passed the test, so that it has no normative value at that level except for definitely retarded cases.

A 11. Winks at Pencil

RATING: 4A+ 6B

Procedure: This is a variation of the test just described. Instead of the hand the examiner takes hold of the end of a full-length pencil and brings the pencil suddenly near the eyes of the child in the central diameters of the visual field alternately in a vertical and horizontal position, being careful to stand at the side and to hold the pencil in such a manner that the stimulus will not be the examiner's hand, but the pencil.

Comment: This test is interesting because it was passed by a small percentage of four-months-old babies and because there is an evident differentiation in the two stimuli. It may be that winking at a pencil represents a somewhat more advanced neuro-ocular organization than winking at the hand.

A 12. Reacts to Paper

RATINGS: 4C 4A

Procedure: While the baby is lying on the table the examiner takes a piece of ordinary letter size paper and, holding one corner of it, places it flat upon the child's face. No pressure except that of the paper itself is exerted. The examiner then peers beneath the paper to note the reaction of the child. Any kind of reaction is sufficient to pass the test as we scored it.

We reserve the 4A rating for those children who make definite defensive movements with the hand which comes up to the paper and seizes it, or knocks it aside.

Comment: Only eight children out of fifty in the four-months group made a defensive hand movement, and this ability seemed to be associated with advanced motor development in other directions. The more frequent reactions varied from mere increase of activity to a crying sound of protest. Often the only reaction is an increase of mouthing movements or of head aversion.

The test probably has some clinical value because it tends to disclose extreme cases of complete passivity on the one hand and of advanced development on the other.

A 13. Regards Spoon or Cube

RATING: 4B+ 4A 6B

Procedure: While the child is seated in a favorable position in the mother's lap a spoon is placed upon the table. The examiner notes whether the child spontaneously regards the spoon. If there is no spontaneous regard, the examiner takes up the spoon, brandishes it before the baby's eyes, and knocks it on the table and

otherwise attempts to attract attention to it. The test is considered
passed even if the child then pays attention to the spoon. The
examiner may also place the spoon in the child's hand to determine
whether it is then regarded. A rating of 4B+ is given in either case.
A cube may be presented in a similar manner, with ratings of 4A
and 6B.

Comment: This test serves to indicate a higher level of perception than that which is called for by any of the preceding four-
months tests. Inspection of the spoon put in the baby's hand is
sometimes more easily elicited.

A 13. Perceives Pellet

RATING: 6B+

Procedure: The examiner takes one of the pellets and places
it on its convex surface immediately in front of the child and within
his easy reach. The examiner notes whether the child perceives
the pellet and makes some effort to secure it. If he at once perceives
it, the fact is noted in the record. If the child does not immediately
perceive the pellet, repeated efforts should be made to draw attention to it; it should be moved from one place to another and may be
brought to the table surface with a swift descending gesture—all
for the purpose of determining whether the child can observe and
react to so small an object. A B+ rating is given if there is a
response at the age of six months. It is not necessary that the child
should actually pick up the pellet to secure this rating.

Comment: This test is comparable to the spoon test at the age
of four months. The development of perception is such in early infancy that selective preference is given to large and massive stimuli,
but at the end of the first half-year attentiveness to small objects,
like crumbs, fibres, and strings, is beginning to manifest itself and
our pellet test is intended to measure crudely the perceptive capacity of the child at the age of six months. The test has not pre-

sented many difficulties in administration and appears to us to be fairly reliable for this purpose and will probably prove to have diagnostic suggestiveness in cases of marked retardation in general development.

A 14. Picks Spoon from Table

RATINGS: 4A+ 6C

Procedure: The procedure is the same as in the previous test, but the examiner attempts to determine whether even under most favorable conditions the child is able to definitely pick up the spoon and lift it from the table.

Comment: Only 10 per cent of the children in our four-months group were able to pick the spoon from the table. This ability is undoubtedly correlated with relatively advanced motor organization. It is important not to credit with a pass those children who simply seize and hold or even manipulate the spoon because of reflex tactual response. There must be an element of definite reaching to entitle the child to credit because the purpose of the test is to make a differentiation between reflex clasping and rudimentary reaching.

A 15. Reacts to Dangling Ring

RATING: 4C

Procedure: The infant is in dorsal position lying on the table. The red ring is dangled before him immediately above his face and swung in different directions to attract his attention. It may even be allowed to fall on his upturned face in order to stimulate a response. The test is passed if he clearly regards the dangling ring or makes incipient hand or arm movements in response. Frequently, however, such incipient reaching is not observable, although the child is very evidently fascinated by the stimulus.

Comment: Nearly all of our subjects (95 per cent) passed this test. Regarding a swinging, dangling object is probably simpler or more frequent at this age than definitely regarding a spoon on the table or held in the hand. Failure to meet this simple test does not by itself establish a developmental defect or retardation, but warrants very careful investigation to determine such a diagnosis.

A 15. Attains Dangling Ring

RATINGS: 4A 6B 6B+ 9B 12B

Procedure: The procedure on the four-months schedule is the same as that just described, but the child is required to actually bring his hands together by a closing-in motion which will bring the ring within his grasp. Definite reaching is not expected in four-months-old subjects. Very few indeed are able to reach directly for the ring, but about 43 per cent close in on it in the manner described. If the child simply makes struggling gestures but does not actually attain to the ring, he is not credited with passing this test.

At the six-months level, the child is not lying down but is seated in the mother's lap. The ring is dangled about a foot above and in front of him. If he seizes it, he is credited with a B rating. If he seizes it when it is straight and well above his head, a B+ rating is given. At the nine-months level, his reaction is more mature and he tries to pull down the ring. At the twelve-months level, we note whether he regards the string which suspends the ring and shows some interest in securing the string. The string may be dangled at the six- and nine-months levels to note grasping and reaching responses.

Comment: It is impossible to standardize this test with complete precision, but experience will help the examiner to formulate his own clinical standards and help him to recognize the differences in attack at the ascending levels. In its present form the test has relatively little value for the twelve-months level, but it is interesting to note whether the child shows any selective interest in the string.

A 16. Reaches for Spoon

RATINGS: 4A+ 6B 9C

Procedure: The spoon is held in full view perpendicularly before the child within easy range for vision and grasping. With older children (six months, nine months, twelve months), the spoon should be kept somewhat outside the range of easy reaching in order to better determine directness and precision of the response. In the case of four-months-old subjects, however, every effort is made to facilitate the reaction because it is relatively rare, even under the most favorable conditions. At six months the reaching must be direct and accurate; at nine months it must also be direct and accurate; at twelve months we wish to note especially whether the hand-to-mouth reaction is inhibited after the child has seized the spoon. At six and nine months he receives credit for the test even if he promptly puts the spoon to his mouth.

Comments: Reaching is a reaction of fundamental importance in infancy. Variations in promptness, directness, and accuracy undoubtedly have a correlation with the developmental status of the child. It is for this reason that definite reaching at the age of four months is particularly interesting. How significant such early reaching may be as an index of intelligence endowment cannot, of course, be stated without further and more precise data.

IMITATION

A 20. Imitates Rattle of Spoon in Cup

RATING: 9A 12B

Procedure: A spoon is rattled in the cup by the examiner by a stirring or oscillating motion. The test is passed if the child succeeds in making a noise with similar motion.

Comment: Our data on this test are insufficient, but it is inserted as being a promising test of the imitative capacity of the nine-months- and twelve-months-old child. The examiner will, of course, appreciate on this and similar items that an action may simulate imitation without actually being so.

A 21. Rings Bell

RATINGS: 9A   12B

Procedure: An ordinary hand bell is placed in the hands of a nine-months-old child, after demonstration of how it is rung. If he rings the bell in a purposive manner, the test is passed. The rating at nine months is A. The rating at twelve months is B.

Comment: The significance of this reaction is not altogether clear. An element of imitation enters at twelve months and this factor may be partly responsible for the increased number of successes. A less ambiguous test should be devised.

A 22. Rubber Doll Imitation

RATINGS: 12A   18B

Procedure: A small rubber whistle doll is placed prone on the table immediately in front of the child. The examiner hits it smartly a few times to produce a whistling sound. The child is then given an opportunity to imitate him. The score is on the basis of simple success or failure at both the twelve- and eighteen-months levels.

Comment: Voluntary imitation undoubtedly has a fundamental relation to intelligence. It is, therefore, worth while to ascertain in different ways whether such imitation is present at the levels in question. Individual differences in precision and alertness of response are revealed by this test. Individual differences in emotional reaction are also observable, and we encountered one subject in whom the situation aroused evident fear.

A 23. Block Building

RATINGS: 12B 12B+ 12A 18B 18A 24B

Procedure: The examiner takes the pile of red blocks and places them in confusion before the child. The examiner then builds a tower of two or three blocks and by motions and command asks the child to build one too. At twelve months, if the child responds adaptively by placing one block on another or on the examiner's demonstration tower, he receives a rating of B; if he piles two, the rating is B+; if 3, A. The rating is raised to A when three blocks are added to a tower of two. At eighteen months the rating is C for piling three and A for piling four; but it is B if he builds a tower of three independently, in imitation of the model. At the age of two years he secures a B rating if he builds a tower of four or more.

Comment: The block building tests, which are rather prominent in our schedules, undoubtedly reveal progressive grades of capacity and motor maturity. The imitative superstructure tower occurs very frequently at the age of twelve months and represents a definitely lower stage of ability than duplicating a model. Motor coördination and painstaking personality qualities are incidentally revealed by the test. Reactions to blocks are so easily evoked, so characteristic and objective, that it will be profitable for the examiner to organize on the basis of his observation concrete mental formulations of these characteristic reactions at various levels.

A 24. Builds Bridge

RATINGS: 24A 36B

Procedure: The examiner builds a simple bridge of three blocks, the third resting squarely on the corners of the two buttress blocks. The child is credited with a success if he makes any arrangement of three blocks which duplicates the model; but he must have arranged the buttress blocks purposefully, not placing the third block by chance on two adjoining blocks.

Comment: This is a definite test of practical comprehension and of the same functions which underlie drawing from a model. At two years a rating of A; and at three years a rating of B is assigned. At two years, one may still find a tendency to add on to the model presented by the examiner. Such a response, however, cannot be credited as a success.

A 25. Building Block Gate

RATINGS: 48A 48B+ 60B

Procedure: The material for this test consists of ten red cubes. Say to the child, "Shut your eyes and I'll make something for you." Record the response but if the child shows unwillingness to close his eyes proceed to build a model gate of five blocks screening it from the child's view by a box cover. Then show the gate. Say to the child, "Now you make one for me just like this." Urge and encourage to secure the initial attempt but give no further guidance unless he begins to build something altogether different.

If unsuccessful tell him to watch while the examiner builds another model for his benefit. Use one hand only so that he can easily see how the parts are combined. With this assistance repeat procedure as above and record the figure which the child makes. Credit only a figure with blocks correctly though not necessarily symmetrically arranged. The rating is 48A if he builds the gate on the first trial without demonstration, and 48B+ if he needs the demonstration model. The estimated rating for five-year-olds (either with or without demonstration) is B.

Comment: This is a useful test. It extends the imitative series begun at twelve months into the five-year level. Rapport is easily secured. Attention and personality traits are readily observed.

A 26. Recalls Block Stairway

RATINGS: 48A+ 60B+

Procedure: The material, as in A25, consists of ten red cubes and the child is again asked to close his eyes with the remark, "I am going to make something for you again." Record any significant personality response and proceed as in the gate test. Make a stairway of four flights out of the blocks and tell the child to look at it saying, "See, four steps, 1, 2, 3, 4. Can you make one like this? Try." Wait a moment and then knock over the block saying, "Now you make the steps for me." Make a record of the time. As it is highly improbable that a four-year-old child will be able to successfully make these steps the test becomes one of perseverance in the face of difficulty. If the child works purposefully for more than one minute and fifteen seconds he may be characterized as very persistent on this test (ten children out of fifty worked in this way). Over thirty seconds has been scored as equivalent to persistent. When the child makes only one attempt and then gives up he is characterized as non-persistent on this test. The term *fairly persistent* may be used to describe a child who makes a few attempts and then is diverted from the main purpose.

Comment: The remarks made in connection with scoring indicate that this should be utilized as a personality observation test as well as a performance test. It may be regarded as the capstone of the series of block tests which appear at every level beginning with four months. It taps the upper range of adaptive imitation as found in normal pre-school children.

A 27. Folds Paper

RATINGS: 18A+ 24B 24A+ 36B+ 36A 48B 60C

Procedure: A piece of letter-size paper is folded transversely by a single crease in the middle. It may be refolded two or three times. The child is then given a second piece of flat paper with the words, "You make one like this." A single fold earns a score of A+ at eighteen months and of B at two years. With two-year-old children the paper is folded twice, one fold at right angles to the other. Imitative success secures a rating of A+ at two years and of B+ at three years. At the age of three years the situation is further complicated by a third diagonal fold, and success earns a rating of A at that age and B on the four-year schedule and C on the five-year schedule.

Comment: This test might have been grouped under the motor items because it makes definite demand upon motor coördination and precision, but it also involves display of intelligence. Furthermore, it brings personality traits into play. The test is most useful and convenient. It is also self-recording, and the paper may be dated and filed away as part of the case record.

RECOVERY OF OBJECTS

A 30. Looks for Fallen Spoon

RATINGS: 6B 6A 9C

Procedure: A spoon is placed at the edge of a table, immediately after the child has been playing with it and while he is still interested in it. The spoon is then suddenly dropped or thrown to the floor. The examiner notes whether the child shows by his facial expression or demeanor that he is conscious of its disappearance, and he also notes whether the child promptly turns its head to look for the fallen spoon.

Consciousness of disappearance should be noted in the record and apparently deserves a B rating at the age of six months. A rating of A, however, is given if the child definitely looks for the fallen object. At nine months the proportion of children who look for the fallen spoon is so great (93 per cent) that the rating sinks to C.

Comment: The characteristic response to a fallen spoon in a nine-months-old child is so prompt, definite, and adaptive that we make a fair inference when we say he "looks" for the spoon. Shall we attribute any "consciousness" or "awareness" of disappearance at the six-months level, when his reaction is signified by a fleeting facial expression or postural alteration?

A 31. Cup-covered Cube Test

RATINGS: 6B 6A+ 9C 9A 12C

Procedure: The examiner takes one of the small red cubes and casts it upon the table to entice the child's attention. He may even allow the child to handle the cube for a moment. While the attention of the child is directed to the cube, the examiner swiftly covers it with an inverted enamel cup and placing the handle of the cup at the child's right, he notes first the reaction of the child to the cup.

If he lifts the cup by any means whatever at the age of six months, he is given B credit. If he regards the handle and seizes the handle, this fact should be noted. Only one child in our group of fifty six-months-old babies showed any interest in securing the cube from its cover. Forty-six per cent of nine-months-old children secured the cube and nearly all of them lifted the cup. We therefore give a rating of C for lifting the cup at nine months, a rating of A if the cube is secured. At twelve months 86 per cent of the children definitely secured the cube, and the rating declines to C.

Comment: This is undoubtedly a valuable performance test. Complicating and distorting factors are relatively few. The test is placed near the beginning at each of the schedules when nearly every child is much interested in the red cube. The mental processes required for the solution of this situation follow closely the paradigm of Binet's definition of intelligence, and it was most astonishing to find one six-months-old child who solved the situation unmistakably, not only once but six times in immediate succession, exhibiting great zeal and concentration.

A 32. Unwraps Cube

RATINGS: 9A+   12B+   18C

Procedure: A red cube is wrapped up in a sheet of letter-size paper before the child's eyes. Before wrapping up, the child should be given the cube to play with and should be interested in it. While attending to the cube, it is hastily wrapped up in a loose, baglike bundle, lightly closed, but completely concealing the cube. The child is then told to get the cube. The test is passed if he immediately secures the cube by unwrapping or by manipulation.

Comment: This test has some historical interest because it is an adaptation of the wrapped-up bonbon test suggested by Binet as being appropriate for the two-year level. We suspected that this was a misplaced standardization and have found an appreciable percentage of nine-months-old children who will definitely look for the concealed cube, and others who will find it as a result of ordinary manipulation. The percentage steadily increases in three months. At the age of one year, 60 per cent of the children recovered the cube from the paper wrapping. At eighteen months, nearly all the children are able to perform the test. It is not supposed that a nine-months-old child unwraps the cube in obedience to the command, but that he is prompted by a native curiosity or explorativeness comparable to the inquisitiveness which a nine-months-old child betrays when he looks for a fallen spoon.

A 33. Removes Pellet from Bottle

RATINGS: 12A   18C

Procedure: A small 1-oz. transparent glass bottle with a 2-cm. opening, uncorked, and containing a pink pellet is handed to the child. Immediately before this he has been permitted to have the pellet, which is unceremoniously taken from him and put into the bottle, before his eyes.—Make a brief descriptive record of his response.

Comment: We do not have sufficient data, as yet, to assign ratings to this test. It may profitably be tried at the twelve- and eighteen-months levels because it is a variation and extension of the concealed-cube situation. The frequent effort to secure the pellet by thrusting the hand through the neck of the bottle at twelve months and the absence of this method of attack at eighteen months are significant.—The spontaneous play with pellet and bottle is interesting and instructive to the examiner.

A 34. Puzzle Box

RATING: 36B

Procedure: The ball which has been used in the preposition test is given to the child and he is asked to place it in a part of the puzzle box described elsewhere. The examiner then closes and fastens the box in view of the child and hands it to the child with the ball showing through the top. The examiner then says, "You may play with the ball if you can get it without tearing the box or breaking the string."

Comment: The children were most interested in this test. The interest seems to be in the puzzle rather than in securing the ball to play with as they wished to be allowed to do it again in almost every case. In order to get the ball three steps are necessary; first, the ball must be slipped from a loop, the loop must be pulled through a ring, and third, the cover must be lifted from the box. The most frequent error was the attempt to pull the ball through the small opening. The test seems to prove that even a child of three has a strong interest in puzzles if the puzzle is within the limits of his comprehension and capacity. Exactly 72 per cent of the children succeeded in opening the box and no difference was found between boys and girls, as the score stood 36 per cent of passes for each.

The test may be tried at two years, but at the risk of arousing considerable emotional reaction in certain cases.

A 35. Garden Maze Test

RATING: 60B

Procedure: A maze 9 by 12 inches in size with fourteen blind alleys is used and a time limit of 110 seconds is set. On this basis 74 per cent of five-year-old children reached the center of the maze and a rating of B is assigned. The test is preceded by the five-year Porteus Maze as a demonstration. The examiner says, "Suppose this is a garden and these are garden paths. These lines are fences which you cannot get over. You have to find your way to the center of the garden." The test is included in the five-year schedule chiefly because of its effectiveness in bringing out personality differences. The child is allowed to correct his own errors. His reaction to the errors may be noted.

Comment: Scrupulous adherence to procedure is not insisted upon in all cases, because the test as used on the five-year schedule is intended largely as a basis for displaying and recording personality reactions.

COMPREHENSION

A 40. Places Cube in Cup on Command

RATINGS: 9A+   12C

Procedure: A red cube is given to the child and the child is told to place it in the cup. The word of mouth is accompanied with gesture. Gesture and command may be repeated several times and the child should be given every possible opportunity to meet the test. Success is scored if he obviously places the cube in the cup in obedience to the command and not by chance.

Comment: The test has relatively little significance at twelve months, where it is rated as C, but it serves to disclose advanced comprehension in nine-months-old babies. Reluctance or motor difficulty in releasing hold of the cube is frequent at the one-year level.

A 41. Places Cube in Cup, Plate, Box

RATINGS: 12A+ 18B+ 18A 24B

Procedure: The table is cleared and a cup and plate are placed before the child. He is given a cube and asked without specific gesture to place the cube in the cup. The cube is restored to him, he is asked to place it in the plate, and this procedure is continued until the examiner ascertains whether the child's response is discriminating or non-discriminating. The word *plate* is preferred to saucer as being the more familiar. At eighteen months, the test is complicated by adding a low box (*ca.* 4 by 6 by 2 in.) to the series. The procedure remains similar. A rating of A+ is earned at twelve months and B+ at eighteen months, if discrimination is made between cup and plate. If made between cup, plate, and box, the rating becomes A at eighteen months and B at two years.

Comment: This test presupposes some familiarity with language, but can be used with a child from a foreign language home if English has not been altogether outside of the child's experience. Tendencies to a kind of perseveration show themselves in an interesting manner.

A 42. Three Commissions

RATINGS: 36A 48B+ 60B

Procedure: Take subject to center of room. Say, "Now, I want you to do something for me. Here's a key. I want you to put it on that chair over there; then I want you to shut (or open) that door, and then bring me the box which you see over there" (pointing in turn to the objects designated). "Do you understand? Be sure to get it right. First, put the key on the chair, then shut (or open) the door, then bring me the box (again pointing). Go ahead." Stress words *first* and *then.* Give no further aid.

Credit if the three commissions are executed in proper order.

Comment: The procedure follows the Stanford Revision. The errand and commission capacity of the child can be determined even below the three-year level. It is reflected in the little errands and chores he can do at home under accustomed conditions. Items covering this point are related to his personal-social behavior and are considered in that connection.

A 43. Comprehension of Questions IV

RATINGS: 36B   36B+   48B

Procedure: Be sure to get subject's attention before asking question. Repeat if necessary. Allow 20 seconds for answer.

> (a) "What must you do when you are sleepy?"
> (b) "What ought you to do when you are cold?"
> (c) "What ought you to do when you are hungry?"

The scoring on this test is as follows: 36B if one question is answered correctly, 36B+ or 48B if two questions are answered correctly.

A 44. Comprehension

RATING: 48A

Procedure: The examiner simply asks the child the question, "What must you do if you have lost something?" and repeats the question, if necessary, as in the Binet comprehension questions, and records response. He also asks "What must you do just before you cross the street?" A correct answer to either question merits a rating of 48A.

Comment: We have included these practical-judgment questions, because they clearly fall within the ordinary experience of four-year-old children and because we wished a more complete scale of comprehension problems. The examiner will, of course, make discounts if there has been inadequate language background.

A 45. Comprehension of Questions VI

RATINGS: 48A+   60B+

Procedure: Say:

(a) "What's the thing to do if it is raining when you start to school?"

(b) "What's the thing to do if you find that your house is on fire?"

(c) "What's the thing to do if you are going some place and miss your train (car)?"

It is permissible to repeat a question, but not to change form.

Credit if two or three responses are correct.

Comment: These questions are adapted from the Stanford Revision. It will be noted that they have a partial applicability to the four- and five-year levels.

DISCRIMINATIVE PERFORMANCE

A 50. Puts Rod into Performance Box

RATING: 12B

Procedure: The examiner gives the child the small red rod and presents the performance box, placing the surface of the box at a level favorable for manipulation. By word and pointing he asks the child to place the rod into the hole. If there is no response, he may demonstrate and let the rod fall with a thud into the box. The test is passed if the child then places the rod into the hole, whether he lets the rod drop or not. We should also credit as a success the occasional instance in which a child thrusts his finger instead of the rod into the hole.

Comment: The interest in the various hole insertion and fitting tests is so nearly universal that it must have some instinctive basis. It is somewhat surprising to find so many twelve-months-old children responding to this problem. We usually accompany the administration of the test with verbal directions, but we should get almost an equally high response if the test were presented mutely. Even the demonstration is superfluous in many instances.

A 51. Performance Box (Square)

RATINGS: 18A 24B

Procedure: The conditions of this test are similar to those just described. The child is handed a square block which is presented horizontally with the rectangular surface foremost, or it is placed flat on the surface of the performance box. A rating of A is scored at eighteen months and of B at twenty-four months if the child without demonstration thrusts the square through the rectangular opening.

Comment: This situation tests the child's power to make an adaptive rotation of the block. Frequently he is foiled by attempting to place the block through the hole diagonally. Then his judgment and power to straighten the block are clearly brought into play. Undue persistence in obvious errors is not without significance here, particularly in retarded cases. At eighteen months the child may also make an effort to thrust the block into the small rectangular hole of the performance box.

A 52. Three-Hole Form Board

RATINGS: 12B 12A 18B+ 18A+ 18A 18B

Procedure: A simplified form board with circular, triangular, and square openings and no bottom is laid on the table. The child is given a round block. No directions are given or gestures made at first. If the twelve-months-old child inserts the circular block without help, he earns a rating of A. If he needs to be shown by gesture or demonstration, he earns a rating of B. At eighteen months the score is B+ if he is not helped; B if he is shown. At eighteen months we also present in turn the square and triangle and he is scored A+

if he puts either one of them into the form board without being shown, and A if he is shown.

Comment: This test is presented after the performance box at both the twelve- and eighteen-months levels and the effect of the previous performance carries over. The response of the children does not depend upon verbal direction or urging. The circle is unquestionably the easiest of these three forms. The selective interest in the circle combined with the priority of the ability to use it adaptively is a pretty example of the specificity and orderliness of development. (Does the child ever *first* acquire equal skill with the triangle?) The graded series of letter ratings on this one test show its differentiating character.

A 52. Adapts Circle to Reversed Form Board

RATING: 18A

Procedure: The form board is presented as before, and after the circle has been placed the board is rotated on the table through an arc of 180° in the child's view. He is again given the circle, and if he does not persist in attempting to place the circle in the square opening but makes the adaptation and places it in its proper hole he is credited with an A score at eighteen months.

Comment: This is a convenient test which takes but a few moments to administer and brings into operation a kind of mental adjustment which may be presumed to have significance as a symptom of intelligence.

A 52. Solves Three-Hole Form Board

RATINGS: Within time limit 24B   36C without error 24B+ Adaptation: within time limit 24B+   36B; without error 24A+

Procedure: The form board is placed before the child. The blocks are arranged so that each block is in front of its appropriate hole. The examiner then says, adding gesture, "Now put all of these blocks into their holes." Three trials may be given if child does not place without error. A trial is concluded at the end of one minute or if the child definitely pushes the board away and does not respond to words of encouragement to proceed. After each trial, a new situation is created by placing the blocks in the holes for him, and then arranged again in front of their respective holes for the second trial. During any trial replace on the table in front of appropriate hole any block misplaced by the child. Three trials are given unless child places the blocks without error. A difference in the scoring is made between placing the blocks correctly within one minute and placing the blocks without error.

Adaptation: When the child has learned to place the blocks without error or at the end of the third trial, the blocks having been placed by the child or examiner in their respective places, the board is slowly rotated through an arc of 180° and replaced on the table (square hole is now in front of circular block and *vice versa*). The examiner says to the child, "Now put the blocks in where they belong." The examiner gives three trials as above, revolving the board before each trial.

The ratings, including estimated ratings for three years, are analyzed above.

Comment: This is a simplified form board which we first devised in our study of two-year-old children. The table top serves as a bottom; the board is light and convenient. Its appeal to children is almost universal. It has been found to be a good reserve breaker in timid subjects of pre-kindergarten age.

A 53. Comparison of Lines

RATING: 36B

Procedure: Show card (Binet IV) and say, "See these lines. Look closely and tell me which one is longer. Put your finger on the longest one." If no response, "Show me which line is the biggest."

Show twice more (reversing card at second showing) and ask "Which one is the longest here?" If only two out of three are correct, repeat the entire test.

Credit if three responses out of three, or five out of six, are correct.

Comment: This test seemed to be quite within the range of interest and achievement of the three-year-old children. The willingness to attend which Terman emphasizes as a necessary part of the test was not lacking in our three-year normative group.

A 54. Aesthetic Comparison

RATINGS: 36A 48A 60B

Procedure: Show pairs of faces in order from top to bottom of card (V 3). Say, "Which of these two pictures is the prettier?" Credit if all three comparisons are made correctly.

Comment: The test was found applicable to superior three- and four-year-old children in our unselected groups and is therefore included with advanced ratings on these levels.

A 55. Comparison of Weights

RATINGS: 36A 48B+ 60B

Procedure: Place the 3- and 15-gram weights before the child, two or three inches apart. Say, "You see these blocks. They look just alike, but one of them is heavy and one is light. Try them and tell me which one is heavier." Repeat instructions if necessary, saying, "Tell me which one is the heavier." If the child merely points without lifting blocks, or picks up one at random, say, "No, that is not the way. You must take the blocks in your hands and try them like this." (Illustrates.) Give second trial with position of weights reversed; third trial with weights in same position as first. Credit if two of three comparisons are correct.

Comment: This is one of the original Binet tests. It proves to have a wide range of application. In spite of its apparent objectivity it must be carefully interpreted. Often children succeed apparently quite by lucky chance. The test must then be entirely repeated.

A 56. Selects Humorous Pictures

RATINGS: 48B 60C

Procedure: Three pairs of pictures, one humorous and one non-humorous in each pair, are presented. The examiner says "You like funny pictures, don't you? I am going to show you some funny pictures." (Smiles.) Record response. "Is this a funny picture?" (Holding the first pair of pictures in the air, waiting for a response). Place the first pair in front of the child and say "Point to the funny picture." Then the second pair and the third pair, covering the preceding pair so that the child has only the two new pictures to consider. Record response as plus, minus, or uncertain. Then show all three pairs of pictures, the first pair placed in the center and say, "Point to the funniest picture of all." Record response. The rating is based on two correct responses out of three.

Comment: This is possibly more a test of comprehension than of the sense of humor. It permits, however, of observation and estimate in regard to the humor sense and also is easily converted into a test of suggestion as in P38. Personality responses are interesting to note.

A 57. Matches Forms

RATINGS: 36B 36A 48B

Procedure: Use the forms described in the chapter on psychological materials. (No. 39.)

Place circle at "X" on card and say, "Show me one like this," at same time passing the finger around the circumference of the circle. If no response, "Do you see all of these things?" (running finger over the various forms). "And do you see this one?" (pointing to circle again). "Now, find me another one just like this." A first error should be corrected thus, "No, find one just like this" (again passing finger around the outline of form at "X"). Make no comment on any other errors, but pass on to the square, then the triangle, and the rest in any order. Commend successes.

A credit of B is given at three years if four of the ten forms are matched. A credit of A is given at three years if seven are matched. A credit of B is given at four years for seven correct matchings and a credit of C is given for seven correct matchings at five years.

Comment: This is a convenient and useful test for its purpose. It is adapted from the Kuhlmann and Stanford Revisions and extended to the three-year level. It is particularly effective as an advanced item on the three-year schedule.

A 58. Four-Block Design

RATINGS: 36A 48B

Procedure: A card with a red square design made of four smaller squares is presented to the child and four red cubes are placed before the child. The examiner then says, "Take these blocks and put them together so that they will look like this," showing the design printed on the card. Repeat the directions with encouragement if necessary.

Comment: This is a simple block design test and complicates somewhat the common problem of duplicating a model. Multicolored blocks make the problem still more difficult. In either form it merits a superior rating at three years.

APPERCEPTION AND COMPLETION

A 60. Watch Naming

RATINGS: 18A+ 24A+ 24A 24B 36B+

Procedure: Six cards representing different stages in the drawing of a watch from a mere circle to a complete watch are presented

in turn, beginning with the simplest or circle form. Show the child
the first drawing and say, "What is that?" Record the response.
Repeat with each card, using the same form of question, and score
as follows: Names watch on fourth view, A+ at eighteen months;
names watch on second view, 24A+; on third view, 24A; on fourth
view, 24B. On third view also score 36B+.

Comment: This is a variety of completion test and also indicates the capacity of the child to overcome infantile perseveration.
The consistency with which the percentages increase at the ascending age levels from eighteen months up would seem to show that
the test is not without diagnostic value. The test is adapted from
one described by Franz as applicable to mature subjects. It would
be interesting to make comparisons between infantile and adult
apperception.

A 61. Picture Completion

RATINGS: 24A+ 36B

Procedure: An outline drawing of a little Dutch girl knitting is
presented complete. Say, "See the little girl." Next ask the child
to point out the dog, bag, and other objects. The picture is then
separated into its two vertical halves. Place the left half two or
three inches to the right of the other piece. Let the child watch for
about thirty seconds, noting his attitude and general response, then
say, "Now you put the picture together again."

Comment: This is a concrete type of completion test and undoubtedly brings intelligence into play. Three-year-old children
respond with eager attention and those who were finally successful
showed, in almost every case, purposeful reaction, holding one piece
in hand and studying the problem before placing it. The test is
applicable to superior two-year-old children. Willingness to attend
is significant. The child who merely manipulates the cards in
inconclusive play usually is unequal to the task.

A 62. Picture Adaptation

RATINGS: 24A+ 36A

Procedure: The material and general procedure are the same as for A61. If the child passes A61 he is shown the complete picture again. The examiner rotates the left half of the picture to the left so that it will be upside down. The child is again allowed to inspect the situation for thirty seconds and then the examiner says, "Now you put the picture together again."

Comment: This makes still greater demands upon adaptive completion judgment. Solution of the problem is perhaps more significant on the two-year than on the three-year schedule. We have quartered the picture to make its reconstruction a grade more difficult. The quartered version is applicable to the (advanced) three- , four- , and five-year levels.

A 63. Form Completion A

RATINGS: 36A 48B 48B+ 48A

Procedure: Bright-colored cardboard designs consisting of a circle, square, rectangle, maltese cross, and lozenge are emptied out of an envelope with the remark, "See these pretty cards." Sheet 1, picturing an incomplete outline of a circle and square, is then placed in front of him. The examiner then picks up all of the cards and hands the circle to the child saying, "Look at the paper. See the marks here and here. Now put this card where it will just fit." If the card has been incorrectly or carelessly placed, make a point of picking it up and laying it down accurately on the line. Then remove the card which has just been placed and hand the child a square, repeating the remark, "Put this where it will just fit." Correct, if necessary, both for the circle and square. Then turn the trial sheet over, expose the reverse side, and hand the forms in the order in which they are mentioned above, continuing the procedure just described. An occasional commendation is necessary with a timid child. (See figure 15.)

Every form is scored as correctly placed even if the form is not accurately to the line. The results on the trial sheet are also included in the final score. The ratings credited are as follows: two out of five correctly, 36A and 48B. Three out of five correctly, 48B+. Four out of five correctly, 48A.

Comment: The test is a convenient and useful one. The bright colors appeal at once to the child's interest. Personality traits are brought freely into play and motor as well as intellectual maturity comes to a test. It taxes the skill of the three-year-old child to match a rectangular form nicely against a straight line.

A 63. Form Completion B

RATINGS: 60A   60A+   60B   60B+   60C

Procedure: The procedure is similar to that just described, but at the five-year level three placement sheets with eight forms are presented in the order and position indicated on the sheets. With five-year-old children there is no preliminary try-out.

The scoring is on the following basis: eight forms correctly placed, 60A+; seven forms correctly placed, 60A; six forms correctly placed, 60B+; four or five forms correctly placed, 60B; three forms correctly placed, 60C.

Comment: With the test are given forms two, three, four, and five. These prove to be relatively easy for five-year-old children but the difficulties presented by forms six, seven, and eight make possible a differential rating into five grades. With improvement in the standardization of procedure, the form completion test can be accurately graded for a range extending at least from two to six years of age. Even below the two-year level we find types of completion behavior which are akin to and preparatory to more advanced form completion adaptations.

A 64. Patience Picture

RATING: 48B

Procedure: Two copies of the home picture (Figure 7) are used, —a complete copy and one diagonally cut. The complete copy is placed in front of the child and a few of the objects and persons in the picture are pointed out; namely, the little girl with the umbrella, the mother, the dog, and the boy washing. The halves of the diagonally cut piece are then placed before the child arranged as in the Binet patience card test. Tell the child to put these two pieces together (touching them) so that they will make a picture just like this (pointing to the complete picture). "Make a nice picture for me just like this one," repeating instructions if necessary. Give three trials, beginning a new trial whenever the child turns the cards and leaves them. The examiner at each new trial replaces the pieces in their original test position with the remark, "See if you can't put them together so that they will look just like this."

Comment: Judgment must, of course, be used to determine the amount of encouragement and urging that should be given. The test has proved to be a valuable supplement to the more abstract and less interesting Binet patience card test. It is superfluous if the child has passed the latter test.

A 65. Patience Card

RATINGS: 48A 60B

Procedure: Use two cards, each 2 by 3 inches. Divide one of them diagonally into two triangles. Place the uncut card on the table with one of the longer sides toward the subject. Then lay the divided card thus $\triangle \triangledown$, and say, "I want you to take these two pieces (touching the two triangles) and put them together so they will look exactly like this" (pointing to rectangle). If the subject hesitates, repeat instructions with a little urging. If the first attempt is a failure, replace pieces, saying, "No, put them together so that they will look like this" (pointing to rectangle). Do not suggest further by face or word whether response is correct. If a piece is turned over, turn it back and don't count that trial. Give, if necessary, three trials of one minute each. Credit if two of the three trials are successful.

Comment: Willingness to attend to the problem is an element or a symptom in this test. It is significant that the counterpart to the patience test can be carried down to the two- and three-year levels as already described. The enlarged pictorial version of the test in A64 makes a stronger appeal to four-year-old children.

A 66. Names Incomplete Man

RATING: 48B

Procedure: Show the child the incomplete drawing of a man as described and pictured elsewhere. Say, "What is this?" Record response. If the child does not respond, tell him that it is a man, without making any comment in regard to the missing parts. Score credit if the child names a man, boy, doll, or something equally interpretative and give rating of B at the four-year level. (Figure 11.)

A 67. Man Completion Drawing

RATINGS: 36 48B 48A

Procedure: The material and introductory procedure are as described in A66. Continue by saying, "The person who made this man didn't draw all of him, don't you see? You finish him. Make the part that's gone. Make a good man; he isn't all made yet." Most children will begin to draw some part. When the child stops urge him at once to "Finish him some more!" If the child is not able to add further parts say, "Where is the man's ear?" Or if this is not sufficient, say, "Where is his other ear?"

and even suggest that he draw it. Let the child act on his own initiative, but if there is no further response suggest once more that he "Finish the man." All parts of the body and any additional feature such as buttons or hat are counted as one completion excepting the ear or other features substituted for ear, the ear having been drawn, which was suggested to the child. The ratings are made on the following basis: 3 completions, 48B; 5 completions, 48A.

Comment: This test has proved highly suitable for the four-year level; and should be carried down to the three-year and up to the five-year levels, to note qualitative and maturity differences. Norms for the adjacent level have not been determined. The test makes definite demands upon the completion type of adaptive behavior which is an important factor in so-called general intelligence. Personality traits and spontaneous conversation are readily evoked by the test. Another advantage is the fact that it is self-recording and permits intercomparison at successive developmental examinations.

A 68. Supplying Missing Parts

RATINGS: 48A+ 60B+

Procedure: Show card (Binet VI 2) and say, "There is something wrong with this face. It is not all there. Part of it is left out. Look carefully and tell me what part of the face is not there." Same for (b) and (c). If the subject gives an irrevelant answer, say, "No; I am talking about the face. Look again and tell me what is left out of the face." If correct response does not follow, point to the place where an eye should be and say, "See, the eye is gone." Then proceed to others, asking, "What is left out of this face?" For (d) say, "What is left out of this picture?" No help except on (a). Order is eyes, mouth, nose, arms.

Credit if correct response is made for three of four pictures.

Spontaneous remarks may be noted and recorded.

A 70. Placing Cubes in Cup

RATINGS: 24A   36B   36B+   48B   48A+

Procedure: Several cubes and an enamel cup are placed before the child. First of all, say to the child, "Put just *one* block into the cup" (emphasizing *one*). If he succeeds say, "Put *two* blocks into the cup." Accompany the statement with a gesture to facilitate response, but do not give him any further guidance. Repeat the test until you are satisfied that he either lacks or possesses the number sense and control to meet the test. A rating of 24A is earned if he differentiates between one and many cubes on the two-year schedule. If he places one and two cubes, discriminatingly, the rating is 36B+ or 48B. Success on 3 cubes earns 48A+.

Comment: This test is useful. Nearly all of the children are interested in handling the cubes and cup. Arithmetical knowledge at this stage of development is so concrete that even counting tests are not always competent to reveal the number sense of the child. At the age of eighteen months he has not developed a clear distinction between one and many. Not until the three-year level does the distinction between one and two assert itself in this test. The rival interest of filling the cup with the several blocks at his disposal helps to make the results of the test more significant when a success is definitely scored.

A 71. Counting Four, Ten, and Thirteen Pennies

RATINGS: 36A   48B+   48A   48A+   60A

Procedure: Place four pennies in a horizontal row. Say, "See these pennies. Count them and tell me how many there are. Count them with your finger, this way" (pointing to the first one on the subject's left)—"One. Now, go ahead." If the child gives the number without pointing, say, "No, count them with your finger, this way," starting him as before. Have him count aloud. Two trials are permitted.

Proceed in a similar manner with ten pennies and with thirteen pennies.

The scoring is 36A for counting 4 and 48B+ for counting 4; 48A and 60B for counting 10; 48A+ and 60A for counting thirteen.

Comment: This is not a test of number sense but of associative verbal-motor association. In our series of fifty three-year-old children the examiner found as many as 72 per cent who could count four pennies correctly. Our data for four-year-old children, however, were supplemented with other tests of counting and number comprehension which cast some doubt on the interpretation of the findings for the three-year-old group. Strict standards in scoring are necessary to preserve the usefulness of this test. More practical tests of the actual number comprehension of young children are desirable. The cup-and-cube tests give a better indication of the actual practical number sense, and even these may well be supplemented for verification by informal number tests of give and take.

A 72. Drawing Bubbles

RATINGS: 48C 48B 48A+ 60B+

Procedure: A picture of a boy blowing bubbles is laid in front of the child with the remark: "Look at this boy. What is he doing? He is blowing bubbles, isn't he?" The examiner draws around the bubble to be sure that the child knows what the bubble is. Then the examiner adds, "Now you make one bubble under the chair, just one bubble under the chair." Emphasize *one* and *under.* Follow this with the commission, "Make two bubbles above his head, *two* bubbles *above* his head." Then say, "Make three bubbles behind him,—*three* bubbles *behind* him." Then, "Make four bubbles in front of him,—*four* bubbles *in front of* him." Record the response to number and direction separately. The scoring is on the following basis: one correct, 48C; two correct, 48B; three or four correct, 48A+.

Comment: This test gives further evidence on the existence and intensity of any number sense which the child has acquired.

A 73. Problems

RATINGS: 48A+ 48A

Procedure: The examiner asks the child, "If you have one penny and I give you another penny, how many pennies will you have? If you have two pennies and I give you another penny, how many pennies will you have? If you have two pennies and I give you two more pennies, how many pennies will you have?"

This is scored as 48A if there is a number comprehension of two. Number comprehension of three or four counts as 48A+.

A 74. Gives Number of Fingers

RATING: 60B+

Procedure: Say, "How many fingers have you on one hand?" "How many on the other hand?" "How many on both hands together?" If the child begins to count, say, "No, don't count. Tell me without counting," and repeat question. Credit if all three questions are answered correctly and promptly without counting (5, 5, 10 or 4, 4, 8).

CHAPTER 11

Norms of Personal–Social Behavior

REACTION TO PERSONS

P 10. Adapts to Nursing

RATING: 4C

Procedure: By questioning determine whether the child makes any recognition responses at the time of nursing. Follow up the questions to determine how definitely the baby reacts to satiety or to loss of the nipple.

Comment: Definite responses are reported by nearly all mothers of four-months-old children. The item ordinarily has little normative significance. In subnormal cases, however, information on this point may be significant. Weak recognition and weak adaptive responses may be associated with deficient endowment at the age of four months.

P 11. Attention to Face

RATINGS: 4B 6B 6B+ 9C

Procedure: The examiner by observation supplemented by interview determines whether the four-months-old child shows selective and responsive reaction to the face. If the fact is in doubt the examiner may try to elicit response by approaching the child with facial animation. A rating of 4B is given if a child shows selective interest in the face.

By observation and interview the examiner can usually determine whether the child shows a definite recognition of persons. A rating of B is assigned at six months if there is a definite evidence of such recognition response. If at six months there appears

135

definite consciousness of strangers, a rating of B+ is assigned. At nine months the rating is C.

Comment: The recognition responses are based upon a simple type of associative memory. The higher rating is assigned to definite consciousness of strangers because it implies an element of discrimination and perhaps a somewhat higher level of emotional development. At nine months this evident consciousness of strangers is so common as to have little significance, although by the same token complete lack of sensitiveness to strangers would be regarded as an unfavorable symptom.

P 12. Anticipatory Motor Adjustment

RATING: 4C

Procedure: In lifting the four-months-old baby from table and in placing the baby on table note whether by facial tension and shrugging attitude of shoulders the baby makes an anticipatory motor adjustment.

Comment: It is possible that a less definite evidence of such adjustment may be found as low down as the neonatal period. Although a habit must be conditioned by experience, the opportunity for experience is almost universal and the response is sufficiently objective to merit further observation and record. The present rating is provisional, being based on a limited number of cases.

P 13. Reaction to Mirror

RATINGS: 6A 9B 12C

Procedure: The examiner should, if possible, put this item to actual test by holding the child near a large wall mirror, taking pains to keep his own image and that of others out of the mirror. Definite motor response at six months is credited with an A rating, if the child shows more than casual manipulatory interest in the situation. A playful response of a somewhat higher grade is credited with an A rating at nine months and C rating at twelve months. This item is difficult to score and there is a large margin of error in interpretation. However, the test so frequently liberates unambiguous and significant responses that it should be made whenever convenient.

The gradation of response from four months to two years is interesting and merits further analysis. At eighteen months the response is so well developed that a child may even reach behind the mirror to get hold of his own image.

P 14. Salutations

RATINGS: 9B+ 9A+ 18B

Procedure: By interview supplemented by actual tests the examiner ascertains whether the nine-months-old child can wave "Bye-bye" or say "Bye-bye" or say "Hello." If he uses either of these two expressions a rating of 9A+ is assigned. If he simply waves "Bye-bye" the rating is 9B+. If he says "Thank you" or its equivalent, at eighteen months, the rating is B. This item is descriptive but has some normative value because it is an almost universal custom to teach a baby to wave "Bye-bye."

P 15. Shows Affection Spontaneously

RATINGS: 18A 24B

Procedure: Interview.

Comment: This item is included because it throws some light on the personality and social maturity of the child. The display of affection may be purely mimetic, and the examiner will have to use considerable judgment in making his interpretations. As a descriptive item this may be well included in a developmental schedule both at eighteen months and at two years.

P 16. Forbidden Acts

RATINGS: 12B   18B

Procedure: By interview the examiner determines whether the child is influenced by ordinary methods of discipline and makes elementary distinction between what is permissible and not permissible. On the eighteen-months schedule the examiner further inquires whether certain of these inhibitions are habitual and are not dependent upon command.

Comment: At twelve months one may expect a baby to withdraw his hand at the expression "No, no," if he starts to touch a forbidden object. At eighteen months a child has learned that certain objects must not be touched and he inhibits without command. This particular item, like the foregoing, does not permit of rigid standardization but contributes to an estimate of personality status in normal children and may be particularly important in seriously retarded cases.

P 17. Tells Experiences and Stories

RATINGS: 24B   36B

Procedure: By interview or by improvising situations, the examiner determines whether the child is mature enough to relate simple experiences or recent occurrences. If he relates such experiences even in a fragmentary manner he is entitled to a B rating at two years and if he can tell a simple story he secures a B rating at three years.

Comment: We do not, of course, expect any accuracy of testimony at these levels and it is significant that at three years children frequently begin to elaborate their stories with imaginary details. This item is included under the present heading because it is the social aspect of the child which is particularly significant. Even though a great many of the items classified under the category "personal social-behavior" do not permit of precise standardization, they have a place in the broad type of developmental examination because of the light which they throw upon the maturity of the child's personality.

PERSONAL HABITS

P 20. Putting on Shoes

RATINGS: 12B   24A   36B+   48B   60A

Procedure: Interview and observation. The examiner by questioning determines on the twelve-months schedule whether the child is beginning to try to put on his shoes. If so a rating of B is assigned on this schedule. If he actually succeeds in putting on his shoes a rating of A is assigned on the two-year schedule. This achievement is entitled to a B+ rating at three years. Lacing shoes is characteristic of the four-year level and earns a B rating on that level. On the five-year level an A rating is assigned if a child is able to tie the laces into a bow knot. The latter ability may be tested out in accordance with the Stanford Revision procedure if desired. A shoestring is tied in a bow knot around a stick or pencil, wings pointing right and left. The examiner then says, "You know what kind of a knot this is, don't you? This is a bow knot. I want you to take this other piece of string and tie this same kind of knot around my finger." The standard of scoring on this basis is tying a double bow knot in not more than one minute of time. If the child can approximate this test on his own shoes a note may be made in the record.

Comment: Although this item is influenced by unequal training opportunities, it is relatively uniform in the difficulties presented and throws some light on the child's ability to profit from training. The insistence which a child shows in regard to dressing and feeding himself is a significant personality trait.

P 21. Uses Knife and Spoon

RATINGS: 12A   18B   24C   48B+

Procedure: By interview the examiner determines whether the child has begun to use a spoon and at the four-year level he also inquires about the use of a knife. Supplementary inquiries with respect to the amount of training received are necessary. Ratings are assigned on the following basis: 12A, if he uses a spoon at all; 18B and 24C if he uses the spoon without much spilling; 48B+ if he uses the knife at the table and can spread his own butter or jam.

Comment: Here again precise ratings are impossible unless the ability is put to standardized test. However, the item belongs on the developmental schedule because marked deviations from the average may have significance with respect to the child's capacity to profit from ordinary home training. Sometimes a child is spoon-fed beyond his pre-school years on account of faulty home training.

P 22. Bowel Control

RATINGS: 12A   18B   18A   24C

Procedure: The examiner interviews the parent to determine the length of period of training and the character of the training with respect to bowel control. If reasonable regularity and control have become established at twelve months a rating of A may be assigned; at eighteen months this rating becomes B. Occasional lapses are not to be counted negatively in considering this item. If a child distinctly asks to go to the toilet a rating of A is given at eighteen months and a rating of C at two years.

Comment: This item is of considerable importance because of its relations to the personal hygiene and home training of the child. It assumes special clinical importance in cases of marked retardation in the acquisition of control. Such retardation must of course be distinguished from specific incontinence. The delay in acquisition of control is psycho-clinically significant when it denotes retardation in the development of the cortical mechanism of inhibition.

P 23. Bladder Control

RATINGS: 12A+ 18A 24B

Procedure: Same as in P 22.

Comment: The comments made on the previous item apply in general here. It will be noted that bladder control is achieved somewhat later ordinarily and receives somewhat higher rating on the developmental schedule. Here again delay in attainment of control must be clinically distinguished from enuresis. Enuresis is a very common defect in pre-school children and is not limited to definitely neuropathic cases. The most favorable time for preventive control of enuresis is in the pre-school period and the item has considerable practical importance. The data regarding four-year-olds, in Chapter 32, are significant on this point.

P 24. Buttons Clothes

RATING: 48B

Procedure: Interview. The child is credited with this capacity if he is able to button his clothes. Back buttons, of course, are too difficult at this age level.

P 25. Washes Self and Brushes Teeth

RATINGS: Washing: 36A 48B 60B Teeth: 36A 48B

Procedure: Interview. The examiner determines whether the child has attained sufficient skill to wash himself without getting his clothes very wet. Similar inquiries are made in regard to cleaning teeth, always of course with supplementary questions in regard to training.

Comment: Items of this character are of course subject to the examiner's own judgment. It is in cases of retardation and of behavior disorder that the broad normative aspect of these items assumes importance.

P 26. Orderliness

RATINGS: 36B 60B

Procedure: On the three-year-old schedule the examiner depends upon interview to determine whether the child has acquired any habits of orderliness in regard to his toys and possessions. On the five-year-old schedule similar inquiries may be made and the orderliness is also observed in the free construction test when the examiner says to the child, "Now put these things away as nicely and neatly as you can for me in this box."

Comment: Personality and intelligence traits which are bound up with orderliness are capable of more systematic and objective standardization. The element of training naturally enters, but under test conditions somewhat novel situations can be devised to measure roughly the capacity for orderly arrangement. Interest in orderliness is in itself a significant item. Our home study of three-year-old children shows that the typical child at this age does not willfully break his toys and that he can put them away. In the case of five-year-old children we found that the free construction test revealed qualities of orderliness. A large percentage of five-year-old children were not only willing to put things away but showed definite interest and ability in arranging the material in an orderly manner. In a certain psychological sense this is akin to the interest which displays itself so early in relation to form-board situations. There is a broader observable difference with respect to these reactions when four-year-old children are compared to five-year-old children in their response to the commission to put things away neatly in a box. This orderliness test has incidental advantages as a means of displaying quality of attention.

P 30. Asks for Things at Table

RATINGS: 12A 18C 18A 24B

Procedure: By interview the examiner determines whether the child is beginning to ask for things at the table. If he merely points at his desires a rating of A is assigned at twelve months and of C at eighteen months. If, however, he mentions the things by words, a rating of A is assigned at eighteen months and of B at two years.

Comment: Because of its association with the fundamental and universal situations which arise in connection with hunger and eating, this item is not without broad significance. Personality features, however, enter. All the child's wants may be anticipated or he may be unduly seclusive and silent. This complication, however, may be an added reason for including the item on a developmental schedule.

P 31. Persistence in Reaching

RATINGS: 6A 9B

Procedure: With the dangling ring, the red rod, or some equally tempting object, persistence in reaching can be tested by holding the object just a little outside the child's reach. The six-months-old child sometimes must be allowed to hold the object momentarily and sometimes to touch it in order to secure his stimulated interest. It is unwise to tease him long without rewarding him with success, although the procedure may be varied with different cases. A marked persistence at six months if shown by three or four successive efforts at securing the ring is entitled to an A rating. Equally marked persistence is so common at nine months that the rating at this level is B.

Comment: Although it is impossible to be definite about the conditions of this test, it is clinically too valuable to forego. In fact, the test should be varied in order to disclose personality differences. It reveals individual differences not only in attention and judgment but in emotional traits. The elements of judgment can be estimated by determining at what distance the child begins persistent reaching and with what directness. If the examiner wishes to make a special determination of this point he brings the ring somewhat slowly toward the child, beginning at a distance of three or four feet.

P 32. Knows Where He Wants to Go

RATING: 18B

Procedure: By interview the examiner determines whether the child of his own volition asks to go to places somewhat remote from his accustomed place of play.

Comment: Definite evidence on this point cannot always be elicited. However, the item is likely to reveal advanced degrees of orientation and independence associated with developmental maturity. The twelve-months-old child wanders about somewhat aimlessly. By the time he is eighteen months old he is beginning to show a higher order or orientation. The psychologically interesting sense of locality could profitably be studied at this age.

P 33. Opens Doors

RATINGS: 18B   24C   36B

Procedure: Interview or test. If the child tries to turn the knob on the door he receives a B rating on the eighteen-months schedule and C on the twenty-four-months schedule and if he actually opens the door the rating is B on the three-year-old schedule.

Comment: Here again the examiner must use his common sense to make allowances for differences in home conditions and also the variations in the difficulty of the problem itself.

P 34. Climbs for Object

RATING: 18A 24C

Procedure: Interview will frequently suffice. The situation may, however, be put to an actual test by placing a small basket or box on a shelf about five feet from the floor. Or the examiner may hold the basket at that level. In either case a chair is placed immediately under the basket. The purpose of the test is to see if the child will climb the chair to reach the basket in which he is interested. If an eighteen-months-old child immediately solves the problem by climbing the chair to secure the basket, an A rating is assigned.

By interview the examiner determines on the two-year-old schedule whether the child ever moves a chair from one place to another in order to use it as a means for attaining some desired object. If he uses a chair in this purposeful manner he is entitled to a 24C rating.

Comment: This simple item is surely related to the traits of initiative and independence; positive evidence on this point is reassuring at the appropriate levels. Negative evidence may indicate personality inhibitions.

P 35. Goes on Simple Errands

RATINGS: 18B+ 36A 48B

Procedure: By interview the examiner determines whether the child can carry out simple commissions and errands in his own home or his own neighborhood. He is entitled to a B+ rating on an eighteen-months schedule, if he carries out a simple errand. On the three- and four-year-old levels this errand must definitely take him outside of the house in order to entitle him to a rating.

Comment: Here again we are dealing with concrete evidence of importance in developmental examination. Although the item is not precisely standardized, it permits disclosures of inadequacy and superiority which contribute significant information as to estimates of personality maturity and personality makeup. Experience will enable the examiner to formulate his questions in such a way that he can very expeditiously ascertain particulars of home behavior which have clinical significance.

P 36. Trusted with Breakables

RATING: 36B

Procedure: Interview.

Comment: This item is based on our survey of the home behavior of three-year-old children. From our results it is clear that by that age children can be trusted with minor responsibilities such as carrying china, glassware, or grandmother's spectacles from one part of the house to another. A moderate capacity in this direction, is, therefore, characteristic of three-year-old maturity.

P 37. Resists Suggestion

RATINGS: 48B 60A 60B

Procedure: Having completed the test described under A56 all the pictures are removed and a nonhumorous picture of a man reading the paper is presented. The examiner says "Is this a funny picture?" in a casual tone without emphasis. If the child resists the suggestion given by the preceding series the examiner smiles and asks, "Oh! but isn't it a funny picture?" He is scored as having resisted suggestion if he maintains that the man with a newspaper is not a funny picture.

The procedure at the five-year level involves the use of a picture of a horse running away with a man about to fall off the horse's back. The following questions are then asked in a plausible tone: "The man fell off and was on the ground, wasn't he?" "The horse was walking, wasn't he?" "The girl was looking over the fence, wasn't she?" "A dog was barking, wasn't he?" There was neither a girl nor a dog in this picture and the proper answer is "No." A rating of A is assigned if the child resists all four questions. A rating of B is assigned if he resists only three.

P 38. Crosses Street Alone

·RATING: 36B+

Procedure: Interview.

Comment: The significance of this item varies with different circumstances, but it is worthy of inquiry as a measure of the child's independence.

PLAY BEHAVIOR

P 40. Playful Reactions

RATINGS: 4C— 4B 6B+

Procedure: Interview. By questioning, the examiner determines whether the child at four months takes evident enjoyment in his bath, which receives 4C rating. The examiner also finds out whether the child ever laughs aloud. This receives a 4B rating. If the child reacts in a responsive frolicking manner when played with, a rating of B+ may be assigned at six months. The playful reactiveness of six- and nine-months-old infants is often readily observed incidentally to the ordinary course of the examination.

Comment: These items are by no means without significance in cases of subnormal development. Enjoyment of the bath is practically universal in four-months-old babies and complete passivity or lack of enjoyment would, therefore, be indicative of an unusual developmental condition at the age of four months. Because of lesser frequency, laughing aloud has more normative value. Four months appears to be the nascent period for laughter and a rating of B approximately represents its developmental significance. Practically all four-months-old babies smile, but the history of laughter ordinarily dates back no further than two weeks before the age of four months. A playful, seemingly imitative response to gayety is developed at the age of six months. There is also a corresponding response to expressions of sternness at this age. If a child responds actively to gayety when played with it signifies a relatively mature social and emotional development.

P 41. Early Play

Plays with hands

RATING: 4C

Procedure: By observation and by interview determine whether the four-months baby is inclined to play with fingers and hands.

Comment: This type of play is highly characteristic of the four-months level of development, particularly when it is associated with visual fixation. The most characteristic form of this play reaction consists in contemplation of the moving hand which simulates, amusingly sometimes, inspection of a wrist watch. Apparently this play reaction and exercise of visual perception are initiated by fortuitous coincidence and are not necessarily voluntary in character. Occasionally the four-months-old child has begun to play with his feet as well as his hands, but this is not characteristic.

Scratches

RATING: 4B

Procedure: Incidental observation and interview. This reaction is found even in the neonatal period when it sometimes becomes inordinate. If, however, the scratching is indulged in as a form of play, whether it be the scratching of the side of the crib, of the table or of pillow or dress, it is entitled to a B rating atf our months.

Plays with objects

RATING: 4B+

Procedure: Observation and interview.

Comment: Ordinarily parents begin to give their children simple play objects at the age of four months. This fact itself is significant. To what extent experience hastens the capacity to play with a rattle or ring it is difficult to ascertain. The four-months-old baby who comes to the examination with a definite history of play with a rattle, ring, or clothespin for a week or more is usually somewhat advanced in development. At any rate such definite play with objects at this period is entitled to a B+ rating.

Pats table

RATINGS: 6B 9C

Procedure: Observation and interview.

Comment: Either patting the table or banging with spoon may be considered typical six months play and is, therefore, rated B. At nine months this type of reaction is so common that the rating falls to C.

Throws objects for play

RATINGS: 6A 12C

Procedure: Observation and interview. Purposive throwing or brushing aside objects because of interest in hearing the fall is rather an advanced form of play for six months. It is frequent at nine months but is entitled to only a C rating at twelve months.

Exploits paper

RATINGS: 6B 6A 9B

Procedure: A piece of letter-size paper is presented to the child so that he may grasp the edge of it. It is desirable to exercise some caution with respect to this detail because we wish to ascertain whether the child will merely crumple the paper or will show a somewhat higher grade response. A higher grade response is favored if he grasps the paper by the edge.

A rating of B is made if the child merely crumples the paper or manipulates it in gross manner. If, however, he shows a more exploratory and restrained interest in the material and inhibits at the age of six months the hand-to-mouth reaction, we make an A rating. A banging or waving reaction is also given the higher rating at the age of six months and a B rating at the age of nine months.

Comment: Subjective factors inevitably come into play in interpreting the response to this test, but these subjective factors will not introduce any serious error in the record. A low-grade response to the paper at the age of twelve months, however, must be weighted unfavorably. Infants hold paper in high esteem as play material. In retarded subjects this item may clearly disclose subnormal attention span.

Puts cube into cup

RATINGS: 9A+   12A   18B

Procedure: The spontaneous playful exploitation of cube and cup is noted in the covered-cube test. If the child spontaneously thrusts the cube into the cup, even if he does not relinquish his hold, it is considered an advanced form of play both at nine months and at twelve months. The rating of eighteen months is B.

Comment: This playful but purposive combination of cup and cube recurred so often in the presentation of this test material and appeared to be so characteristic of a certain stage of play development that the item is inserted here as one for observation and record. It reflects objectively the maturity of the child's play at the ages of nine months and twelve months.

P 42. Reaction to Music

RATINGS: 4C 4B+ 6B 6A 9B 9B+ 12B 24B 36B

Procedure: By interview or by observation the examiner determines whether the baby shows any motor reaction to music or turns his head to listen to a voice or the ringing of a bell. If there is an adaptive motor response either to music or voice, a C rating is assigned at four months. Turning definitely and promptly to the sound of a bell is entitled to 4B+ and 6B ratings. If the child coos or laughs on hearing music, the ratings are 6A, 9B+ and 12B. A smiling or dancing reaction at nine months is entitled to a B rating.

The examiner should give the bell-ringing test with some care. It is best to approach the child from behind and to ring a hand bell gently either two or three feet from the child's right or left ear. This is repeated at intervals with each ear. If the approach is not made cautiously from behind, the response is ambiguous; the turning must be definitely to a sound stimulus and not a visual one.

On the two-year-old schedule the examiner may ask whether the child ever requests by name or title familiar tunes. On the three-year level the examiner may inquire whether he definitely recognizes favorite tunes on the phonograph or on musical instruments. Ratings of B are assigned.

Comment: Further investigation and experiment would, of course, enable us to standardize reactions in this field with more precision. We have noted that vocalization is not only initiated but obviously increased by the stimulus of music. Here also is a field for more objective measurement and observation.

So many four-months-old children respond with head turning to the voice that this reaction may have more diagnostic significance at the age of three months than at the age of four months. It is, however, one symptom of normal developmental maturity at the four-months level. It is interesting that babies who turn to the voice frequently do not turn to the bell.

P 43. Plays Peek-a-boo or Pat-a-cake

Ratings: 9B+   9A   12B   12C

Procedure: Interview or observation. A rating of B+ is given at nine months if a baby plays pat-a-cake or peek-a-boo or has acquired a similar playful trick. At twelve months these accomplishments sink to a C rating.

Comment: These nursery reactions are significant because they are ordinary and normal indications of the development of social capacities.

P 44. Pictures and Stories

Ratings: 18B+   18A   24B   36C

Procedure: By interview, or by actual trial if he desires, the examiner tests whether the child shows any interest in picture books or listens with some continuity to a simple story based on the pictures. The average eighteen-months-old child has no pronounced fondness for pictures. His interest is ordinarily of a fugitive character. If the interest is a pronounced one a B+ rating is assigned. If in addition he is interested in a story an A rating is assigned. At two and three years the trait is more common and the ratings are B and C.

Comment: Although this item is conditioned by experience it is fundamentally determined by maturity of attention. Positive evidence on these points is, therefore, significant.

P 45. Dramatic Play

Ratings: 18A   24B   36B   48C

Procedure: By interview chiefly, the examiner determines whether the child shows any form of dramatic play. Ratings are made on the following basis. Imitative reproduction of simple acts like mimicry of an old man's walk or smoking or reading, receive ratings of 18A and 24B. A higher grade of dramatic pretense in which a child plays out a part a little more elaborately, such as telephoning for the doctor, merits a B rating at the three-year level. At four years it justifies a C rating.

Comment: This item provides the examiner with an opportunity to record specific forms of play which have considerable developmental significance. The differentiations sketched above are very crude, but they furnish some basis for developing an estimate of the child's mimetic, dramatic play capacity.

P 46. Dramatic Drawing

RATINGS: 48A   60B

Procedure: By interview, supplemented if necessary by trial, the examiner determines whether the child can make representative drawings. If the child makes such drawings either spontaneously or on suggestion and gives them a definite dramatic interpretation, an A rating may be assigned at four years and a B rating at five years. Here again a more precise standardization is necessary, but drawing is here considered as a vehicle for dramatic expression which is used by a sufficiently large proportion of children to make it noteworthy in the schedule of four and five years.

P 47. Constructive Play

Combining play with spoon, cup, and saucer

RATINGS: 6B   6A   9B   12C

Procedure: Spoon, cup, and saucer are placed on the table within reach of the child. The three objects are separated because we wish to note whether the child makes constructive or combining use of these materials. If he merely manipulates one or more of these articles at the age of six months, we give a B rating. If there is an element of exploration in his manipulation, we give an A rating at six months, a B rating at nine, and a C rating at twelve.

Comment: Again the subjective factor inevitably comes into play. The test, however, is too useful and convenient to be discarded, because it permits a broad distinction between low-grade manipulation and restrained "purposive" exploratory play. The test is more useful at six and twelve months than at nine months. It is useful at six months to display a high-grade type of reaction, and conversely at twelve months the persistence of infantile banging and mouthing might be suggestive. There is an objective basis for the impressions which one derives from an observation of the reactions to the cup, spoon, and saucer. These objective differences could, with further investigation, be formulated and classified, but even lacking this precision, the test unquestionably retains clinical utility.

Free construction

RATINGS: 48B 48A 60B

Procedure: Emptying the contents of the box containing construction material on the table, say, "Here are some things you will like. Look at all these nice things. Now, make something." Record immediate response. There will probably be no hesitation, but in a few cases it may be necessary to add a few encouraging words. After the child starts to examine the material, do not encourage or urge again, unless at the end of one minute the child is merely looking at the flag or handling the material. At the end of one minute, urge the child "to make some more" or "make something." At the end of three minutes record what he has made. It may be of interest to observe how much longer he is willing to work with the material, but the scoring has been based on the amount and type of construction in a three-minute interval. Record also personality responses such as the following: Initial responses—immediate or delayed. Imagination—by spontaneous comment and ability to name the object. Spontaneity—expression of eagerness and satisfaction in the work. Purposefulness—

sustained interest in construction with only a comment on the diversions, or non-purposefulness—irrevelant conversation and attention diverted from work. Critical ability—expressed by comments on work.

Scoring on the amount of material used, although it has the advantage of being entirely objective, seemed less satisfactory than the more subjective scoring on an estimate of purposefulness and imagination displayed in the manner indicated above. The responses fall fairly easily into four groups:

Rate as 48B any systematic arrangement of the pieces, even though there may be little attempt to define their construction; for example, placing all the sticks in the timber or making a houseboat with several sticks and pieces of timber, with only a comment or two made by the child on his constructions.

Rate as 48A to 60B more elaborate constructions accompanied by interpretative comment. For example, (1) letters A and L and a boat made of three sticks; or (2) a well constructed house made out of all the timbers and sticks; or (3) though diverted at first by distraction material, a gate was constructed out of three pieces of timber and a plaque, showing a good imagination; (4) A "roasting thing" was made out of sticks and timber with remarks made about roasting marshmallows on a stick but without distraction from construction; (5) A bridge, a fence with steps, and a boat, all named as made.

ACQUIRED INFORMATION

P 50. Asks Questions of Elders

RATING: 36B

Procedure: Interview.

Comment: This is an objective point readily determined by interview and, if the child has not been repressed, is of significance. Here as elsewhere a negative evidence must not be weighted as heavily as positive evidence.

P 51. Points to Parts of Body

RATINGS: 18B   18A   24B

Procedure: After getting the child's attention, say, "Show me your nose. Put your finger on your nose." Proceed in like manner with eyes, mouth, and hair. A rating of B is assigned at eighteen months if the child points to one part of the body. A rating of 18A or 24B is assigned if he points to two or more parts, or if he signifies by facial gesture that he understands which part of the face is alluded to.

Comment: It is necessary in some cases to overcome timidity or to exclude the test altogether because of self-consciousness. The test is assigned to the three-year level by Binet, but we find it applicable in partial form to the eighteen-months and two-year levels.

Distinguishes right and left

RATINGS: 48A+ and 60B+

Procedure: Say to the child "Show me your right hand." Stress *right* and *hand* strongly and equally. Proceed likewise for left ear and right eye. If there is one error repeat the whole test, using left hand, right ear, left eye. Avoid giving aid in any way. The ratings are assigned if three out of three or five out of six responses are correct.

P 52. Verbal Facility

RATINGS: 18A+   36A

Procedure: By interview or trial the examiner determines whether the child can count or repeat part of the alphabet or recognize any letters or rimes. The latter ability merits a 36A rating; verbal counting or repeating of part of the alphabet receives an 18A+ rating.

Comment: A corresponding number sense is not implied in the ability to count. The ability is presumed to be purely verbal but is considered an index of the imitative and discriminative capacity of the child. It therefore has some significance at eighteen months. It is unnecessary to add that the type of home in which the child has been reared must be taken into account. It is also true that specific delay in speech is not infrequently associated with normal intelligence.

P 53. Tells Name, Sex, and Age

RATINGS: 24B   24A   36B+   60B

Procedure: The examiner asks the child "What is your name?" If the first name only is given, the examiner adds, "Yes, but what is your other name, Walter what?" The rating is 24B for the first name; 24A for the full name. If the subject is a boy, the examiner further asks, "Are you a little boy or a little girl?" If a girl the question is framed, "Are you a little girl or a little boy?" The ratings are 24A and 36B+.

The examiner also asks on the five-year schedule, "How old are you?" A correct answer receives a B rating.

P 54. Knowledge of Money

RATINGS: 48C   48A+   60A

Procedure: By interview the examiner determines whether the child has definite conception of the fact that money is for purposes of purchasing. Nearly all children four years of age have attained this conception and a rating of C is assigned at that level. If in addition on the four- and five-year-old schedules the child names three or four common coins, he receives a rating of 48A+ and 60A. The procedure for the coin naming test is as follows: Show in order a nickel, penny, quarter, dime, asking, "What is that?" If the answer is "Money" say, "Yes, but what do we call that piece of money?"

P 55. Distinguishes Forenoon and Afternoon

RATING: 60B+

Procedure: The examiner asks (if it is morning), "Is it morning or afternoon?"; if it is afternoon, "Is it afternoon or morning?"

P 56.   Gives Color Names

RATINGS: 24A   24A+   36B+   48B+   48A   60B

Procedure: By interview or trial ascertain whether the child ever uses the names of colors in designating particular objects or parts of clothing or when presented with a variety of colored cubes or similar material.   A rating of 24A is assigned if he uses color names whether they are used appropriately or not.   If the child is using color names, a white card with rectangular shapes of red, white, blue, and yellow is presented to him.   Pointing to one color the examiner says, "What is the name of the color?"   If the response is correct and no other color is confused with it, ratings are made on the following basis: One correct, 24A+   36B+   two correct, 48B+;   four correct, 48A   60B.

CHAPTER 12

ACTION PHOTOGRAPHS

In this chapter are assembled a large number of photographs which were taken in the course of our investigation. The chief value of these photographs lies in the fact that they were taken when the subjects were exactly or almost exactly at the age level indicated. The pictures portray the developing child in characteristic behavior situations. They are called action photographs because with few exceptions some form of action enters into the picture. Most of the pictures were taken by the writer under the ordinary lighting conditions of the laboratory. A small Graflex camera, size 3½ by 2½, with rapid lens, was used.

In addition to these photographs we have taken clippings from two reels of cinema film provided by the Pathé Review. The cinema pictures were taken in the psycho-clinical laboratory under high-power arc lights. The lights proved to be less disturbing than we had feared. The children adjusted readily to the novel situation. The mothers of children usually came in pairs and it proved that this arrangement facilitated the adjustment of the children and reduced any alarm which they or their mothers might have developed. Most of the children looked intently at the four high-power lamps and listened to the intermittent humming noise but were not seriously distracted. The lights, strangely enough, proved to be more of a distraction to the older than the younger children. This might have been due partly to the fact that the four- and five-year-old children were pictured on a dull day when the glare of the lights was more accentuated. The disturbing influence of the lamps is lessened if the pictures are taken in bright diffused daylight, which makes the lights less apparent. The problem of adjustment to the photographic situation, therefore, did not concern so much the physical as the personal and social factors of the whole situation. When social confidence was established, the children adjusted readily.

The pictures are arranged in an orderly and so far as possible normative series. They are not inserted to embellish the text nor even to illustrate the developmental examination. They are grouped in this chapter so that the examiner may actually use them on occasion as an instrumental aid to classification. In later chapters on methods of developmental diagnosis, we shall emphasize the importance of a comparative approach. A graded series of photographs should prove of some practical value when used in a comparative manner as a means of matching a given case against certain standards such as are portrayed in the photographs themselves.

Gilbreth has invented the magster as a device for picturing and studying the dynamic elements which are at the basis of various forms of skill. This device enables the user to view stereoscopic stilled pictures of moving pictures and to compare in a leisurely manner "all the details of the phenomena of precious skill, automaticity, comparative lag, and relativity or simultaneity of the anatomical members and other elements of behavior of the superskilled and the champion." That an analytic device like the magster has clinical possibilities is apparent. Lacking this luxury, we have assembled our action photographs as the first leaves of a clinical album which may be used for normative reference and comparative purposes. We hope sometime to have the opportunity to make such a collection more complete and serviceable.

A reproduction of Paul Manship's sculpture of his infant daughter is inserted as a frontispiece to the series of action photographs. This marble image is remarkable for its beauty and for its realism. And, it might be added, for its daring. When it was first shown in the New York Metropolitan Museum of Art it created a stir, and not a little comment from those who suggested that "so young an infant was not a fitting theme for a work of art." Rarely in the history of art has either painter or sculptor attempted to portray so young a child. We are told that even among the numerous and various representations of Christ there are almost none which present him as a very young infant. Manship's Pauline, therefore, is a unique artistic achievement. (Figure 17.)

Much of the charm of this marble portrait lies in its veracity. The subject is not overidealized. If it is symbolic it is so because it conveys an impression of a real baby, the sculptor's own daughter, at the age of three weeks. It even conveys, though of marble, a suggestion of action. There is a characteristic incoherent fanning in the fingers, one of which has touched the cheek which yields to the impress.

In a critical and discriminating appreciation, M. G. Van Rensselaer makes the following comments: Pauline is "portrayed with exact truth and all possible respect for the nascent personality, studied with the utmost care and rendered with the most delicate precision." "It seems to us that in recording an aspect which is soon outgrown—that air of infinite wisdom which vanishes when intelligence develops—he has produced a little masterpiece, valuable alike for its unusual documentary and for its purely artistic qualities, highly individual, distinguished, interesting, and also charming to the eye."

"We may safely believe that so fresh and so vital a work of art will prove to be one of those that repay their debt to nature by opening many eyes to the interest and the significance of natural things which they have never really seen before."

FIGURE 17. INFANT, AGE THREE WEEKS
Sculpture by Paul Manship

162

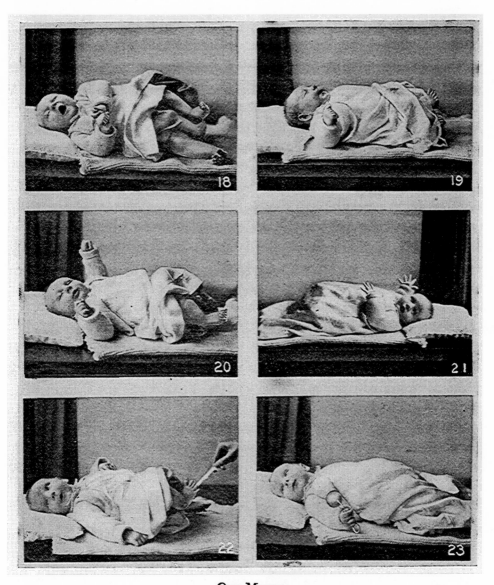

ONE MONTH

18. Yawning   19. Sleeping.   20. Waking and stretching.   21. Awake.   Finger fanning.
22. Babinski toe fanning.   23. Reflex holding.

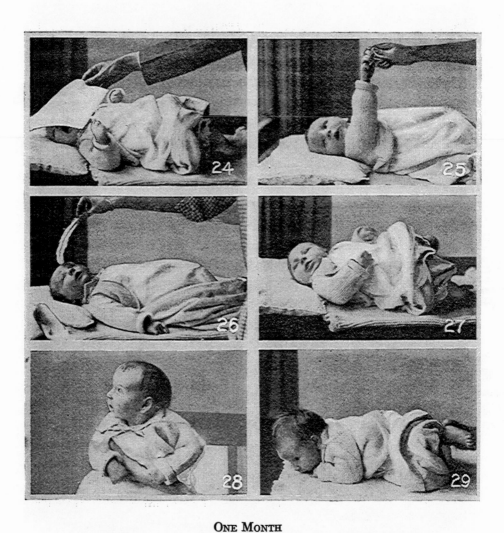

ONE MONTH

24. Reacts to paper cover.   25. Resists rod withdrawal.   26 "Attends" to tactile stimulus.
27. Random head play.   28. Transient head posture.   29. Lifts head.

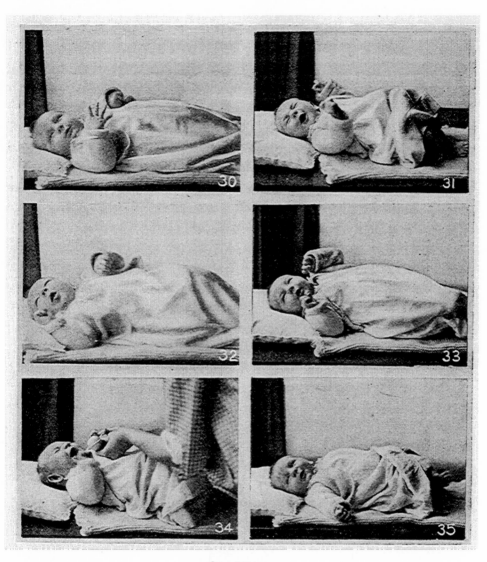

ONE MONTH

30. Fanning finger play.   31. Sound play (expiratory wheeze).   32 Mouth and tongue play.
33. Stretching.   34. Sneezing.   35. Resting.

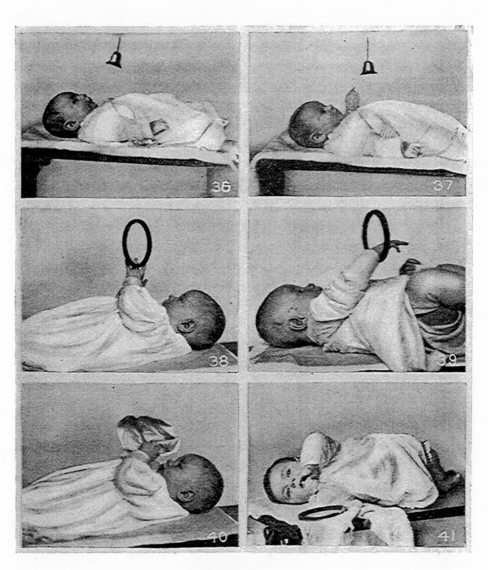

FOUR MONTHS

36. Regards bell.   37. Incipient reaching.   38 Closes in on dangling ring.   39 Attains ring without grasping.   40. Simple paper play.   41. Hand to mouth.

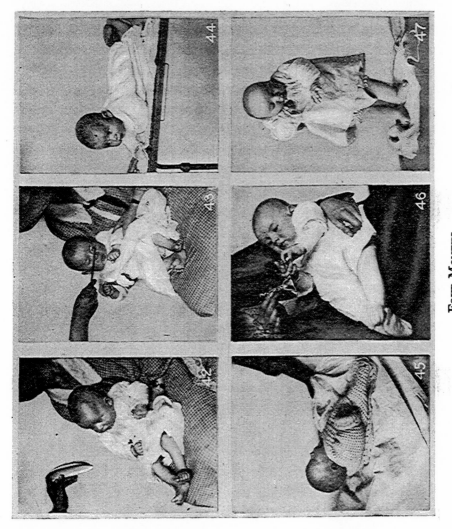

FOUR MONTHS

42. Blinks at saucer. 43. Fails to blink at pencil. 44. Erects head when prone. 45. Tries to "sit up."
46. Plays with hand. 47. Regards hand attentively.

167

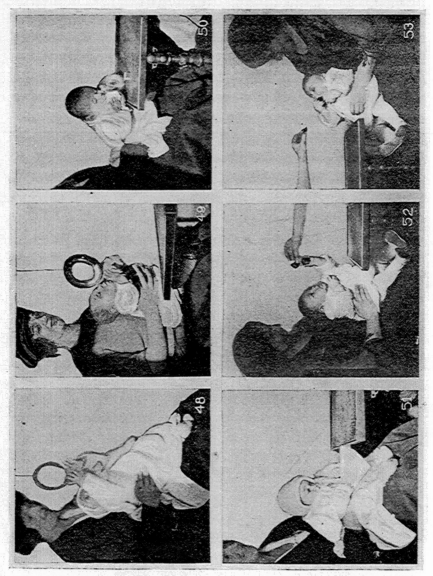

Six Months

48. Reaches directly for ring. 49. Mouths ring. 50. Picks up cup. Disregards cube. 51. Crumples paper. 52. Holds two cubes. 53. Does not take third cube.

168

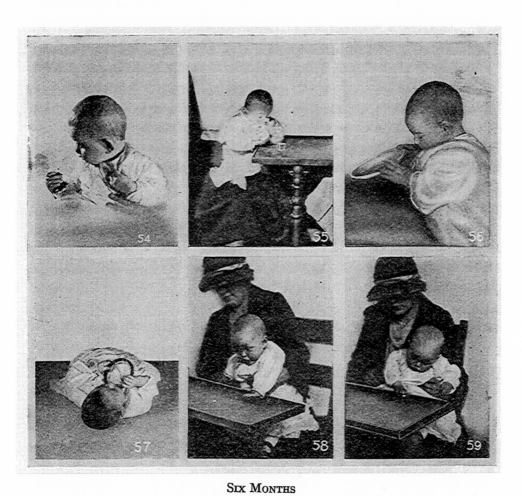

Six Months

54. Grasps bell. 55. Vigorous mouthing 56 Rocks saucer 57 Bites ring. 58. Regards pellet.
59. Scoops up pellet.

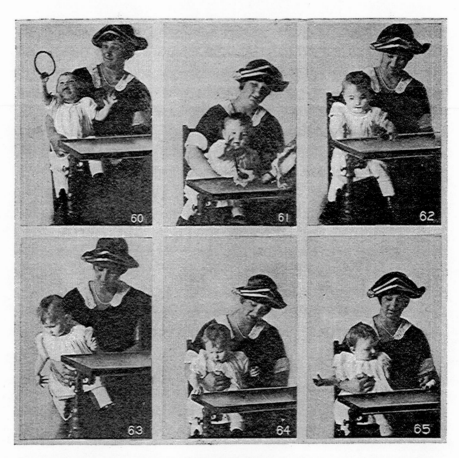

NINE MONTHS

60 Reaches directly for ring with one hand (also regards string) 61. Reaches insistently, using one hand 62. Lifts cup. Secures cube 63 Looks for fallen spoon. 64. Picks up pellet. 65. Inspects pellet.

170

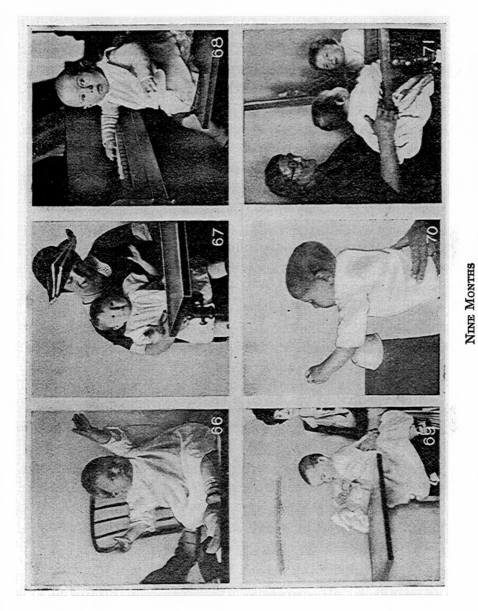

NINE MONTHS

66. "How big is the baby?" 67. Pat-a-cake. 68. Plays piano (sits alone). 69. Crumples paper "purposively." 70. Bangs cube on cup. 71. Reacts to mirror image.

171

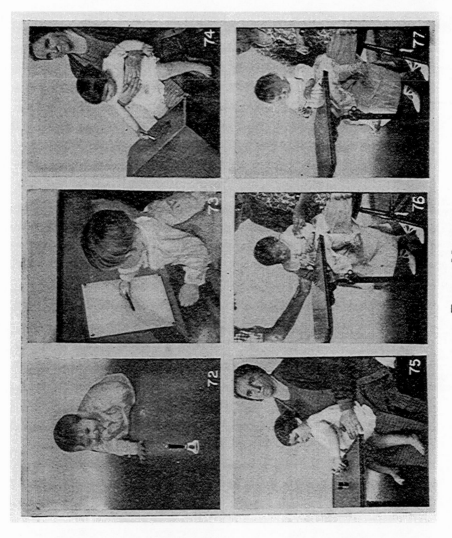

TWELVE MONTHS

72. Crawls for bell. 73. Scribbles. 74. Thrusts rod in hole. 75. Combines cubes. 76. Watches cube disappear. 77 Unwraps cube.

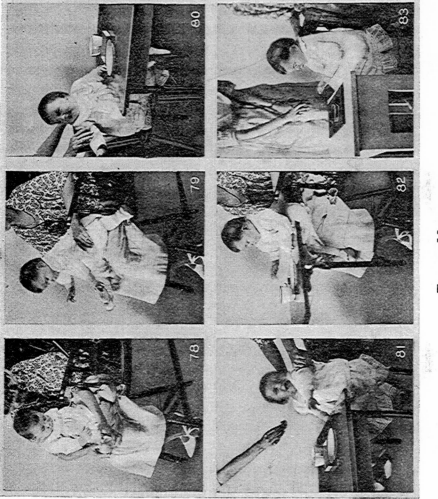

TWELVE MONTHS

78. Watches very intently while shoe is put on foot. 79. Tries to put shoe on foot. 80. Alarmed by moving of table. 81. Will not be persuaded. 82. Promptly readjusts in mother's lap. Obeys multiple choice command. 83. Puts circular block in form-board when shown.

173

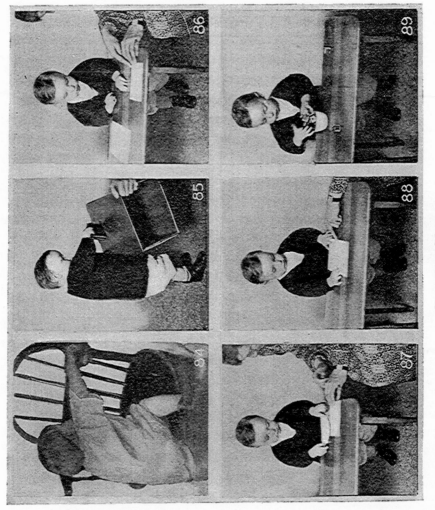

Eighteen Months

84. Climbs into chair. 85. Inserts block in box. 86. Watches paper fold. 87. Folds paper. 88. Points to pictures. 89. Piles cup full of blocks.

174

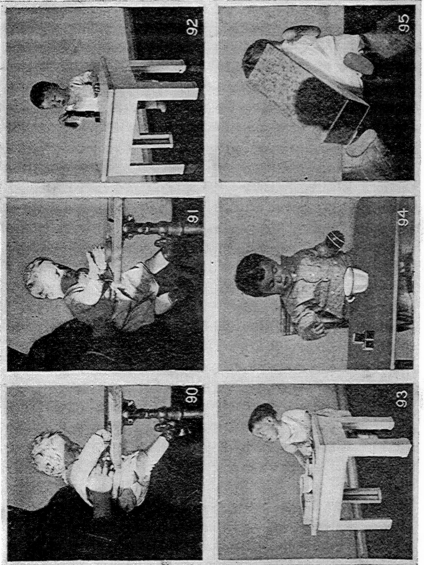

EIGHTEEN MONTHS

90. Scribbles spontaneously. 91. Puts round block in form-board. 92. Builds a tower. 93. Places cube in cup, plate, box. 94. Plays with cup and cube. 95. Spontaneous performance box investigation.

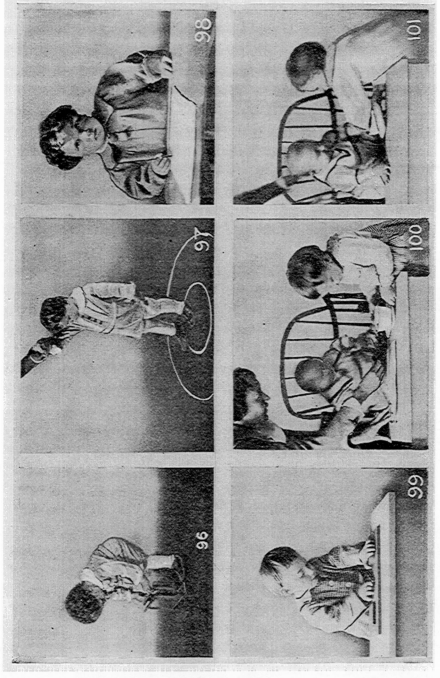

TWO YEARS

96. Revolves toy clown. 97. Tries to stand on one foot. 98. Draws vertical and horizontal lines imitatively. 99. Solves three-hole form-board. 100. Plays very purposively with cup and saucer. 101. Until interfered with by brother, age 1.

176

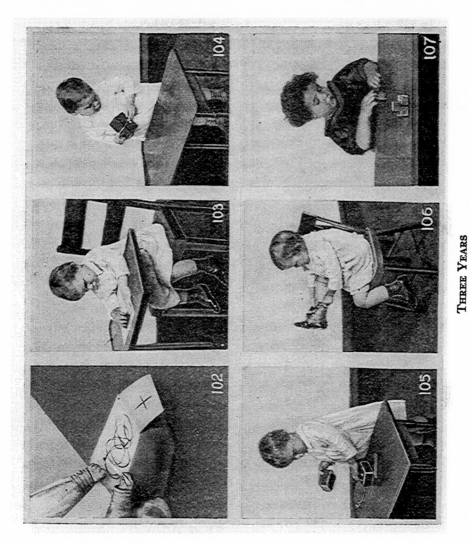

THREE YEARS

102. Copies circle but may fail on cross. 103. Aligns card. 104. Tries to get ball from box. 105. Succeeds. 106. Puts on shoe. 107. Builds bridge.

177

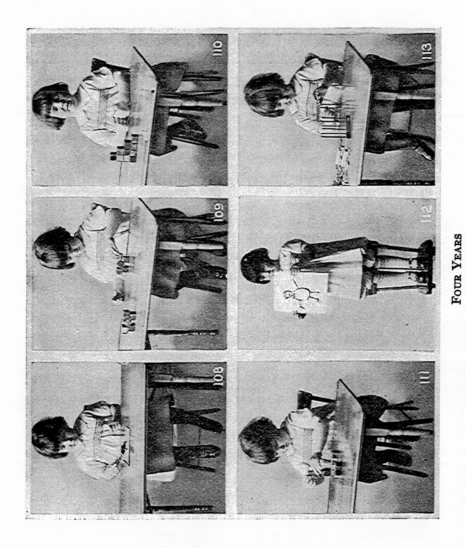

FOUR YEARS

108. Hooks fish. 109. Builds gate from model. 110. Closes eyes on command. 111. Tries to build memory steps. 112. Completes man. 113. Builds constructively with play material.

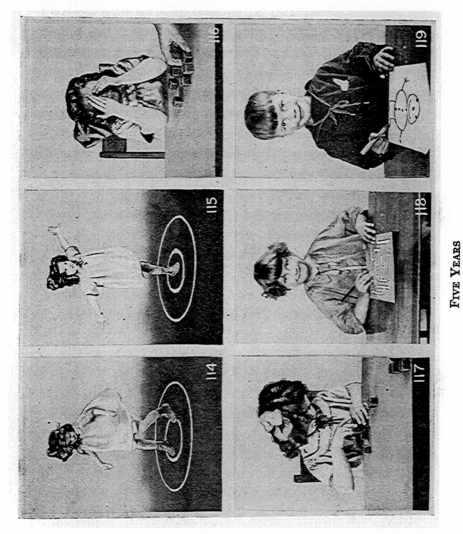

FIVE YEARS

114. Whirls gracefully in circle.   115. Balances on one foot.   116. Closes eyes for test.   117. Builds memory steps.   118. Traces maze.   119. Draws a recognizable man.

179

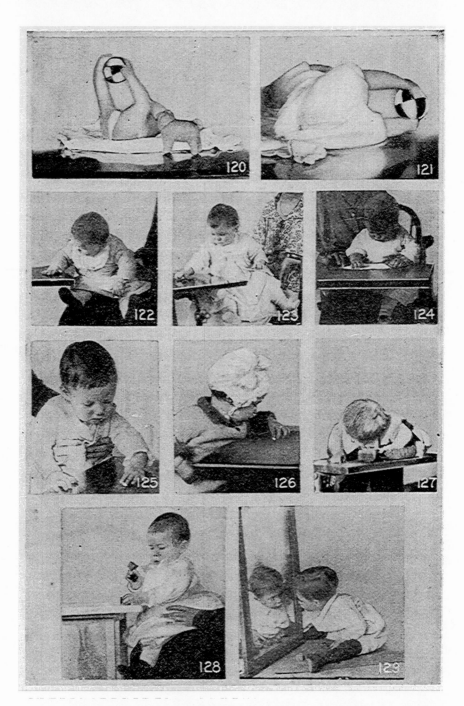

PREHENSION

120–1. Pedal prehension, age 6 months. 122. Fine prehension, lateral attack, age 9 months. 123. Same subject, age 12 months, overhead attack. 124. Trying to pick up a hole in paper (9 mos.). 125. Defective prehension at 9 months. Thumb does not participate. 126. Same subject, age 12 months. 127. Three-year-old Mongolian, picking up pellet with six-month palmar scoop. 128. A high grade 9 months solution of third cube problem. 129. Retarded two-year-old girl reaching behind mirror to apprehend image.

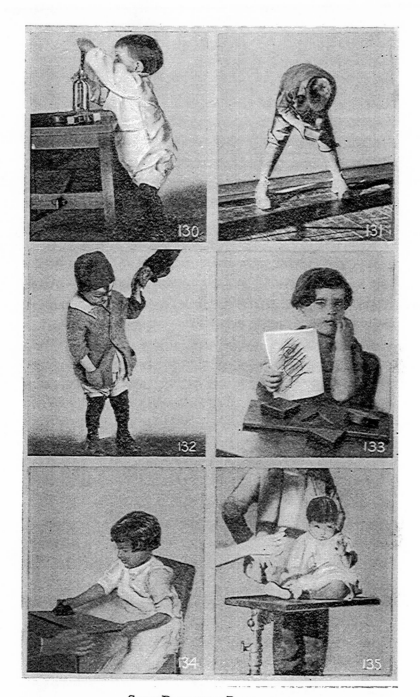

SOME DEFECTIVE REACTIONS

130 Two-year-old girl tries to put bell in bottle 131. Defective Seven-year-old boy trying hard to shake ball out of puzzle box. 132. Two-year-old boy extremely fearsome and shrinking because of abnormal home conditions. 133. Cannot solve formboard; makes scribble response to man completion test 134. At four years persists in obvious impossibility of forcing square block through rectangular opening of formboard. 135. Three-year-old Mongolian disregards cube but contemplates hand.

181

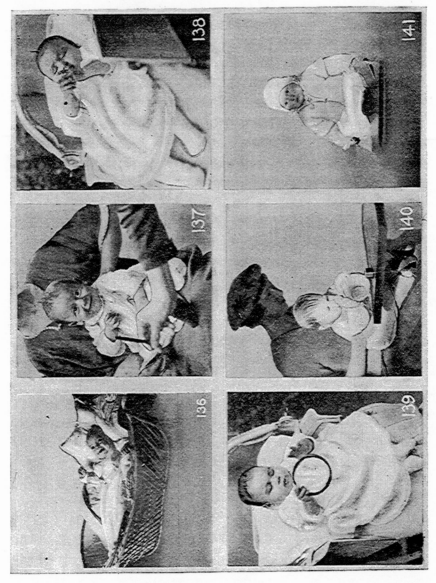

ADVANCED REACTIONS

136. A "social" smile at two months. 137. Direct reaching at four months. 138. Prolonged hand play at four months.
139. Advanced manipulation of ring. 140. Definitely lifts cup to secure cube at six months. 141. Sits alone at six months.

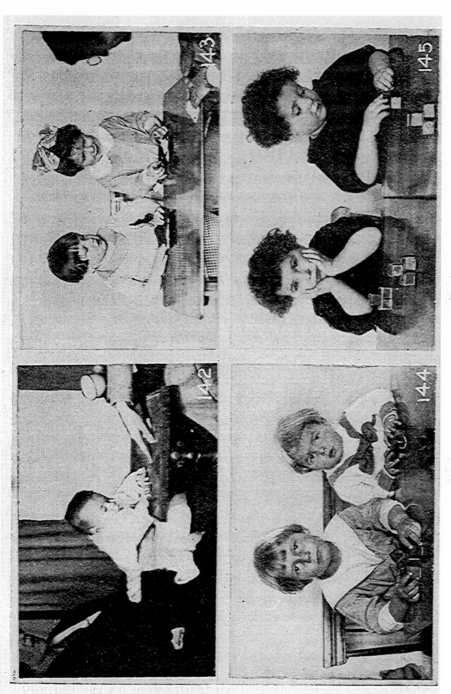

CLINICAL AND COMPARATIVE EXAMINATIONS

142. Developmental examination of six-month-old infant, seated in mother's lap, reaching for the pellet which the examiner has just placed on the table. 143. Two girls, both four years of age but of unequal capacity, are being comparatively examined (paper folding test). 144. Three-year-old boy and four-year-old boy, under comparative examination (Chapter 23). 145. Three-year-old duplicate twins. The resting twin consistently showed greater speed than her sister (Chapter 27).

183

PART THREE

COMPARATIVE STUDIES OF DEVELOPMENT

CHAPTER 13

The Foetus

Does the foetus belong to psychology? This question is not quite so startling as it was some fifty years ago when it was first asked by Perez. If we are at all sympathetic to the behaviorist point of view, we can readily see that the foetus falls within the scope of psychological interest. The foetus manifests behavior mediated by its own nervous system. Whether that behavior is associated with consciousness or not, it is associated with the early growth of the nervous system; and the first, albeit blurred, chapter in the book of development falls within the prenatal period. This chapter is not completely cryptic; nor is it altogether unique; but it has much of the obscurity that attaches to beginnings.

The prenatal development of the nervous system is significant in this connection. We single out the nervous system for special discussion, because of its numerous and intimate relations to the problems of development. Every organ of the baby is in a certain sense vital,—his liver, his heart, and his bones; but his nervous system has a peculiar importance. It is relatively the most complex, the most highly elaborated of all his tissues, and it is closely connected with every organ of the body. It is the nervous system which, in conjunction with the blood and lymph, makes of the body a living unit and makes all parts interdependent. It, in conjunction with bio-chemical mechanisms, regulates and integrates the organism.

The nervous system mediates the regulation of the lower vegetative functions of digestion, excretion, secretion, respiration, pulse. It determines the sensitiveness of the body to temperature, pressure, sound, light, and other stimuli; it determines also the responses of

187

muscles and glands to stimuli. Finally it is necessary for the higher ranges of conduct in the sphere of memory, of ideas, symbols, emotions, and voluntary action. The nervous system is the physiological basis and instrument of behavior in each of its three levels— (a) the vegetative level, (b) the sensori-motor level, (c) the higher psychical. Moreover it normally brings these three levels or aspects of human behavior into healthy coördination and balance. It is therefore the key to interpreting or formulating many of the problems of development.

The general significance of the nervous system in the maturation of the pre-school child can be suggested by a sketch of its prenatal development.

This development begins with the union of two minute gametes, as the two parental germinal cells are called. The mature nervous system consists of some 10,000,000,000 cells, but it is literally derived by a process of differentiation and specialization from the fertilized ovum. Indeed the growth intensity of this ovum is so remarkable that the full quota of neurones becomes established before the fifth month of the prenatal period.

The ovum at the time of impregnation is about .2 mm. in diameter. By a process of development which man shares with all animals and even with plants, this tiny globule of protoplasm divides into two cells, which presently divide in the same manner producing four cells, which likewise produce eight and so on until a solid sphere of segmenting cells forms. A cavity soon develops within the sphere, which becomes a vesicle over 1 mm. in diameter, with three primary layers of embryonic cells from which all the tissues of the organs arise. These layers are called the ectoderm, mesoderm, and entoderm. The ectoderm is particularly interesting to us because from it the nervous system is derived.

The stage of the ovum lasts two weeks, and in this time the segmenting ovum attains a length of about 4 mm. The stage of the embryo begins with the third week and lasts until the sixth week. During this period the various organs take recognizable form, the nervous system taking the lead. The embryo attains a length of about 14 mm. With the sixth week begins the stage of the foetus. This lasts until the end of the prenatal period of forty weeks or ten lunar months. By this time the child attains a length of fifty centimeters.

The first indications of the nervous system are found as early as the second week of prenatal development. There is a thickening of the ectoderm in the longitudinal axis of the tiny ovum. Presently this neural plate becomes depressed throughout its length, forming the neural groove. The sides of this groove speedily become accentuated, forming the neural folds, which close in, meet, fuse, and thus form the neural tube. This tube is never completely obliterated but persists throughout life as the cerebro-spinal canal. At its head end the tube expands into three dilated vesicles from which the entire brain finally develops.   (See Figure 146.)

It is not important here to follow the complex anatomical changes which take place in the course of this development. It concerns us more to grasp the underlying microscopic features, which can be understood in a general way by a study of the accompanying illustrations.

Figure 147 shows a series of cross sections. The first is from the cerebral cortex of the human foetus at about the second month of its development, when the neurones are at a rudimentary stage of their development. Indeed at this stage they are only potential neurones and are therefore called neuroblasts. The second section shows the cortex a month later (foetus of the third month).

The third section is of the cortex of a child a month old (neonate). The tiny processes at the end of the neuroblasts develop into the more elaborate processes of the neurone, called the dendrite and axon. In some nerves these delicate fibers may attain a length of two or three feet. Whether short or long the function of the fibers is to conduct and discharge impulses and to establish intercommunications within the nervous system. The relative complexity of any nervous system therefore depends not only upon the number of neurones but also upon the variety and character of the con-

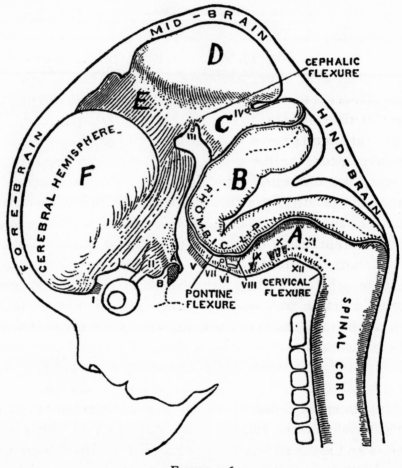

FIGURE 146

The central nervous system of the human foetus of six weeks. Profile view showing an early stage, before the cerebrum (fore-brain) expands and envelops the mid-brain and hind-brain. The Roman numerals indicate cranial nerves. (*After Dunlap.*)

nections between them. The development of the nervous system consists in a series of changes in which a relatively small number of embryonic cells become transformed into billions of neuroblasts,

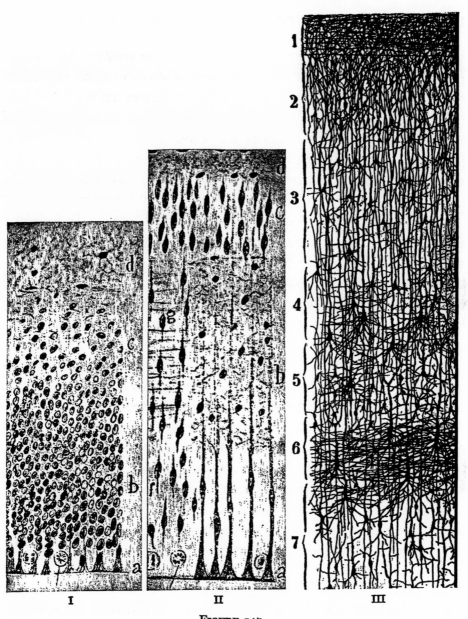

FIGURE 147

Early stages in the development of the human cerebral cortex. Enlarged microscopic sections.
I Two-month foetus. II Three-month foetus. III. Child one month old (neonate)
(*After Cajal and His*)

which in turn become neurones with innumerable interrelations established through an orderly network of protoplasmic fiber processes.

The embryonic cell division takes place, as already noted, within the walls of the neural tube. This cell multiplication is so rapid that the full quota of nerve cells is attained by the end of the fourth prenatal month. Whatever may be the influence of hygiene and education on the capacity and behavior of the individual, the number of neurones is part of his original nature fully determined before the intra-uterine period of his existence is half over. Inheritance also seems to determine the primary connections between the neurones, and the order in which these connections shall be established. Through the influence of training and experience the child will acquire many important connections between his neurones, but even these will be grafted upon the connections which are inborn.

The nervous system does not mature at a uniform rate and in a homogeneous manner. It develops somewhat as does a new country when opened for settlement. Certain districts and living essentials are first provided for, while whole areas lie relatively dormant. Naturally the most important lines of communication are the first to be laid down. These, in the human organism, have to do with such fundamental functions as blood circulation, digestion, respiration, suckling. Infant mortality would be still higher than it is, if vegetative and self-preservative functions did not have this priority in the growth of the nervous system.

Before the fifth month of the gestation period the physician can detect with his stethoscope a double sound, closely resembling the ticking of a watch under a pillow. The frequency of the beats is from 120 to 140 to the minute, almost twice the frequency of the maternal pulse. From the standpoint of the development of the nervous system, what does this observation which was first made a hundred years ago, mean? It means that certain neurones, connected doubtless with the medulla, have established functional connections with cardiac muscles of the foetus and brought them under a rhythmic control which will not cease until death. The foetal heart sounds therefore indicate that an appropriate group or network of neurones has in a sense matured. Such a group of coördinating neurones is called a "neurone pattern."

This is a convenient term. Every specific response of the body, every reflex action, every habit, memory, idea has its appropriate neurone pattern. Anatomically the nervous system is the sum total of all its constituent neurones. Physiologically it is the sum total of all its functional patterns. For a neurone pattern is a group of functionally associated neurones; it is the protoplasmic route over which afferent, efferent, and controlling nerve energy passes in any given situation.

To the student of behavior the neurone pattern concept is as useful as the molecular theory was to the physicist. It does not, to be sure, explain the ultimate mystery of life, but it is a formula which assists interpretation and observation. Even the mental development of a baby becomes somewhat less elusive if we regard the progress of his attainments and his propensities as the maturation of both inborn and acquired neurone patterns. The accurate observation and measurement of the behavior of an infant will furnish an objective index of the maturity of his nervous system. It is impossible to ascertain the maturity of the brain by a fluoroscope or skiagraph; but the reaction of the child to a test problem or situation may give a clue. We may be sure that the child will never make any adaptation to a stimulus unless he has the requisite neurone organization.

The foetal heart sound, therefore, may be considered as a very early expression of the growth of his nervous system. Like so many objective signs of development it has a diagnostic and prognostic significance. The rate of the foetal heart beat is subject to many variations and Williams considers it a fairly reliable means of estimating the well-being of the prenatal child.

After the fifth month, the foetus actually moves of his own spontaneity in the womb. These movements, at first like faint flutters, become quite pronounced in the later prenatal period. Here again, we have a recognizable bit of behavior, which is doubtless the manifestation of maturing neurone patterns, involving the spinal nerves and spinal cord.

Microscopic studies by the neurologist also show that the spinal cord neurones are among the first to mature. The neurones which preside over most fundamental reflexes take the lead in development, and these are normally ready for the crisis of birth. If they are not ready the child dies. The adjacent levels of the spinal cord are brought into connection before the remoter, and the connections between the spinal cord and the cerebrum as a rule mature still later. The cerebral cortex, which presides over the higher forms of behavior, is relatively late in development. Those portions of the cortex which, like the infra-granular layers, may be concerned with instinctive and sensori-motor responses apparently mature earlier, and certain regions like the frontal and parietal association areas are the last to ripen. In the frontal lobes of the seven-months foetus, the nerve cells are still in the neuroblastic stage, and they do not form into the characteristic layers until the eighth month. Even at birth the cerebral cortex as a whole is so undeveloped that the question has been raised whether the newborn baby has consciousness at all!

However this may be, he is ready with parental care to begin the struggle for existence; for he "knows how" to take his food, to swallow, to breathe, to cry, to hiccough, to yawn, to sneeze, to sleep, as soon as he is born. During the latter months of his prenatal development the inner architecture of his nervous system has been so perfected that he can make all these fundamental self-protective adaptations.

The growth of the brain is of course reflected in the size of the cranium. The cranium taken by itself shows a regular increase throughout the whole growing period. This increase in relation to stature is so great in the early stages of development that relative to the total dimensions of the body its growth shows a consistent decline. At the beginning of the foetal period the head is in size and bulk about equal to the whole body. Even at birth the "height" of the cranium is almost one-fifth of the stature. As Godin has said, this means simply that the brain of the child is from birth much nearer its adult dimensions than any other organ and that its content has much less need to grow than does stature.

But the brain still has need to grow. In six months it attains almost half of its adult weight. Neurone patterns grow and multiply at an amazing rate and the infant makes impressive gains in his conquest of the world during the whole preschool period. From the standpoint of psychology and of hygiene it would be very useful to have even approximate norms with which to measure the completeness of his development at any stage during these important formative years.

CHAPTER 14

The Neonate

It has been found necessary to adopt a distinctive term for the earliest period in the life of the new-born infant. His medical and his public-health significance during the first month of existence is so great that we render him a real service when we bestow upon him the distinguishing cognomen *neonate* for that one critical month. When he attains the age of three or four months, more general terms like baby and infant and pre-school child will suffice.

Not only from the standpoint of child hygiene but also from the standpoint of developmental diagnosis, the neonatal month proper and the two or three months succeeding it constitute a period which presents problems of peculiar interest and difficulty. These problems warrant special research and clinical procedure. We have scarcely grasped the importance of the genetic problems with which this period bristles. It may well be that some happy method of precise physiological investigation will reveal facts relating to the growth of the nervous system which will be of such basic import that they will have unusual diagnostic and predictive value.

What do we see when we look into the basket which has just received a newly born child? He is wrapped up snugly in a warm blanket because of the immaturity of his mechanisms of temperature regulation. But we may ask at once,—Are these mechanisms absolutely immature and must this neonate start from a zero line in achieving powers of temperature control? Has not this control been anticipated in the foetal period? Why not? It has been said that the temperature of the foetus is one degree higher than that of the mother. If this is true there must be a measure of independence in this matter of temperature regulation. Even if the temperature of the foetus and mother are identical, we may still believe that the maintenance of this identity falls upon the former as well as upon the latter, and although the foetus is nourished by the maternal blood stream it must be remembered that there is no complete physical union between his own circulatory system and that of the mother. There must be a degree of physiological independence in his status from the time that his own circulatory system becomes established and functions. The fact that he is coming into possession of a functioning nervous system at that same time is significant. He lives and moves and has his own physiological being during the foetal as well as the neonatal period of his existence. His quickening movements originated within his own organism. In a like manner much of his behavior during the foetal period must be indigenous.

These facts from a developmental point of view must be emphasized because there has certainly been a tendency to exaggerate the differences between prenatal and postnatal existence. Compayre calls birth "a veritable metamorphosis which changes the child from a parasite to a personal human being who becomes individualized and lives by himself." This is undoubtedly an overstatement. Although birth does represent a drastic alteration, it carries with it no marked developmental transmutation. Strictly speaking, the mother even in the foetal period is in the relation of a nurse to the child. With birth there is a fundamental difference in method of food and oxygen intake, but this difference scarcely confers upon him a decisive independence; moreover his basic metabolism remains much the same.

But we must return to the baby who, newly born, has been deposited in the basket with blankets and hot-water bottles to keep him warm. If we peer under the blanket's edge what picture of behavior do we see? A very interesting one. Even though we look at no more than his head we find three or four distinct forms of activity. There is a rhythmic tensing movement of the eyelids and associated movements. There is a slight frown and corrugation of the brow, but the muscular action seems to be confined chiefly to the lids and simulates a gross blepharospasm. This is one form of activity. Near by we see an equally vigorous rhythmic dilatation and partial closure of the nostrils. This is no doubt a part of the respiratory adjustment which the child is making to his neonatal environment. Dominating the scene, however, are the rhythmic mouthing movements. They are more frequent than the movements of the eyelids. The mouth not only closes tight but opens wide; the tongue protrudes as much as half an inch. The frequency and continuousness of these movements are pronounced. In the margin of the picture we see vermicular rotating movements of the baby's hand, which is held near the mouth. Occasionally this activity withdraws the hand from the oral zone, but most of the time the hand keeps coming into rhythmic contact with the lips and sometimes protrudes into the mouth, increasing by contact the mouthing reactions.

The picture presented is, therefore, one of intense, diversified activity. One of the most interesting features of this behavior picture is the fact that there is apparently a high degree of independence in the activity of these three or four zones. There is no synchronization in the activity of the eyes, of the nostrils, of the mouth and of the hands. The moving and energizing factors seem to be unrelated and surely unintegrated. Yet as one looks at this first visible scene of the drama of development one gains the impression that a process of organization and growth is going on even while his observations are being made. The babies in near-by cribs, who are several days the senior of this freshly born baby, already display certain evidences of higher organization and adaptation. The rate of growth during the first week of neonatal life, could we measure it, doubtless far exceeds that of any comparable interval of growth in later infancy.

This incoherent and apparently useless pristine behavior

must be a kind of fore-exercise which has a preparatory or adaptive relation to innumerable useful forms of behavior which the child is about to acquire. And again the behavior may be given a backward reference. It is not unlike that mode of fore-exercise which was present in the antenatal period. There is, however, one unmistakable exception which we failed to mention. While the baby's eyes, nose, mouth, and hands were in activity we could hear from time to time a clearly defined expulsive "eh, eh, eh" which was scarcely a cry but was a part of the respiratory adjustment which the child was making to his new aërial environment.

This vocalization was increased to a definite crying when a physician lifted the child from the basket and placed him upon the table to take several measurements of the head with a pair of calipers. The crying was intense but not prolonged. With each new adjustment or shift of position the crying was repeated. When drops of silver nitrate were instilled in the eye the crying was again repeated and there was a definite head aversion of a defensive character. At one time the steel tape came within the baby's grasp. He seized it reflexly and held on tightly. Indeed he held on so tightly that his whole body weight might almost have been lifted from the table. This reflex grasp disappeared during the period of sleep which followed as soon as the baby was reinstated in a warm basket. While he was sleeping he could not be aroused by a stamp of the foot but he immediately began to cry when the physician's finger touched his cheek. A more massive touch, which we call a caress, however, would have an opposite effect.

The next episode in the life of this newly born baby is the first bath and the first dressing, which may come, let us say, in four hours. How does the baby react to these unique and in a sense violent though protective events?

We sketch here roughly the behavior picture as we saw it a few hours after birth. While he lies in his crib just before he is lifted out for his first bath he is busily engaged in making mouthing movements. He turns his head with almost rhythmic regularity at about forty-five degrees. He yawns from time to time with amazing expertness and apparently with all the skill of an adult. His eyes continually move back and forth with a slow semi-rhythmic regularity. He cries momentarily, apparently not from any distress, about six times within a period of five minutes. His fingers are active and move independently, assuming many positions. At one time his thumb is curled inward; his index finger is sharply flexed; his little finger as sharply extended; and the ring and middle fingers in intermediate positions. The examiner tries to duplicate this postural arrangement of the fingers in his own hand and is unable to do so. The baby is mildly startled if his mattress is suddenly pushed against his back, but he is not startled by a loud sound.

Mild vocalization is sharply increased when he is lifted onto the table for the ministrations of the nurse. The vocalization is as sharply concluded as soon as he is allowed to rest free on the table surface. It is renewed as soon as the nurse begins to wash and wipe the eyes. There are definite head aversion movements and an increase of leg movements. There is a quieting down while the neck and body are sponged; a marked stiffness of the arms and legs when the nostrils are cleaned. There is facial and bodily squirming when the baby is lifted from the table into the weighing pan, but random movements resume as soon as he is laid down. The great toe displays a surprising mobility and remains separated for a few moments by as much as one centimeter and one-half from the adjacent toe. When the baby is placed on the table he tolerates the prone position; he flexes his legs in a manner which simulates mild crawling movements. His right cheek, however, rests with a hapless heaviness upon the table top. He closes his right eye protectively while in this position, but his left eye is wide open. He cannot erect his head to relieve any discomfort from his head posture, if indeed he feels discomfort at all. He cries again lustily for a brief moment when the nurse begins to shampoo him; but he does not cry during the process of shampooing. Indeed it appears that he cries at the moment when there is a marked transition from one condition to another as though he were protesting against the transition rather than the result itself. He protests against the constraint that goes with putting on the first garment but relaxes with evident motor expansiveness when replaced snugly in his crib after this, his first bath and first dressing.

His facial expression takes on an aspect of increased alertness; there is a mild vocalization expressive of organic satisfaction. His lips resume their previous activity; his mouth closes and opens about a dozen times a minute; he sneezes, yawns, and falls to sleep.

In two weeks this child will be able to graduate from the maternal ward in the hospital and will go to his own home. In that fortnight he undergoes remarkable development which we shall not attempt to summarize. How precociously and efficiently he exhibits his powers of learning is illustrated by a certain infant who recently came to our attention. In the first day of life this infant cried at every new pronounced stimulus—as soon as he was picked up he cried;—he ceased to cry when allowed to lie quiet. In two weeks his social environment induced a complete *reversal* of this relation between stimulus and response. He cried while he was in the crib; he ceased to cry when picked up. If he learned this in two weeks what can he not learn in twice two weeks, in two months and in four months?

We can give a concrete indication of his repertoire of behavior at the age of one month by referring the reader to a foregoing set of action photographs. Part of the significance of these photographs lies in the fact that all of them, eighteen in number, were taken in the short space of one hour while the child was deploying himself on the table in our laboratory. No apparatus was used to display his various achievements except a piece of paper and a white feather presently to be mentioned. The arrangement of pictures roughly duplicates the order in which they were taken and they furnish a succinct cross-section view of a healthy one-month-old baby who has just had his afternoon meal and nap. Only brief comments are necessary by way of explanation. (See pages 163–66.)

Figure 18 (p. 163) represents the child in the act of yawning. He has not yet fully awakened from his sleep. In this picture leg stretching is more conspicuous than arm stretching. He does not succeed in arousing himself with this initial yawn or several yawns which follow.

19. His nap continues as is shown in this picture. His fingers, but not his toes, are flexed. His legs also prefer a flexed posture.

20. He is now waking. The picture represents him in the act of stretching. During the transitional period his eyes are only half open and he is only half alert.

21. Here he is fully alert. He has begun to play. The picture indicates an active playful fanning movement of the fingers of both hands. His playful activity extends from his finger tips to his oculomotor mechanism because there is an alarming strabismic droop of the left eyeball. This "functional strabismus" might be described as being playful in character; nature's method, perhaps, of exercising the ocular muscles. Normally this strabismus is "outgrown."

22. It persists, however, for some time and shows itself in the present picture. This picture also shows a pretty Babinsky's response to the feather stimulus to the ball of the right foot. The great toe is extended and there is a spreading or fanning reaction of the toes.

23. This shows the type of reflex hold which the child of this age is equal to. This baby held the rattle for fully a minute, but the duration of the hold in any given instance depends altogether on the state of his reflexes at the time. When the impulse to random or playful movements asserts itself and he begins to spread his fingers and wave his arms the rattle drops.

24. This shows the baby's reaction to the paper-covering test. There is an increase of head aversion or head-rolling movements but particularly an increase in mouthing activity. The picture clearly shows the vigorous mouth-opening reaction which the paper stimulus evoked.

25. This picture shows the strong resistance to the withdrawal of a small rod which has been put into the baby's hand. He grasped the rod firmly but the thumb maintained its characteristic curled-in position.

26. This interesting picture would be a very significant one if we could adequately explain the nature of the evident response. We should know something very fundamental about the laws of attention if we could adequately explain this simple picture. The child is unquestionably "absorbed" by the tactile stimulation of the feather tip. There is a temporary cessation of his random movements and his arms lie relaxed by his side. He showed a similar reaction to the massive light stimulus coming through a sunlit window.

27. This photograph indicates an important form of play activity which was prominent in the behavior picture at this time. This play activity consisted in a vigorous, frequently recurring, rhythmic movement of the head. The body participated only moderately in the general reaction, which was confined largely to the head and neck muscles. These movements were almost too rapid for the camera as adjusted.

28. The baby's head play was so vigorous and abundant that it must have contributed to the postural control shown in this picture. It is evident from this picture that the child is beginning to hold his head erect. He maintained erect head posture for a few minutes at a time but this posture was far from established. His head readily slumped to a wobbling position and only feebly resisted lateral pressure from the examiner's hand.

29. This picture also shows the partial attainment of head posture. The baby is scarcely able to lift his head from the blanket

but his attitude is considerably beyond the passive limpness of the first week. This picture shows too how feebly the legs flex when the child is in the prone position.

30. This picture shows a fanning kind of finger play in the right hand with fingers flexed in the left. It is very evident at this tender age that movements are by no means bilateral and simultaneous but that there may be independent activity of the right and left members.

31. The camera caught this picture at the very instant at which the subject made a loud expiratory sound. Although this sound was an explosive, expiratory kind of wheeze it could not be considered a sneeze. It was very evidently not a response to an irritation but a playful kind of vocalization which the child indulged in freely as part of his total play.

32. This shows the prominence of mouth play at this period. Indeed in several of the pictures this characteristic activity of mouth and tongue is indicated. The present picture is included to show the marked active extrusion of the tongue.

33. This picture represents the subject in the act of stretching.

34. Here he is sneezing.

35. Here he is resting with very evident facial expression of a state of profound organic satisfaction. A mother and even a psychologist might be permitted to describe this expression as bordering on a smile. The baby's capacity to smile was no longer in doubt eleven days after, when he definitely smiled at his grandfather and definitely and still more frequently smiled at his grandmother in response to a squeaking sound made by her for his benefit.

The foregoing summary gives a fair indication of the baby's developmental status at the age of one month. It is clear that in these first four weeks the child makes an amazing advancement. If the reader is curious to know how far another month takes the baby some inference can be made from the following abstract of a detailed record of one full day of activity at the age of two months.

6:00–6:45 Nursing. 6:45–7:00 Quiescence. 7:00–7·45 Sleep. 7·45–8:05 Quiescence. 8:05–8:15 Crying. 8:15–8:20 Motor activity, —moving of arms. 8:20–8:23 Fretting. 8:23–8:29 Quiescence with fretting and slight motor activity. 8:29–8:41 Dozing—occasional moving of arms during sleep. 8·41–9:10 Quiescence with a little fretting and slight motor activity. 9:10–9:20 Experimentation,—looking about, waving hands before eyes, apparently experimenting with various sounds. 9:20–9:30 Crying. 9:30–9:35 Held by father— quiescence—evident enjoyment of being held. Smiling and "talking." 9:35–9:55 Bath—quiescence. Enjoyment while in tub. Motor activity,—kicking. Slight crying while being dressed, stopping when placed on stomach. 9:55–10:20 Feeding. 10:20–11:39 Quiescence with occasional motor activity and some experimentation,— noting of surroundings, noises, etc., playing with hands, and a little vocalization. 11:39–12·15 Sleeping. 12:15–12:20 Quiescence—one cry. 12:20–12:23 Motor activity,—trying to put thumb in mouth. 12·23–12:26 Crying. 12:26–12:32 Drinking water. 12:32–12:35 Quiescence. 12:35–12:40 Crying. 12:40–1:30 Sleeping. 1:30–1:40 Crying. 1:40–1:58 Sleeping. 1:58–2:50 Nursing. 2:50–3:10 Motor activity,—arms and head. 3:10–4:10 Sleeping. 4:10–4:12 Crying. 4:12–4:14 Quiescence. 4:14–4:22 Drinking water. 4:22–4:45 Quiescence. 4:45–5:25 Crying. 5:25–5:45 Being dressed for night,— played with a little. Enjoyment at being talked to. Smiling. Vocalization. 5:45–6:10 Nursing. 6:10–11:25 Sleeping. 11:25–11:55 Nursing. 11:55–4:10 Sleeping. 4:10–4:40 Intermittent crying and dozing. 4:40–5:20 Nursing. 5:20–5:35 Quiescence and slight motor activity. 5:35—Sleeping.

This behavior can conveniently be subdivided into seven categories, namely: Sleeping, Nursing, Quiescence, Emotional Activity, Motor Activity, Vocalization, Experimentation. Although no rigid line can be drawn between these various aspects of behavior, the classification permits us to draw up a distribution polygon which shows how the two-months-old child apportions his twenty-four hours.

Figure 148 brings into comparison the behavior charts of an infant at two months and again at six months. The observations on

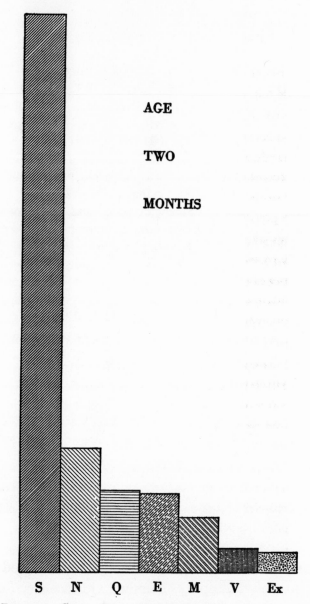

FIGURE 148.   BEHAVIOR CHART SHOWING DIURNAL DISTRIBUTION OF ACTIVITIES AT
TWO MONTHS

S	Sleep	14 hrs. 14 min
N	Nursing	3 hrs 9 min (12 min water)
Q	Quiescence	2 hrs 5 min
E	Emotional activity	2 hrs. 2 min (crying, 1 hr 47 min, enjoyment 15 min)
M	Motor activity	1 hr. 25 min.
V	Vocalization	40 min.
Ex	Experimentation	30 min
	Total time	*24 hours*

206

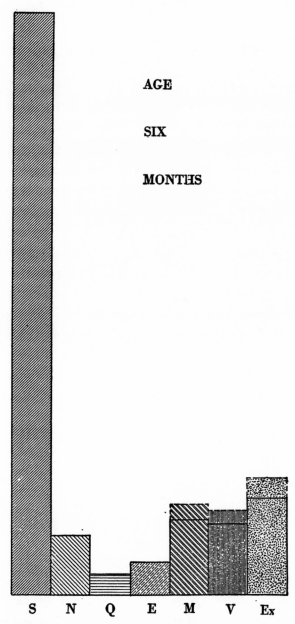

FIGURE 148A. BEHAVIOR CHART SHOWING DIURNAL DISTRIBUTION OF ACTIVITIES AT
SIX MONTHS

S	Sleep	14 hrs. 50 min.
N	Nursing	1 hr. 30 min.
Q	Quiescence	39 min.
E	Emotional activity	46 min. (crying, 14 min., enjoyment, 32 min.)
M	Motor activity	1 hr. 53 min. (2 hrs. 23 min.)
V	Vocalization	1 hr. 49 min. (2 hrs. 19 min.)
Ex	Experimentation	2 hrs. 28 min. (2 hrs. 58 min.)
	Total time	*24 hours.*

207

which these charts were based were made by a trained observer, who found, however, that as the child grew older it proved more difficult to make a behavior record in accordance with the adopted classification. The charts disclose certain interesting differences between an infant day at two months and at six months.

The total time awake at two months was nine hours and forty-six minutes, and one third of this time was expended in nursing. It would, however, be most inconsistent with the facts to conclude that the baby at this time is merely a vegetative creature. Even at the age of two months it is evident by the way in which he cries, by the time at which he cries, by the abruptness with which he stops crying, by the manner in which he smiles when a sister or grandmother is in his vicinity, by the directness with which he responds to or is startled by the sound of a voice—by all these and similar tokens it is evident that he is being socially conditioned and that personality is in the making.

CHAPTER 15

An Outline of Pre–School Development

In the previous chapters we have attempted to demonstrate the basic continuity of development. There are no sharp beginnings and abrupt endings; no chasms of cleavage. If one takes a bird's-eye view of the whole span of pre-school development one is everywhere impressed with the dynamic unity and interrelation of all the manifold phenomena. It is very difficult to get a bird's-eye view because of the bewildering multiplicity and complexity of these phenomena. The mountain climber gets his most comprehensive view by mounting a high point and looking down; but he can acquire a real familiarity with the landscape only by exploring its terranes and by approaching them from various angles.

Perhaps the most concentrated synopsis of pre-school development which we can offer is that contained in the syllabus of normative items (Ch. 7) and in the series of normative summaries (Ch. 32). The syllabus classifies the various items of behavior into four groups which do not, of course, possess any sharply defined independence, but which bring together symptoms of development that are psychologically akin. The normative summaries formulate the items of behavior in such a manner as to bring out distinctive characteristics of ascending age levels.

In the present chapter we aim to sketch the general course of development in the four major fields of the map of behavior:— 1. Motor Development. 2. Language Development. 3. Adaptive Behavior. 4. Personal-Social Behavior.

1. MOTOR DEVELOPMENT

The postural limpness and motor incoherence of the new-born babe are amazing. They would be depressing as well if the chaos were not relieved by very prompt evidences of nascent coördination and cumulative organization. Out of the wealth of random movements those which are useful or adaptive are, as it were, invested, and he acquires a rapidly growing capital of motor achievements which lead to progressive postural control of his lips, his head, his back, his legs. In four months he holds his head erect; in nine he sits erect; in twelve he stands erect; in eighteen he walks with a skill which is distinctively human. Hopping, skipping, jumping, standing on one leg, dancing, perhaps even pirouetting may all come before the school age.

It is not implied that all these motor attainments are the outgrowth of habituation and training. Inborn propensities assert themselves at ascending stages. While he is acquiring head posture he is impelled to raise his head from the pillow; while he is gaining back control he has an urge to raise his back; when this is raised and he sits, he has a similar propensity to stand, and thus he both propels and is propelled along his upward course.

It must, of course, be understood that the term *motor development* is so sweeping and general as to be almost metaphorical in character. It is the general name for an almost endless array of specific forms of motor ability. These specific forms do not develop abreast; for example, the child who is not actuated to use his legs may be developing considerable skill in a fine prehensive use of the fingers. Physiological conditions, disease, and social factors all leave their impression on various forms of motor behavior. However, there are underlying laws which give orderliness to these manifold phenomena and there are developmental correlations which give them diagnostic significance. As a group, mentally defective children walk several months later than unselected normal children, and low-grade deficients walk later and usually more clumsily than high-grade deficients. Motor tests and items have a fundamental place in developmental diagnosis because they reveal significant facts relating to the maturity of the neuromuscular system.

The motor development of the pre-school child records itself with approximate precision in drawings which he makes with chalk, crayon, and pencil.   In the case of young children, drawing is not a form of draftsmanship and individual technical skill.   It has many of the characteristics and impulsions of play activity.   In rare cases a child at nine months will make marks and scrawls in which he takes at least fleeting interest.   At twelve months spontaneous scribbling begins to assert itself, and at eighteen months it is an almost universal trait.   Scribbling and scrawling represent the random-movement stage which precedes almost every form of organized skill.

It is apparent that imitative drawing represents an earlier and simpler form of psychomotor control than does copying from a model.   Indeed the crudest kind of imitative drawing is hardly above the level of mimetic gesture, which is well developed at nine months; in fact, one reason that we cannot be sure whether certain nine-months- and twelve-months-old children are scribbling imitatively is because we do not know whether they are simply reproducing a gesture or whether in addition to this they are also taking some interest in their workmanship.

Spontaneous scribbling (often conditioned, however, by imitative factors) asserts itself frequently enough among twelve-months-old children to warrant the conclusion that the evolution of drawing begins at that level.   The eighteen-months child is still largely in the scribble stage of development.

It is a sign of relative superiority if he makes a discriminative imitative distinction between a scribble and a stroke.   At the age of two years this differentiation is made by most children.   The average two-year-old child can make an imitative vertical stroke but he takes no particular interest in such defined imitative performance.   It is significant of the specificity of motor development that he has greater difficulty in imitatively reproducing a horizontal stroke than a vertical one.   It might be suggested that vertical strokes are more in accordance with movements which are racially important and that, therefore, he shows perceptible precocity in making vertical strokes as distinguished from horizontal strokes. At the age of three years he is ordinarily able to make this distinction and he is also able to copy a circle from a model. Again he shows no marked interest in this type of circumscribed drawing but, if he is held to the task, he shows that he has a certain conception of beginning and end when his circle is complete. He makes a circumscribed curved mark in duplication of a model. Curiously enough, however, we cannot expect him to copy a cross. In another year he is able to copy the cross of St. Andrew, making two straight right-angle strokes, but he has difficulty in completing the oblique cross of St. George.

The ability to copy a square cross and the inability to copy an oblique one presents us with a definite objective cleavage which has considerable psychological interest. From a purely logical point of view these two problems are equally difficult; they require the same amount of energy and both crosses are made up of two short strokes, one applied across the other. Why is it that one is possible and the other impossible? Is there some incompleteness in the oculomotor mechanism? Is this incompleteness peripheral or is it central and if it is central, as it possibly is, is the incompleteness due to lack of training or to a lack of native racially determined neural patterns?

The copy of a square is somewhat too difficult for the median four-year-old child. The copy of a triangle is a little more difficult. At the age of five years the median child can copy both a square and a triangle but he shows an inability to copy a diamond, which recalls a similar lack of mastery over oblique strokes which he displayed a year earlier when called upon to differentiate between the cross of St. George and the cross of St. Andrew.

Imitative drawing and copying, although conditioned by social factors, are primarily affected by the maturity of the neuromuscular system. In the field of dramatic spontaneous representative drawing, social factors and personality traits come more conspicuously into play but, basically again, drawing even in this field is determined by broad developmental factors. It is for this reason that normal three-year-old children as a group do not draw a man or even the semblance of a man and that five-year-old children draw a recognizable man with relative anatomical completeness (not to mention superfluities). The characteristic or median four-year-old child's drawing of a man lies midway between the primitive scrawl of the three-year-old and the recognizable five-year-old man. Since we must be brief we may allow the accompanying drawings to speak for themselves (Figure 149).

2. LANGUAGE DEVELOPMENT

The very first behavior event after birth belongs in a sense to the field of language. Indeed the philosopher Kant imputed to it definite language value for he called it nothing less than "a cry of wrath at the catastrophe of birth." The respiratory tricks, the cooing and babbling of even the young infant are a preparation for language. Out of many varied vocalizations, articulate speech finally emerges. There is an increasing range and diversity of sound play during the first half year of life. During the first day of life the ordinary listener could perhaps distinguish not any more than an "eh and ah" in the audible behavior of the infant, but at the age of six months it requires diligent observation to record the wealth of vocalization which presents itself in the course of one day.

Through the interest of Mr. L. M. Malmberg, we were able to get a complete twenty-four-hour record of the vocal activities of a six-months-old child. The accompanying graph analyzes and summarizes the results of this day of observation. It was calculated that 3 per cent of the waking time of the child was expended definitely in some form of speech or language activity. At nine months this same child expended 6.66 per cent of its waking time in such

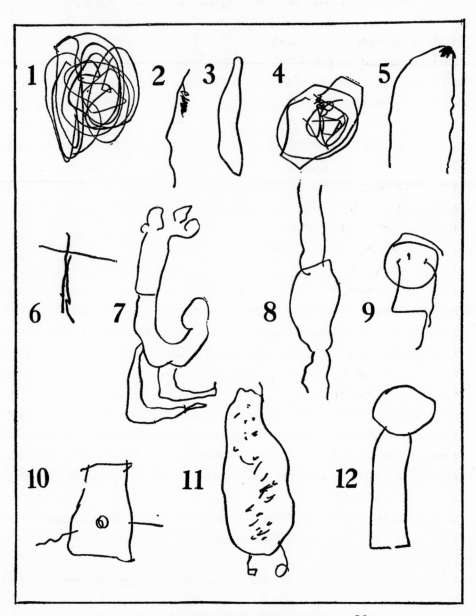

FIGURE 149. FOUR-YEAR-OLD DRAWINGS OF A MAN

Every one of fifty unselected children just four years of age was asked to draw a man.   No model or help was provided.

FIGURE 149 (CONTINUED)

Twenty samples from these fifty drawings were arranged in a graded order   Number 12 may be regarded as a typical or normative specimen   Number 21 was drawn by a superior four-year-old girl not in the normative group   (Note duck, ducklings, and worm.)

activity. It will be noted from the six-months record that the most frequently recurring sound was *da*. When itemized this sound showed a frequency of 63, followed by *a* without a consonant with

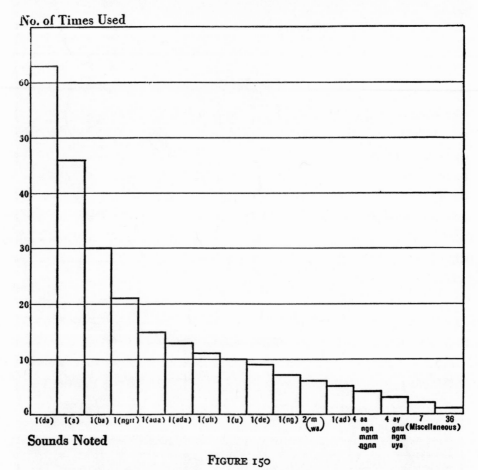

FIGURE 150

Vocalization chart of L. M., age 6 months   Sixty-four different sounds were distinguished and their frequency is shown in the diagram.

a frequency of 46. The next in order was *ba* with a frequency of 30. *Ngrr* (which the reader may read silently) was a very popular sound and occurred with a frequency of 21. There were many variations of the *n* sound which were indicated in the tabular summary.

Summing up the vocalization activity from the full day's behavior chart, we find that there were 104 separate moments of vocalization during the day, varying in complexity from a one-letter sound to thirty-two repeated syllables; seventy-five sounds and combinations of sounds were used.

It is not surprising, therefore, to find that some six-months-old children are credited with the ability to say *dada* and that a very high percentage of nine-months-old children are credited with the same ability. At twelve months the acquisition of vocabulary is definitely under way. The median twelve-months-old child not only can say *dada* or *mama* or its equivalent, but has mastered at least three or four distinguishable words which he articulates with much precision. In one instance the vocabulary in a retarded case consisted of *mama, papa* and *shut up*. It is worth while to record below in the tabular summary the words reported by the fifty mothers of our twelve-months-old normative babies. The most popular words, other than *mama* or *papa*, are *bye-bye* and *baby*.

WORDS REPORTED BY MOTHERS OF
12–MONTHS–OLD BABIES

Oh my mama	Bad	Dirty
Oh my papa	Up	There
Dog (3)	Ettie	Baba (grandmother)
Horse	Ice	Yea
Baby (6)	Harry	Ah!
Bow-wow (2)	Ru (Russel)	Boy
See that	Tit (sister)	Anna
Doll	Aaeku (2)	How-do-you-do
Ball (2)	Bread (2)	Who's that
Bye-bye (31)	Rompers	No
No no (2)	Animals	Yes
Ba-ba (for bye-bye)	All gone	Grandma
Ta-ta (10)	Upidee	Dolly
Down (3)	Bang	Stop
Birds	Meat	Tish (kiss)

Bobby (2)	Brother	Egg
This (2)	Frankie	Money
That (1)	Eddie	Gidap
See (2)	Cat	Hiyo
Kitty (4)	Ida	Oh don't
Tecky (name)	Peek-a-boo	Doggie
Gone	Three names	Nice doggie
Moo	Hello (2)	Car
Dot (2)	Sit down	What
Good	Auntie	How

At eighteen months this vocabulary list has expanded in a significant manner. Since we were able to ascertain these vocabularies of individual children exactly at their eighteen-months-old birthday, it will be desirable to reproduce the complete list of both words and phrases reported. *Bye-bye* is again in the lead with other salutations like *ta-ta*, *hello*, and *how-do-you-do* scoring high.

VOCABULARY AT 18 MONTHS

Words Reported by Mothers of 50 Babies

Words

Drink	Please (2)	1, 2, 12
Bye-bye (48)	1, 2	Stop
Ta-ta (30)	Thank you	Gi-gi (bottle)
Hello (15)	Georgie (2)	Up
How'do (19)	Helen (3)	Me (2)
Man (2)	Thanks	Lizzie
Coal (2)	1, 2, 3, 4, 5 (3)	Take
Meat	Alphabet except Q	Eddie
Pie	Come	Cocoa (3)
Cake	Bobby	Chan-chan
Hat	Auntie	Ru-ru (Russel)
Baby (3)	Coatie	Sistu (2)
Ball (2)	To	Yard
Good	Stop	Trolley car
Yes (3)	Kitty (3)	'Night
No (3)	Hot (2)	Home

Ice	Hat	Movies
Bread (6)	Boy (2)	Nana (eat)
Water (3)	Go	Here
Milk (4)	Bottle (3)	Moon (2)
Egg (2)	See	Light
Soup	Emma	Horse
Day	Shame	Good morning
Noni (eat)	Ah-ah	Cracker
Butter (2)	Elsie	Doll
Bow-wow	Robert	B (ball)
1, 2, 3, 4, 5, 6	More	Grandma
Spoon (2)	Dog	This
Hurrah	Rose	Cold
'Um 'um	Apple	One
a, b, c, d	Spoon	Ten

Phrases

Yes, I can	Oh, mama	All gone
I want to go out	That's a chair	Wo ist mama
Lady and baby	Hello, mama	Who's it
Helen made me bebe (cry)	Try and get it	Over there
Take baby	Are you afraid	Baby's hat
Oh stop, Roy	Out walk	Give me spoon
Look out	I get it	I fix it
Oh, putty!	All right	Get down
Come in	Shut the door	Put back
Daddy's great big boy	See up there	Bread and butter
I want money	Grandpa—pie	See kitty
Some of that	Give me	Bye-bye—going
Pulled my hair	See the pants	

TOTAL: 93 different words, 38 different phrases.

There is a remarkable increase in language power in the interval between eighteen months and two years as shown by the ability of our two-year-old children to meet rather exacting language tests involving the use of pronouns, color names, etc. Our figures on the language ability of two-year-old children are especially significant because they are based upon a study of fifty representative children who were of American parentage and reared in English-speaking homes. The data tabulated from Muntz's findings are reported herewith.

LANGUAGE ABILITY AT TWO YEARS

Based on a study of fifty children of American parentage in English-speaking homes.

1. CORRECT USE OF PRONOUNS *I*, *you*, AND *me*.

    (No records where confusion)

No. who use all 3 appropriately......................	24	48%
No. who use only 2 appropriately....................	3	6%
No. who use only 1 appropriately....................	4	8%
No. who use none appropriately	19	38%
No. who use *I* appropriately	23	46%
No. who use *you* appropriately	27	54%
No. who use *me* appropriately	29	58%

2. CORRECT USE OF PLURALS AND PAST TENSES.

No. who use the plural form correctly...	21	42%
No. who use the past tenses correctly.	20	40%
No. who use both correctly.......	18	36%
No. who use only one correctly..	5	10%
No. who use none correctly.......................	27	54%

3. MERE WORDS AND SENTENCES.

No. who use mere words...........................	20	40%
No. who use sentences..	30	60%

4. LONGEST SENTENCE.

No. whose longest sentences 0–2 words inc.	16	32%
No. whose longest sentences 2–4 words inc.	7	14%
No. whose longest sentences 4–6 words inc.	7	14%
No. whose longest sentences 6–8 words inc............	20	40%

That the acquisition of words undergoes a consistent increase as the child grows older is amply borne out by our studies of the three-, four-, and five-year-old children. This increase in vocabulary is an index of maturity and also in a measure an index of intelligence. Conversational facility which involves emotional readiness and sociability is more powerfully influenced by personality traits and environment factors.

From the standpoint of mental hygiene and developmental diagnosis, conversation characteristics are more important than vocabulary index. Vocabulary, however, reflects the ability of the child to assimilate and utilize words, and therefore has a fundamental relation to endowment. The language progress which a child makes from three years to five years of age is typified by his ability to use prepositions appropriately, his employment of descriptive words and his tendency to deal with larger units of thought, his ability to bring clauses and sentences into logical relation both in imaginative and in practical narration. Indeed within his limits he becomes an entertaining raconteur, whereas four years earlier he was unable to articulate a single word.

3. ADAPTIVE BEHAVIOR

The progress of the pre-school child in the sphere of adaptive behavior is most concretely and strikingly summed up by re-capitulating his reactions to the little red cubes which figure prominently in our developmental schedules. Even at the age of four months we may present one of the cubes to the child to note whether he perceives it as it lies on the table before him. In the absence of any overt response we cannot, of course, be certain of the presence or character of such perception. We can, however, note objectively whether he regards the cube. If there is definite fixation of the eyes upon the cube we may infer that this is itself a simple, selective, adaptive form of behavior.

At six months this adaptation is elaborated by a definite reach-ing response. The infant seizes the cube and puts it in his mouth or bangs it up and down on the table. At nine months he will not only take one cube but he will take a second in the other hand and often he will accept a third; but the range of his adaptation is still very narrow. To accept the third cube he ordinarily drops one or both of those he has in his hand or adopts the expedient of reaching with his head and taking it by mouth. This is a low-grade adaptation in a certain sense, but at the age of nine months it does him no little credit and psychologically might even be described as an intelligent form of behavior.

It is very difficult to determine the exact point at which the adaptive behavior of the infant may be safely described as intelligent. We have no authoritative definition of intelligence at our disposal. There is uncertainty even in regard to the existence of general intelligence. Binet defined intelligence as a form of mental adaptation with three characteristics; first, a tendency to take and maintain a definite direction; second, the capacity to make adjustments for the purpose of attaining a given end; and third, the power of autocriticism. Such a descriptive statement does not clarify the problem of the genesis of intelligence in infancy. Some of the elements of intelligence may be found in the simple act of perception ascribed to the four-months-old child who takes definite notice of a cube before him. Fundamentally there is a relation between perceptual processes and the more elaborate intellectual processes which are classified under the head of intelligence.

We have seen a six-months-old boy seize with executive directness an enameled cup which was turned upside down and concealed a cube; we have seen him lift the cup adaptively to seize the coveted cube. Not only once did he make this adaptation but five times in succession. Here again is a form of adaptive behavior which lies at least on the borderline of intelligence. The advantage of the broader term "adaptive behavior" consists in the fact that we do not need to settle decisively any of the mooted questions regarding the genesis of intelligence.

As we ascend the developmental scale and follow the child's reactions to the cubes we find an increasing amount of constructive combining activity. At the age of twelve months he begins either voluntarily or in an imitative manner to bring cubes into relation. He bangs one cube upon another, ranges them side by side, or places them one on top of another. His span of attention, however, is still so narrow, his range of adaptation so confined when measured by the cube, that we rate him as somewhat advanced for his age, if he can, even under the influence of imitation, pile three cubes one upon the other. At eighteen months and two years, however, he builds ambitious towers with the cubes, and at three years he can so adjust two cubes that they will support on their corners a third cube, making a bridge. At the age of four years he can build a relatively elaborate gate, consisting of five cubes, in which the keystone cube is tilted diagonally between supporting cubes. At the age of five years he can not only make a simple construction by directly copying a model but he can duplicate from memory a ten-block staircase which he has seen a moment before.

The reactions to the cubes which we have just described, beginning with the visual fixation and ending with the memory steps, can be arranged in an almost linear series of gradations. There is a quantitative progression with regard to the range of adaptation and the number of elements constructively combined. We have in this series of progressive responses a paradigm of the evolution of intelligence.

In the block tests which have just been outlined an external situation is always presented to the child, and his adaptiveness in meeting this situation is brought to expression. The blocks are equally useful in revealing his spontaneous adaptiveness. Simply cast a handful of blocks on the table before him. You need not do more. He will reach in some way that is characteristic of his capacity at the time. Exceptional indeed is the child who will not react at all. Even the four-months child is likely to bring his hand into casual or accidental contact with the blocks. We are scarcely justified in entirely excluding these reflexive and perceptual responses of the four-months level from our hierarchy of adaptive acts. They are after all adaptive and, in their underlying neuro-physiological mechanics, they may well be quite akin to the higher orders of performance which we call intelligent or intellectual. The futility of determining the exact point where "truly" intelligent behavior begins is itself a very significant psychological fact and justifies, clinically at least, such an inclusive conception as adaptive behavior.

It is impossible to draw an absolute line of demarcation between spontaneous adaptive behavior and what might be called accommodational adaptive behavior. In the latter we always set a problem of some kind, a tower to build, a bridge to copy, a stairway to recall. In the former, the child does what he pleases; but what he pleases is perceptibly affected by what he has previously done; and how he will dispose his pile of blocks proves to be an index of his docility as well as his initiative. If he does something to which we are unaccustomed we call his behavior bizarre or original (our own personal equation comes in here). If he does something which is definitely beyond the level for his age we call his constructiveness superior. Here our personal equation counts for less, because we are making a normative judgment.

When we supplement the blocks with rods and plaques and timbers and other construction materials, we encourage expressions of elaboration and of individuality. The free construction test taps personal, aesthetic, and motivational factors which we should like to exclude (but never do) from "pure" tests of intelligence.

When we substitute words for blocks, as we do in certain tests of comprehension, reasoning, and verbal discrimination, have we shifted to an altogether different field of psychological observation? From a clinical point of view, particularly since we are dealing with the youngest of age groups, we should recognize the fundamental behavior identities between the use of things and the use of words; between blocks and prepositions. To be sure, the child can use blocks prepositionally before he uses prepositions, but the one is simply a more difficult and delicate instrument of adaptation.

For all these reasons, we may repeat that the gradation of reactions of the child to that time-honored vehicle of play and work —the building block—portrays in outline the infirmities and growth of human intelligence.

4. PERSONAL–SOCIAL BEHAVIOR

The development of personal-social behavior is in general coordinate with that of adaptive behavior. What distinction can we make between the two? Only one of convenience. In psychology most of our distinctions have the same excuse. They are not necessarily artificial but they are largely pragmatic, aiming to aid us in interpretation or application.

Under adaptive behavior we classify those items of behavior which are relatively impersonal, which deal with such (relatively) colorless situations as blocks, form boards, number relations, puzzles, and intellectual discriminations.

They involve general and special forms of that mental adaptability ordinarily called intelligence; but they do not markedly involve personal inclinations, prejudices, social compulsions or compunctions. As a matter of fact, impersonal adaptive behavior is rarely altogether impersonal. Obscure, oblique personality factors assert themselves even in what are apparently most indifferent situations.

Under personal-social behavior we classify, for the most part, those items which are heavily conditioned by social impressions and represent the responses or habituations of a personal being in a social environment. Obviously these personalized responses do not function in any independent compartment. They are so ubiquitous and multitudinous that they resist enumeration. In our developmental schedules we have simply gathered a few specimens which have a normative or clinical aspect. We have grouped here also

play activities, most of which have a social as well as merely biological significance.

Personal-social behavior, of course, presupposes a certain degree of intelligence—a capacity to profit by experience. In a
psychological sense it also implies the existence or the gradual
organization of a personality. Indeed the child's "personality
make-up," so far as it is a describable, subsisting reality, consists
in the countless conditioned reflexes, associative memories, habits,
and attitudes which it acquires as a result of being reared by other
personal beings. If he were never touched by ministering hands;
if he did not see and hear the evidences of humanity, if he could
grow up in an absolutely asocial vacuum, it is difficult to believe
that he would have any recognizable "personality make-up" at all.

No such fate awaits him! Only in the poet's pathetic line
does the poor babe like a seaman wrecked, thrown from the waves,
lie naked o'er the ground. He is cared for with such directness and
constancy that even in the first fortnight of infancy there must be
some rudimentary growth of personality. Whether he has any personality sense is not a pressing question. In ten days or less he
may "learn" to stop crying when he is lifted. He "associates"
certain tactile impressions with comfort. It is really the nurse who
establishes the association; but he at least incorporates it in his
neurological make-up. By a similar process of incorporation or
accretion he acquires a large fund of material for what we later call
his personality make-up.

If this were all of the story, the relation between parent and
child might become a kind of symbiosis leading to a parasitism
disadvantageous to both alike.

But the child is an individual, after all, who has his own desires
and his own propensities. Feeding, fearing, fighting, and affection
—these impulses at least are not implanted from without. They
are primarily personal. They are satisfied, deflected, thwarted, delayed, and crystallized through environmental or social influences;

but naturally it was intended that there should be at least a certain working partnership between adult and child in this constantly repeated miracle of personality formation.

This partnership, paradoxically enough, often takes on the guise of conflict in the child's psychology. White and Jelliffe described the facts in a few striking passages from which I select the following:

> As development progresses . . . desires become more and more numerous, because the baby touches reality at more numerous points. . . . Thus growing up in the life of the baby, beginning even in the earliest days, an ever-increasing discrepancy between desire and attainment takes place, and as the years go on it will be seen, . . . that the amoral, egocentric baby must gradually take into consideration the world about him. . . . Conflict is, therefore, at the very basis, the very root of mental life; the adjustment of the individual to the world of reality is by no means the passive moulding by external forces, but the individual is constantly and actively, in his mind at least, reaching out and trying to mould the world to suit himself.

The term conflict must here be construed in a broad psychological sense. It does not necessarily mean that there is deliberate open battle, nor does it always imply insidious unconscious repressions and morbid complexes. It is but another name for that indestructible tendency toward self-preservation which is at the root of the child's life and enables him to achieve a vital personality.

The tendency is inherent but not the result. The completeness and balance of personality depend upon social factors. The child may become extraordinarily dependent upon his mother; he may become extraordinarily tyrannical; he may become "spoilt" in other ways. To detail all the ways would be to write a treatise on mental hygiene.

Mental hygiene is chiefly concerned with the normality of personality trends and personality make-up. The key to the mental hygiene of childhood lies in building up adequate self-reliance and independence. Even in infancy this principle must be regarded. Not only from the breast must the child be weaned. Slowly but progressively he must attain befitting fortitude and detachment. He cannot always play in his mother's lap; he must in time begin to play on the floor; he cannot always play in the same room with his mother, he must learn to play in an adjoining one, first for a few minutes, later for an hour at a time. If the mother must leave the house to hang up the clothes, he must be content to watch her through the window—even though it costs him a struggle. He must even learn to go to bed alone, and later to school alone.

These are very elementary lessons in self-reliance, but, psychologically, in spite of their seeming triviality, they involve the same stern stuff out of which mature morale is made. The personal habits, inhibitions, and items of independence which are specified on the developmental schedule have significance, therefore, in estimating the maturity of personality. Many of the emotional states like those of fear, anger, jealousy have a similar significance, but they are either inaccessible or difficult to evaluate in any normative manner. Emotional control, however, is such an important index of personality maturity that it deserves critical inquiry in all cases of conduct disorder or deficiency which require careful developmental diagnosis. No such diagnosis can be comprehensive unless it includes an estimate of personality as well as of intelligence.

The phenomena of personality development are so complicated that it is difficult to find solid ground for generalization. Many writers have emphasized the fundamental and pervasive importance of sexual and pre-sexual factors even in the pre-school age; others have stressed the coördinate importance of hunger and nutrition. Paoloa Lombroso explained much of the child's behavior by her formula of self-conservation. Other writers together have supplied a rather liberal array of specific instincts to account for the elaboration and upbuilding of the child's psychological constitution.

There always is danger of over-simplification in theorizing about the personality aspects of the child's behavior. The psychology of fears shows how ramified and complicated the child's mental structure is. These fear reactions trace back at least to the fourth month of infancy. Every one of the fifty babies of this age blinked when an enamel saucer was sharply rapped with a spoon. We need not dignify this response with the name fear; but it is not unrelated to the wincing, jumping, startling, and crying which four-months-old babies exhibit when they hear sudden noises like the slam of a door, the rumble of an auto, or the ringing of a telephone. Any sudden alteration of accustomed conditions may provoke fear responses. One four-months baby cried with amusing regularity every time the clock near her crib struck the hour. The clock did not change its habit; but the baby did; "he overcame the fear," "he got used to the clock," he entered the fifth month unafraid— of clocks. Fears are evidently conditioned as well as inborn.

As the child grows older fears multiply and show much variety. The most common fears that we have discovered in our survey of pre-school children are:—loud or portentous noises (like raps on the door, or a rushing train or fire engine); strange, ominous persons (like the ragman, drunken men, the policeman, the colored garbage man, Old Man Katchem—a local bogey in the flesh); animals (dog, cat, horse, rooster); fire; dark.

A record of the fears of fifty unselected four-year-old children showed that the most common fear was that of a dog. In twenty-one, or forty-two per cent, of these children, it was only a moderate fear expressing itself in clutching the mother's hand or unwillingness to pass the dog. In the other cases, however, there was screaming or running home in terror. Three more children in the group were formerly afraid of dogs but had overcome their fear.

It would be most difficult to make a complete census of fears at all ages of childhood. Many fears are secret; many are inarticulate; some are highly imaginary, others are nightmares or night terrors. As the child gets into his teens his doubtings and misgivings attach themselves to social, intellectual, and abstract items like death, disease, gaucherie, school examinations, poverty, perdition. In morbid cases ordinary worry becomes an obsessive delusion or a chronic, vague anxiety. Recently we heard of an adolescent girl who developed a strange anxiety that the United States Government could not pay the national debt.

The pre-school period is of all periods the most prolific for fears. Many of these fears are passing and inconsequential, but in their totality they are a faithful indication of the personality status of the child. It would be idle to classify the fears; but there appears to be one common characteristic. Whether it be in children or adults, fear always has to do with escape from imminent pain or danger. It is "anticipatory pain." Its antibody is fortitude—the capacity to endure and cope with pain.

Again we see how the principle of "conflict" operates in the development of personality. Fear and fortitude are opposites, but both are necessary for the growth of character. To omit fear altogether from the child's life, were that possible, would be like omitting vitamins and salt from his diet. If he has normal experiences in the anticipation of pain and evil, he may gradually develop a normal immunity against pain and evil. If fear and fortitude are developed hand in hand, he will become resistant and sympathetic. Indeed, the elements of character are so paradoxical that the full development of fortitude depends upon the experiencing and overcoming of fear. Wholesome fear generates its own mental antibodies. It is a kind of vaccination.

It is, therefore, apparent that nothing is quite so significant of the maturation of the child's personality as the evidences of self-reliance and of independence which bespeak his growing morale. Normally these evidences undergo consistent increase. Abnormally there are partial or complete arrests which leave aspects of his personality stranded on some pre-school level.

CHAPTER 16

COMPARATIVE CROSS SECTIONS OF DEVELOPMENT

The following is a brief account of an investigation which entailed considerable planning, but which covered the short space of eight successive afternoons. Convinced of the value of the comparative method, we undertook to put this method to a test and arranged to make an ascending series of comparisons which would span the whole period of pre-school development. Eight afternoons were set aside for the *simultaneous* observation of two normal children of similar endowment, but differing always by one developmental interval. Sixteen different subjects, or eight pairs, were studied during eight consecutive sessions. These comparative pairs were seen in progressive order as follows:

1. FOUR months *versus* SIX months
2. SIX months *versus* NINE months
3. NINE months *versus* TWELVE months
4. TWELVE months *versus* EIGHTEEN months
5. EIGHTEEN months *versus* TWO years
6. TWO years *versus* THREE years
7. THREE years *versus* FOUR years
8. FOUR years *versus* FIVE years

The children will be referred to in the discussion by the numeral which indicates their age in months or years.

Selection of Subjects

The cases were carefully selected as to age, capacity, and social status; so that they would be truly representative of their age levels. Many children were considered, and no cases which were in any way highly selected were included. All the children came from

231

English-speaking homes, and with one exception they bore definitely "non-foreign" names. The unequal influence of siblings on the behavior picture was pretty well ruled out. In eight instances there were no siblings; in three instances there was only one sibling.

The subjoined table summarizes the exact ages and facts relating to the sex, developmental status, and siblings of all the children compared. No attempt was made to take account of sex differences. General caliber and comparability were emphasized. On the basis of clinical evidence all of the sixteen children were rated as of average developmental status. Three of the list were rated as high average, but none could be considered either inferior or exceptionally superior. For twelve-months subjects we selected children who could stand alone, but who had not yet learned to walk; because our percentages show that the former is a more characteristic attainment at this level.

PAIR	SEX	EXACT AGE	SIBLINGS	DEVELOPMENTAL STATUS
a	G	3 mos. 23 days	none	average
	B	6 mos. 8 days	none	average
b	G	6 mos. 4 days	sister, age 3	average
	G	8 mos. 27 days	none	average
c	B	9 mos. 4 days	none	average
	B	11 mos. 27 days	2 older sisters	average
d	B	12 mos.	none	average
	G	18 mos. 10 days	4 older	high average
e	B	17 mos. 25 days	2 older	average
	G	2 yrs. 4 days	1 younger	average
f	G	2 yrs. 13 days	none	average
	G	3 yrs. 12 days	2 older	average
g	B	35 mos. 20 days	1 older, 1 younger	high average
	B	47 mos. 3 days	none	average
h	G	47 mos. 17 days	1 older	high average
	G	5 yrs. 29 days	none	average

With only one exception the mothers of these children attended a baby-welfare conference conducted in a prosperous semi-residential district of the city of New Haven. In every instance the home from which the child came was in a "good neighborhood," and the housekeeping and child-care standards were well up to a good average grade. Sample occupations of the fathers were electrician, salesman, clerk, machinist. A fair index of the mothers' status consisted in the coöperation and intelligence with which they participated in what was to them an altogether novel and disinterested project. They entered into the spirit of the undertaking. All the children came washed and neatly dressed for the occasion. And, it may be added, the experience was apparently enjoyed by all concerned.

Procedure

Our general procedure was the same for all the developmental levels. Similar situations were repeated throughout the whole series of comparisons in order to bring developmental differences into relief. The children always came with their mothers, by baby carriage or auto, and were carried or walked up one flight of stairs into a reception room where their initial reactions to a new situation were noted. After a brief interval the mothers took the children into a large, attractive examination room. Both mothers were then seated side by side at a broad, five-foot table, and the children sat in their mothers' laps. This was, of course, the most natural arrangement for the younger age pairs; but we were able to continue it throughout the whole series of comparisons, at least for the first part of the examination.

With the younger subjects, the whole examination was conducted while they were seated at the big table. Older subjects were later transferred to small chairs and small tables in the same room or in adjoining rooms. The mothers were always in the near vicinity, but in some instances the children were temporarily separated from the parent to test their reactions.

While the children were seated at the table their response to the bare table and to the new scene was noted. Psychological test material was then served to them in duplicate, beginning always with the enamel cup and saucer and spoon. It required two clinical assistants, one for each child, to provide this material and to synchronize the test situations so that simultaneous observation would be possible. The two regular assistants of the clinic were assigned to this part of the program, Miss Washburn working with the younger and Miss Lord with the older member of the comparative pair. Each assistant took her station at the side of and behind her subject. The directing examiner (the writer) moved about somewhat freely and was sometimes in front of the subjects, and always near enough to observe (or to attempt to observe) all the behavior in progress. In some instances, in order to alter or to intensify the conditions of a test, he presented the material and the stimulus to both children at the same time. His chief business, however, was to witness and record what was going on. Notetaking was impractical. He, therefore, dictated in subdued, conversational voice, a running record to a stenographer who was concealed behind a screen in a corner of the examining room. The comparative cross sections presented herewith are unvarnished transcripts of this stenographic report.

The above description of procedure probably makes the conditions of the experiment appear more formidable than they actually proved to be. To be sure there were nine persons in one room; but one of these (the stenographer) was hidden; two were assistant examiners who operated partly from the background and were associated with interesting toys; two of the persons were mothers who had a stabilizing and normalizing influence upon the whole situation. Moreover (and this, of course, was the essential thing) the children offered no resistance but reacted characteristically. We did not find it necessary to reject a single subject or pair of subjects from our experimental series; we relate what happened as it happened, without editorial rearrangement or embellishment.

The main body of our account is, therefore, simply a recital of observed facts. A slight amount of interpretation has, of course, crept into the impromptu formulation of these facts, and we have added a few supplementary comments and generalizations. Our main purpose, however, has been to furnish an objective record from which the reader may develop his own reflections on the limitations and possibilities of a comparative method in clinical psychology.

It cannot be said that the conditions of the experiment were such as to lead to an exaggeration of the cleavage between adjacent developmental levels. This possibility was more apparent than real, for the reason that the senior age level was always scheduled to reappear as the junior age level in the next succeeding comparison. To exaggerate the superiority of the nine-months child at the expense of the six-months child would have caused embarrassment when the next nine-months child was brought into comparison with a twelve-months child. The fact that seven age levels are represented twice in the series has helped to set forth individual as well as interval differences; and has also protected us against undue accentuation of developmental disparities.

Italicized headings and phrases in the following account will enable the reader to follow the comparative test situations as they arose in the examination. The procedure followed in these tests was that which has been described in connection with clinical procedure. In reporting the children's behavior no attempt was made to avoid altogether the language of common sense. We have permitted the sun to set in the west, technical astronomy notwithstanding. When necessary this language can always be transposed into "behaviorese."

Whatever shortcomings may appear in this comparative account, we hope that the thoughtful reader will glimpse in it an objective epitome of the general course of pre-school development from the fourth month to the sixth year of life.

CHAPTER 17

Four Months *versus* Six Months

Initial Reactions. Baby FOUR not startled in any way by entrance into examination room. Moves head from side to side and also up and down. Apparently regards massive objects, like the large window and moving persons. Does not, however, retain continuous attention for moving persons.   Reacts to stamp of foot with blink.   Shows definite increase of attentive regard when window shade is rolled up and down.

Baby SIX shows much greater selective attentiveness to various objects in environment. Suggests even a little initial timidity due to strange circumstances. Looks with prolonged attention·at examiner; also follows a moving person but with more steady attention than FOUR. Attention, however, is sometimes diverted to mother and other objects in the room.

Mothers take places side by side at table, holding babies in lap. The chief noticeable difference as the subjects are sitting in their mothers' laps is in the relatively fixed posture of the head in Baby SIX. Baby FOUR's head turns somewhat awkwardly to right and to left and shows a slight tendency to wobble downward. There is much activity of the hands and arms. Baby SIX turns more definitely toward mother from time to time. Both babies fix their attention on *curtain* as it is *moved up and down* but Baby FOUR again shows greater distractibility. Both show tendency to blink as curtain is rolled.

When babies are laid on table in dorsal position, Baby SIX shows greater resistance and shows desire to sit up. Baby FOUR coos with contentment (sounds *e, eeh,* and *ooh*). Baby SIX continues to show visual interest in environment and moving objects.   Baby

236

FOUR seems now to be content with merely motor activity.
After about two minutes of lying on table Baby SIX vigorously tries to sit up.

Both babies regard *dangling ring*. Baby SIX closes in on it with both hands and manipulates it with both hands and puts to mouth.

Increased activity of arms, suggesting incipient reaching, by Baby FOUR. Baby SIX pulls vigorously at the ring and waves it back and forth. He has lost his discontentment from not sitting up.

Marked hand to mouth reaction in Baby SIX but this gives way to a transverse waving motion.

Ring is withdrawn and held just out of baby's reach. Eagerness to grasp expresses itself in trembling motion of legs and arms; this trembling motion extends even to lips. Vocalization increased during play with the ring. Baby FOUR smiles responsively, when examiner assumes highly animated expression of face. Baby SIX is much interested but more solemnly intent under same circumstances.

Incipient response on part of Baby FOUR when *examiner starts to play* with him. Vigorous frolicking response on part of Baby SIX, including motor activity and vocalization. Baby FOUR has laughed loud but did not do so in frolicking situation. Anticipatory motor response by Baby FOUR on being *lifted*, involving head and whole body.

When in prone position Baby FOUR makes simple playing hand movements regarding the movements of the fingers. · Baby SIX when prone plays vigorously with blanket and table, putting blanket to mouth.

When put in sitting position there is no protest. Baby FOUR maintains good back posture but imperfect balance.
Baby SIX maintains sitting balance for about a minute but shows a tendency to fall to the side. Baby SIX now responds to facial animation very definitely with smile.

Babies are restored to laps to note reactions to table. Baby SIX responds actively to table surface with banging movements followed by scratching movements. The scratching movements are by the left hand. Banging movements are by one hand or both simultaneously.   Baby FOUR after delay puts hands to table edge and also makes scratching movements but more feebly; then pushes against table edge.

Reactions to spoon placed on table. Baby SIX promptly takes spoon in hand and bangs it. Baby FOUR accidentally touches spoon and grasps it reflexively and in the same manner loses it.

Baby SIX retains hold of the spoon; is conscious of its disappearance.   Perception of spoon by Baby FOUR is somewhat in doubt because she ignores it for long periods and makes no definite reaching motion.   Her actions are not altered by withdrawal of spoon.   Baby SIX reaches with both hands when spoon is slowly withdrawn.   Baby SIX looks momentarily at Baby FOUR, something which Baby FOUR has not done with reference to Baby SIX.

Babies are laid on table and sheet of paper is placed on face. When paper is placed on Baby SIX's face, mouth is opened, hands go up to paper, it is vigorously seized, crumpled, and put into mouth.   Baby FOUR shows slight distress when paper is placed on face. Hands finally go up to paper, which is seized reflexively. There is, however, no immediate adaptive defensive hand movement.   The reaction is apparently the result of increased motor activity.   Baby SIX is very good-natured but showed signs of anger about five minutes ago when in the dorsal position. These signs have altogether disappeared with an opportunity of playing with spoon and other objects, and he is now very contented. Baby FOUR also gives evidence that change of position increases satisfaction and reduces tendency to crying.

With both babies in dorsal position, examiner rings bell midway between them. They are separated by about three feet. Baby FOUR regards the bell and makes a doubtful head-turning movement. Baby six makes an instantaneous head-turning movement and maintains a fixed listening adjustment for fully one minute while the bell is gently rung.   Baby four shows no such fixation, soon turning her head to regard the ceiling.

On four successive trials Baby four held in lap smiles responsively to ringing of bell.   Baby six shows great intentness in same situation and his motor adjustment involves the whole body.   Baby six also makes reaching movement when bell is rung near by.

A piece of paper is offered to each baby. Baby four's response to paper is purely reflexive; no increase of reaching movements and no resistance to withdrawal.   Baby six resists withdrawal of paper with vigor.

Baby six enjoys being *held up so that feet touch table.* Reacts with jigging movements.   Baby four makes pushing movements but does not sustain as much weight as Baby six. Reaction apparently altogether reflex, whereas, in Baby six, a quality of attention is associated with the reaction, which seems to absorb him for the time being.   When Baby six is put in standing position and is lifted gently up and down this play becomes a consuming object of interest. There is no such focalized attention with Baby four, although there are momentary fixations of attention.

A pellet is placed in front of each baby. Baby four disregards pellet completely. Very doubtful whether she perceives pellet. Baby six notices pellet promptly and makes persistent efforts to pick it up by means of a scratching motion which involves four fingers. The thumb does not coöperate. This persistence of effort is expressed first by the left hand and then by the right hand. He does not, however, use both hands to close in upon the pellet. This is somewhat different from the response to the dangling ring in which both hands closed in.

In *cube prehension* Baby FOUR's reaction is altogether reflex. The thumb does not participate.   In Baby SIX the grasp is vigorous and thumb participates in reaction.

While the *two babies* are being *photographed*, the most noticeable difference is the greater activity on the part of Baby SIX and his vigorous attack upon objects in his immediate environment, including Baby FOUR. His exploratory seizure of Baby FOUR is so forcible that it becomes necessary to separate the two babies.

This comparative examination has occupied over an hour; but there are no noticeable signs of fatigue.

CHAPTER 18

Six Months *versus* Nine Months

Initial Reactions. Baby SIX is brought into the room by mother and betrays a feeling of strangeness at first but is not much disturbed by the novel situation, for she readily smiles as soon as examiner begins to play with her. Shows selective attention with preferential interest in faces, turning definitely from regarding one face to a second, shifting in turn to third face. When she becomes more accustomed to surroundings she begins to regard big window. Showed momentary uneasiness on looking at one of assistants.

Turning to mother she notices pin on dress and begins to play with it.

Baby NINE also shows selective attention to various objects in the room and also turns her regard from one person to another. She inspects the light on the ceiling and the arm of the chair. Her whole demeanor is more mature and deliberate with less evidence of disturbance by new scenes.

When seated at the examination table both babies regard each other for a short period. There is no prolonged regard for any one person or object in the room. Both babies vocalize, the vocalization expressing contentment and interest.　　Baby SIX turns her attention to the arm of chair as did Baby NINE but Baby SIX's attack is apparently more muscular in character, and less restrained.　　Both babies wriggle in their mothers' laps and laugh; Baby SIX more than Baby NINE.　　Baby NINE makes movements of sociable character toward Baby SIX. These advances do not seem to be merely exploratory as when Baby SIX attacked Baby FOUR.　　A pat-a-cake response was initiated by accidental meeting of two hands in Baby NINE; this reaction was

241

prolonged and increased by watching examiner pat-a-cake.   Both babies show regard for *bared table*.   Baby SIX manipulates the table edge; Baby NINE takes evident pleasure in making a patting motion first with one hand and then with both hands.

Reactions to spoon. Both babies promptly pick up a spoon from the table and Baby SIX immediately puts it to mouth.   Baby NINE waves the spoon up and down.   Baby SIX takes up spoon more slowly and with less directness and coördination. Baby NINE looks after the *spoon* when it is *dropped* out of sight. Baby SIX shows only momentary consciousness of its disappearance.

Both resist *withdrawal of spoon* but Baby NINE's resistance is much tempered by interest in the examiner. She is aware of both spoon and examiner. Baby SIX concentrates resistance on the spoon.   The hand to mouth reaction is decidedly more prominent and recurrent in Baby SIX.   Baby NINE momentarily inspects and handles spoon in seemingly exploratory manner.

Baby NINE is much more frequently and readily diverted by changes in her environment. (This simulates greater distractibility but may also be described as greater sensitiveness to changes going on about her.)   Both play with spoon for fully five minutes. The variety of the play is decisively greater for Baby NINE.

Baby NINE bangs the under side of the table as well as the surface; but SIX is noisier.   Baby SIX pays more exclusive attention to spoon.   Baby SIX cries because spoon is accidentally dropped. This is merely a reaction to deprivation. There is no looking for the spoon.

A saucer is placed before each child. Both babies transfer interest from spoon to saucer and put saucer to mouth.   Baby SIX is very vigorous with saucer and bangs it strenuously.   Baby NINE is content to manipulate in a quiet contemplative manner with very little banging but not without mouthing. She transfers readily and repeatedly from one hand to another.   Baby SIX also transfers once or twice, but the transfer seems more accidental in character, perhaps due to chance stimulation of free hand. Even the mouthing of the saucer in case of Baby six is more intermittent. Saucers were played with for four minutes. Both babies resist *withdrawal of saucer*. Both babies protest by vocalization but not by actual crying.

Dangling rings are presented just out of reach. Both babies attend. (They are in their mothers' laps.) The chief gross difference as they reach for the ring consists in the more stable posture of Baby NINE. Baby six shows wobbling. Baby NINE regards string and Baby six shows no regard for it.

When *string alone is dangled* before babies, both regard string but attention of Baby six is soon transferred to the ring. Baby six immediately puts ring to mouth on seizure. Baby NINE examines the ring after seizure and very deliberately transfers from one hand to the other hand; the hand to mouth reaction is delayed for about a minute in Baby NINE. Baby six now directs transient attention to string. Baby NINE definitely follows with eyes when the ring drops to floor. The manner in which the ring is dropped suggests purposeful throwing. (The mother reports that Baby NINE is beginning to throw things.)

Both babies regard the *bell* intently while it is *rung*. The regard of Baby NINE is more fixed. When the bell is placed on the table Baby NINE makes definite reaching movements for it.

Baby NINE *picks up pellet* with characteristic pincer prehension. Baby six regards pellet and picks it up with a scooping motion; is conscious of disappearance of pellet when dropped. Baby NINE holds up pellet momentarily for inspection.

Both seize and crumple *paper*. Baby six's reaction is more vigorous and the hand to mouth tendency asserts itself promptly.

In case of Baby NINE manipulation of the paper is apparently more deliberate and controlled.

Baby SIX makes reaching actions toward *mirror image*. Baby NINE gazes intently and looks around inquiringly.

Two and three cubes are offered. Baby SIX accepts both cubes; promptly puts one and both to mouth. Notices third cube but does not accept it.   Baby NINE promptly accepts third cube and drops one and then the other, but shows definite desire to play with only one cube. This desire is marked and she cannot be readily diverted from her purpose.

There is no marked outward difference in the response to the *wrapped cube* situation, although Baby NINE seems aware of disappearance of cube when it is wrapped up; and her manipulation is consistently more deliberate.

Baby SIX reaches for *rod out of reach;* vigorously bends body and thrusts forward both hands, mouth and head participating in reaching. The rod when grasped goes promptly to the mouth. Baby NINE suppresses the left hand and reaches with the right hand.   Head and body participate very little in the reaching reaction.   There is a definite delay in the hand to mouth reaction, but this reaction asserts itself even in Baby NINE after a preliminary period of exploration.

Both babies show resistance when their *feet are placed on table.* Baby SIX's reaction is in the nature of rhythmic pushing upward. Baby NINE's action is more stable and approximates standing. Both seem to take pleasure in the situation.

Both tolerate *prone position.*   Baby NINE raises herself on her arms.   Baby SIX remains prone, erects head, but chest rests on table.

Baby NINE *sits* alone.   Baby SIX sits with support.

Both babies thrust arms forward in anticipatory manner *when being taken up.*

Babies are placed on table, side by side. When they are sitting side by side both take certain interest in each other.   Baby NINE makes a tentative reaching gesture toward Baby SIX.   : Baby

NINE's interest in Baby SIX is prolonged. Baby SIX turns almost immediately to mother, and is much interested in pin on dress.

Selective interest in faces, though present in both children, is unquestionably more marked in Baby NINE.

Duration of examination about one hour.

CHAPTER 19

NINE MONTHS *VERSUS* TWELVE MONTHS

Initial Reactions. Both babies are brought upstairs simultaneously, in their mothers' arms, and survey with interest their new surroundings. There is no marked difference in their reactions on entrance into the reception room. Both babies are unperturbed and view each other with interest. They both smiled when approached by the examiner.

NINE waves his hands up and down and TWELVE is more quiet and sober. His fixation of attention is more prolonged.
Both babies unmistakably show preferential interest for faces and persons and comparatively ignore inanimate objects in the room.

Both are attracted by the *electric light* when it is *turned on* and gaze at it intently but NINE again shows his preferential interest in persons by turning from the light to watch Miss L., who is at the door. Although the fixation and attention of TWELVE is obviously more prolonged than that of NINE, TWELVE more frequently turns toward his mother for recognition and caress.   Neither baby betrays timidity or sense of strangeness when carried to examination room.

The babies with their mothers take their places at the large examining table. Both babies intently watch examiner preparing boxes and examining material. Attention of TWELVE to this is slightly longer than attention of NINE. Both of them respond with active exploration movements to the table.   TWELVE begins to crawl on table.   NINE pats and scratches the surface. TWELVE regards NINE for a long time and readily breaks into smile, makes advances toward NINE, who now is evidently more interesting than the table. NINE responds to the advances.   Both

246

vocalize freely, reaching out to each other and touching hands. The attention of TWELVE to NINE is more prolonged than that of NINE to TWELVE. The interest of NINE soon goes out to the millinery of TWELVE's mother. He inspects hat intently.   TWELVE is much more restless in the lap than is NINE. TWELVE repeatedly puts his mother's beads to his mouth and leans far over the table top. If released would crawl on table or floor. NINE is more content on lap. TWELVE more frequently breaks out in vocalizations.

Cup, spoon, and saucer are placed before each child. Both react to cup and saucer and at first ignore spoon. Twelve at once combines cup and saucer in his play, holding one in either hand. Attention of NINE is restricted to the cup and then to the saucer with very little combining reaction.   TWELVE also plays for a while with cup, first patting it, but soon takes cup and puts it onto the saucer.   Both blink with amusing frequency at the noises made while playing. On the whole TWELVE is the noisier.

TWELVE takes evident delight in pushing cup across saucer. He does the same thing when spoon replaces cup.   NINE occasionally brings spoon and saucer into relation but plays more exclusively with one object at a time. There is, however, frequent transfer of the play objects from one hand to the other in both children.   Both are content with their play material but TWELVE shows much more tendency to look at persons in the room while NINE seems to be more completely absorbed in the manipulation of his saucer. Occasionally he puts saucer to mouth but this reaction is pretty well inhibited.   Both mildly resist withdrawal of cup and saucer. Both put spoon to mouth.

Reactions to cubes. The babies play actively with cube. Both put cube to mouth and transfer from one hand to the other; thumb opposition shown in both cases. Both lift reversed *cup when it conceals cube,* but TWELVE definitely attends to cube and secures it while NINE plays with cup instead of cube.   TWELVE does not release cube when told to put it into cup. Both hold two cubes, one in each hand. NINE shows interest in a *third cube* but does not secure it immediately but later drops one cube to take third. TWELVE solves the situation much more directly, putting one cube into mouth in order to accept third.

NINE secures the third but abandons second cube; TWELVE shows definite interest in securing all three cubes.

Both pick up *pellet* with pincer prehension. TWELVE puts pellet promptly to mouth.

Both show persistence in reaching when *ring is dangled* before them. TWELVE, however, makes definite squirming and climbing efforts to reach the ring. NINE does not raise himself out of lap but tenses body and pushes forward.   TWELVE definitely shows interest in string and pulls down string to get ring. Both regard and seize string when it is dangled. TWELVE pulls down *string* in purposive manner to secure ring.   NINE is more content to wave string and to play with the end of it. TWELVE shows more restlessness than NINE when deprived of play material. His fretting, however, immediately disappears when he secures new material. Both children vocalize, TWELVE vocalizing more than NINE.

Reactions to paper and crayon. Both children find great pleasure in playing with paper, NINE takes it more vigorously and tears it; TWELVE brushes it from side to side and upon table. Neither child puts paper to mouth.   Both children vocalize while playing.

TWELVE scribbles imitatively; NINE simply plays with the crayon and transfers it from one hand to the other. The scribbling reaction in TWELVE is momentary, and is speedily replaced by a banging reaction.   When TWELVE drops crayon he wriggles out of lap and crawls for it and recovers it from floor.

Both children react to their *image reflected in mirror*. TWELVE reacts with a forward reaching gesture; NINE also reaches forward but apparently watches image of hand rather than personal image.

Both children make utterances of pleasure at experience.

Both children are sensitive to changes in their near environment.

A piece of *paper was placed at either corner of the table.* TWELVE made a vigorous crawling effort to get paper, NINE noticed it but made no corresponding effort. It is apparent that the reaction radius of TWELVE is greater than of NINE; TWELVE has a wider range of motility.

When presented with a *performance box with insertion rod,* TWELVE clearly shows an exploratory interest in the holes, putting hand in the rectangular hole and putting index finger in small round hole; approaches hole with rod in hand in purposive manner. After repeated demonstrations he thrusts rod through the small circular hole. Baby NINE shows no exploratory interest in the holes but bangs rod on surface of box, puts it occasionally to mouth and makes no effort whatever to place it in hole.

Form-board is presented. After three demonstrations TWELVE persistently tries to put the round block in hole and finally succeeds. His initial response, however, is more elementary and consists in banging the block up and down. NINE'S interest is purely of a manipulatory kind, consists in turning the block about in various positions. He never brings the block into relation with the form-board except for momentary banging.

TWELVE has been responding very satisfactorily to the test situations but is evidently somewhat relieved at being permitted to *crawl* about *on the floor.* This means that there is a specific drive behind creeping and it is at this age in the nature of permanent competing interest. If it had not been satisfied it is quite likely that the child would find an outlet in fretting. There is no such competing locomotive drive in NINE.

TWELVE evidently has not acquired the ability to release hold of an object. He plays at putting the *cube in the cup* and repeatedly lets it drop by fumbling it but definitely shows that he has not the voluntary releasing ability.

When placed in *dorsal position* both attend with interest to the *ringing of the bell;* NINE makes a reaching gesture but TWELVE gets up and crawls to the bell, takes it by handle and waves it.

Both children show selective adjustment to handle of bell. NINE is able to ring the bell only a few seconds at a time and he holds it in a rather high-handed reeling manner which in an adult would suggest failing motor coördination.

TWELVE hits *rubber doll* imitatively; NINE simply bangs it and plays in characteristic manipulatory manner.

When three cubes are placed before children on table, NINE shows interest in only one cube but TWELVE definitely shows a desire to obtain a second cube and later shows additional interest in the third cube by picking it up in his mouth. He thus secures three cubes while NINE is content to play with one.   TWELVE enjoys throwing cubes but shows that he has not fully acquired the ability to release hold; sometimes he makes a throwing motion without letting go of cube.

Baby TWELVE does not manhandle baby NINE as baby NINE did baby SIX at former comparison. He shows a definite caressing response, patting baby but not hitting. *The examiner, seated in a chair five feet in front of the babies, brings two blocks together regularly with loud report.* Both babies are at first much interested and both blink regularly. After about thirty seconds, however, NINE loses interest and begins to wriggle in mother's lap. The attention span of TWELVE keeps him spellbound so that he watches with intent expectancy.   There is a recurring interest on the part of NINE in the procedure but it is intermittent while the fixation of TWELVE lasted fully two minutes and might have been still prolonged. The blink on the part of NINE was slower, cruder, and more vigorous than the blink on the part of TWELVE.   The test shows the possibility of devising a conditioned reflex experiment utilizing the blink.

The examination up to this point has lasted seventy minutes; there are no signs of fatigue or protest in either baby.

CHAPTER 20

Twelve Months *versus* Eighteen Months

Initial Reactions. Both babies enter room without being disturbed by the new scenes. Both of them continue to attend chiefly to new persons, but after a while TWELVE gazes out of window. EIGHTEEN regards TWELVE more than TWELVE notices EIGHTEEN.

When cup, spoon, and saucer are presented, TWELVE takes spoon at once and plays with it, directly putting spoon in cup; and EIGHTEEN is still under the spell of the new situation and does not play spontaneously with material. He looks about from person to person.

TWELVE takes evident delight in putting spoon in cup and withdrawing it and replacing it. He shows skill in releasing hold of an object and does not play with material in a restrained manner. EIGHTEEN looks from time to time at the examiner but is more absorbed in watching TWELVE. (Mother of EIGHTEEN suggests that she has recently been trying to teach her child not to play with dishes!) TWELVE readily surrenders material and gives it to examiner on command. When a cup alone is presented TWELVE picks it up directly, EIGHTEEN again shows delay and offers it to mother. EIGHTEEN continues to be much interested in TWELVE.

Reactions to cubes. TWELVE accepts two cubes, one in either hand; also accepts a third cube, dropping that in left hand. When a *third cube* is again presented near his face he seizes it in an adaptive manner with mouth. EIGHTEEN is much impressed by what is happening about her and looks on, with very little interruption, at TWELVE. For a few minutes she has not touched two blocks in front of her. Now she begins to play with one and when offered a

251

third seizes it with the right hand, holding two cubes in one hand and makes a request for more. This reaction is markedly in advance of that of TWELVE.

When a *fourth cube* is offered she holds two in either hand; when a fifth is offered she manages to hold three in one hand, when a sixth is offered she holds the sixth by pressing it with her left hand.

When a fourth is offered to TWELVE he drops the third one in his mouth and opens the mouth expectantly to receive the new block. Begins to play with blocks by throwing them on the floor.

When all the blocks are gone he amuses himself by striking and pounding the table. His coördination in this reaction is manifestly superior to that of the nine- and six-months levels. EIGHTEEN continues to play somewhat constructively with blocks, putting them close together, but can scarcely take her attention away from TWELVE. Prattles as she plays with her blocks. Takes two blocks and offers them to examiner. (Perhaps she wishes to revive the multiple cube game.)

When a *tower of three blocks is built* for EIGHTEEN, she tries to put a fourth block on tower. She successfully builds an independent tower of five.   The reaction of TWELVE consists in throwing down each model tower as it is built.

When cube is wrapped up in paper TWELVE puts bundle directly to mouth; EIGHTEEN directly takes cube from wrapping. On second trial there was a suggestion of interest in the cube on the part of TWELVE. On third trial paper was cast aside.

When *edge of paper is presented* vertically to TWELVE, he seizes with both hands and plays with it in a vigorous crumpling manner.

EIGHTEEN seizes it in a coördinate manner with the right hand and makes a gesture with articulate appeal for the cube. When this is presented she carefully lays paper on table and wraps it up as in the paper and cube test. Although much interested in the test situations and apparently free from initial timidity she continues to direct her attention to TWELVE. TWELVE occasionally regards EIGHTEEN but only for short periods.

When cube is covered with cup both lift cup, TWELVE shows interest in cube, and EIGHTEEN in both cup and cube. TWELVE lifts by the bowl; EIGHTEEN by the handle. On command both children place cube in cup; the control is clearly better for EIGHTEEN. When given a double choice of placing it either in cup or box, TWELVE succeeds the first few trials but does not obey later. The reaction of EIGHTEEN does not show this confusion.   When left to her own devices, EIGHTEEN sometimes pounds table with cup but plays with a more controlled manner than TWELVE.

When presented with paper and red crayon, EIGHTEEN scribbles imitatively. TWELVE repeatedly puts crayon to mouth and does not scribble. Láter on he casts crayon to floor. EIGHTEEN scribbles more than once but also shows a tendency to bang with the crayon. No imitative attempt to copy a circle but a suggestion of imitation in making a vertical stroke.

When TWELVE is *taken to window* he very evidently surveys the scene outside. (He is much interested in horses and moving autos.) When EIGHTEEN is taken to window she also shows fixation of attention and begins to talk in an untranslatable chatter.

Both children smile at *mirror image;* TWELVE puts hands out, EIGHTEEN investigates behind the mirror.

When presented with form-board, EIGHTEEN promptly puts circular block in round hole and also places it in after form-board has been reversed. Occasionally, however, she tries to put circular block in square hole.   TWELVE places block on board and brings block near circular hole but does not actually place it in even when shown. He, however, is very near to this performance and a few times places the block almost in the depression. He also has exploratory interest in the board itself.

As happened in two or three previous situations, TWELVE, on losing interest, begins to throw blocks on the floor. The attention and interest of EIGHTEEN do not come to such a termination. EIGHTEEN places triangle in proper hole when shown and makes an intelligent effort at adaptation.   Also puts square in hole on being shown. Puts triangle in promptly when favorably placed in her hand.

Both children are interested in *performance box, and* EIGHTEEN promptly puts *rod* in circular hole.   TWELVE explores hole first with rod and then with index finger of either hand but does not drop rod in until shown.

The general qualitative difference in this situation is the greater fixation on the part of EIGHTEEN.

The square block is presented for placement in performance box. TWELVE is absorbed by interest in the holes themselves and is inclined to cast aside the block after a fleeting trial in order to explore the edges of the holes with his hands.   EIGHTEEN retains a persistent hold on the block and makes a prolonged effort to place the square block in the rectangular hole. She thrusts it in diagonally and after trying for one whole minute she casts the block aside.

Both children are given *a ball* which interests them greatly. On command, TWELVE alone puts ball in the box.   EIGHTEEN is too enamored of the ball to let it go in this manner, but she was willing to pick up the second ball and return it to TWELVE. She is perfectly willing to put cube in box but will not put ball in.

Both promptly pick up *pellet* with pincer prehension; TWELVE puts it to mouth.

TWELVE holds up *rubber doll* for inspection; EIGHTEEN shows a still higher grade response, squeezes it purposively, also places doll in her arm.   TWELVE later on squeezes doll but not in the same deliberate manner as EIGHTEEN.

Both babies are spellbound with interest when *examiner brings blocks together with rhythmic report.* Both of them smile with pleasure and also in expectancy at each imminent report. The attention of

TWELVE is unbroken and he sits transfixed.   EIGHTEEN, however, after about a minute, turns to her mother and makes urgent request for blocks to play with.

The same attention is shown when examiner alternately operates the *snapper* held in each of two outspread hands. Interest in this, however, is not as prolonged or as intense.   The factor of motion was apparently important in transfixing the attention in the previous situation.

Independent play. When EIGHTEEN is taken to the adjoining room and given access to a table full of play material she shows no marked preference for any one of the objects but plays in turn with the blocks and box, teddy bear, picture cards, and ball. She places four cubes into a cup. She shows characteristic eighteen-months shifting from one position to another, handling objects for short periods and moving about from one point of interest to another.

She is able to point to her nose, ears, and eyes; and Baby TWELVE, when asked to show where his teeth are, places his hand in his mouth. It is a domestic trick.

While TWELVE *remains in his mother's lap,* EIGHTEEN *plays at the small table.* Her play is of a simple combining type, putting one thing into another, lifting objects from place to place, shoving them about and bringing them into simple combination without, however, carrying out very elaborate plans.

The rattle becomes disjointed while she plays. She brings it to the examiner to have it remedied. She has lost all her timidity and wanders about the clinic as freely as if she were at home.

How long will she play all by herself? Her mother says a half hour.

CHAPTER 21

EIGHTEEN MONTHS *VERSUS* TWO YEARS

Initial Reactions. The babies are brought simultaneously into reception room. EIGHTEEN shows no marked initial timidity but begins to wander about room. TWO clings to mother and returns to her two or three times, but soon gains confidence, and both children move to small table covered with nested blocks, toys, and teddy bear. EIGHTEEN begins to chatter (unintelligibly) and carries blocks around room. TWO regards EIGHTEEN intently and says, "See the teddy bear." General reaction and attitude of TWO is more mature and restrained. TWO takes notice of pictures on blocks and names one of them a chicken.

Attended by mothers, children walk into examination room. They take their places at the big table, seated in mothers' laps.

Reactions to cup and cubes. When presented with *empty cup and cubes* both children play spontaneously, filling the cup with the cubes. There is a decided qualitative difference in favor of TWO, who is more executive in the manner in which she handles the blocks. She uses both hands in filling cup.   EIGHTEEN's play is less varied than TWO's; he persists longer in the same activity.

TWO plays spontaneously with blocks and places one block upon another; EIGHTEEN later on does the same thing but in a much more tentative and inconclusive manner.   TWO is obviously more purposive and vigorous in manipulating the blocks. EIGHTEEN prattles softly to himself. TWO utters sentences calling attention of mother to blocks. TWO from time to time regards EIGHTEEN; EIGHTEEN occasionally glances at TWO.

Both children *give blocks to examiner on request.* When pile of ten blocks is again placed before children, EIGHTEEN shoves them about; TWO also shoves them a short time.

256

EIGHTEEN builds an *imitative tower* of three blocks. TWO builds an imitative tower of five blocks and laughs with glee when tower falls down.

When asked to *imitate train* with blocks, EIGHTEEN does not imitate model but persists in tower-building reaction; TWO makes a partial imitation and says "Choo choo" to imitate sound of the train. When asked to build *imitatively* a *bridge* both children respond by building a tower. EIGHTEEN, however, builds on model while TWO builds with his own blocks.

When offered multiple cubes, EIGHTEEN, by pressing cubes to the chest, takes five. TWO also accepts five but manipulates more skillfully, holding three cubes in one hand.

In multiple choice and commission test, TWO distinguishes consistently between plate, cup, and box.   EIGHTEEN places the cube by preference in the cup but makes no discrimination for the box. In *performance box*—TWO promptly puts double cube into rectangular hole. EIGHTEEN makes a purposive attempt but does not succeed even after demonstration.

On three-hole form-board, TWO places all three blocks in holes, and adaptively turns triangle to fit hole.   EIGHTEEN takes up blocks, one in either hand, and puts circle in hole with assistance. Makes attempt with square but does not succeed. TWO adapts promptly with circle.

Both children scribble spontaneously *when presented with crayon and paper* and both prefer lateral stroke.   TWO imitatively makes a vertical mark but is unable to differentiate between a vertical and a horizontal stroke She makes a crude imitative attempt at circular motion.   EIGHTEEN makes no vertical stroke, or effort at one, even after repeated demonstrations.

On *imitative paper fold*, TWO makes a consistent effort, without bringing edges neatly together; makes a crude crease. EIGHTEEN handled the paper but without effective results.

When presented with a one-ounce empty bottle and pellet, EIGHTEEN promptly puts pellet into bottle. When asked to give back the pellet he makes a responsive but not adaptive effort; he tries to take pellet out of bottle with his fingers. TWO promptly puts pellet in bottle and when asked to hand pellet back to examiner turns the bottle upside down and releases the pellet.

Independent play at small test table covered with play objects, including bell, ring, spoon, doll, ball, rattle, blocks, pellets, bottle. When EIGHTEEN approaches test table he at once seizes the bell, holds it in one hand, and begins to remove articles from table with the other. He plays in rather an inconclusive manner with spoon and ring and then drops spoon on floor. Tries to reach rattle and is impatient because he cannot do so. He might easily solve the problem by coming to the other end of the table, but he does not make this adaptation.

Begins to wander from table. When he notes that door is closed, returns to table and takes more objects from it; places ring on floor; uses bell to push blocks and rattle. Makes an effort to put bell into bottle though the mouth of the bottle is only half an inch wide.   After about a minute and a half he again leaves table and rings bell up and down. He wanders to and from table from time to time.   Again makes effort to put bell into bottle and then takes doll and hands it to examiner. He walks to near-by shelf and shoves bell under bundle of papers.

Most of activity may be described as diverse, piecemeal exploratory exploits of short duration which involve little elaboration and only simple combination.   He shows no alarm when left alone in examining room. He does not, of his own accord, sit in the chair, but when placed in chair begins to take objects from table and throw them to floor.   Plays with rattle or about a minute.

He takes all three pellets from table and puts them on floor or chair. He tries to pull handle from rattle and is interested in the discovery that the spherical part of the rattle turns on its axis.

His marked but transient interest in this discovery is characteristic of the type and range of his attention. He makes very little effort to bring two objects into relation but is content to exploit the object which is immediately at hand, whatever that object may be. He does try, however, to put the cube into the bottle. This is partly a carry-over from the pellet and bottle test. When given a pellet he places it immediately in the bottle. When, by chance, his left hand takes hold of a cube he bangs the cube up and down and shoves it back and forth.   After remaining in chair for about four minutes he spontaneously makes an effort to get out and crosses the threshold into the adjoining room.

When TWO approaches *the test table* she takes up the doll with one hand and then with the other promptly picks up one pellet and puts it to her mouth; likewise the second and the third. All three are swallowed with splendid dispatch. She then takes the ball and plays with it momentarily. After this she returns to the door and asks for her mother but is readily diverted back to the table. Places ball on table and takes up bell, then takes position in chair and begins to play with objects on table.   She does not lose consciousness of mother but wishes to show objects and toys to mother. She says, "Show it to Mamma" when playing with bell. Her objects of choice are evidently the ball and the bell, both of which she wishes to show to her mother, and she is not willing to have some one else take these objects and show them. Her whole reaction to the test-table situation is altered by the presence of an observer and also by the memory of her mother in the adjoining room. Every object is reacted to with the sentence, "Show it to Mamma."   She asks that the door be opened so that she may go to mother. Restlessness is appeased after she has shown objects to mother. This marginal consciousness of other persons is much more highly developed in TWO than in EIGHTEEN. EIGHTEEN was content to stay in room alone for a while.

When the mother is permitted to enter room the reaction of

TWO is much the same; objects are taken from table and brought to the mother for inspection.   When TWO is placed in chair with her mother near her she begins to play in a combining manner with box and blocks, putting one on top of the other.

That her previous reactions are not altogether preconditioned by association with mother is indicated by the fact that she also inquires about her EIGHTEEN-months-old companion while she is seated at the table. She evidently takes quite as much delight in carrying objects to other persons and receiving recognition as in playing with the objects themselves. She is about to bring crayon to examiner but instead begins to scribble spontaneously. Even this does not hold her attention for any length of time. She holds up the paper for inspection from time to time and says, "I made this." After scribbling on both sides of the paper she begins to play with blocks but at the same time keeps talking about the baby in the adjoining room.

Catching sight of the examiner she takes up the blocks and brings them to him. At no time is her attention completely absorbed by the material, even the doll she brings to the examiner.

She plays for a short time with the string attached to the dangling ring and makes explanatory comments and brings the ring to the attention of her mother and examiner.   She returns to the paper and crayon, picks them up and asks to be placed in mother's lap, and then begins to scribble on the chair arm.

When the electric light is turned on in rhythmic succession the attention of both children is attracted. TWO laughs aloud with pleasure; EIGHTEEN watches TWO. When this game is changed by the examiner to *bringing two blocks together with rhythmic report*, the attention of both children is held momentarily, but there is no such fixation as in the previous comparison. TWO soon loses her attention and tries to get on the floor. EIGHTEEN watches and listens a little longer but soon turns his attention to TWO.

Reaction of children to each other. Both children are very decidedly in the runabout stage. The locomotive drive is strong. It requires more managerial effort to keep the observations under clinical control than on previous comparisons.   The children are interested in each other but show no disposition to play together for any length of time.

On departure from the clinic, TWO displays an unambiguous attitude of seniority toward EIGHTEEN. She bends over with tenderness in her manner and voice and takes EIGHTEEN by the hand to lead him out of the room.   She is somewhat awkward in the way in which she tries to take hold of his hand. She soon loses hold of him. The span of her attention is not as highly developed as her social attitude; she walks on ahead alone, continuing to talk tenderly, unaware that she is leaving EIGHTEEN behind.

CHAPTER 22

Two Years *versus* Three Years

Initial reactions. Both children enter reception room dressed in cloak and bonnet. Mild timidity is evident in facial expression. When it is suggested that the children take off cloak and bonnet, TWO begins to cry and clings to skirts of mother. This fear subsides in a few minutes, as soon as she is shown a few toys. Both children remove their wraps without assistance. TWO is talkative; THREE is silent during the initial period of adjustment. Both children enter the examining room in confident manner; they show a real interest in their new surroundings; but there is a trace of anxiety.

When presented with saucer, plate, and cup, TWO at once utilizes them as play material, taking up each object in turn and bringing the spoon into relation with the plate and cup. She plays in a combining manner. THREE is more interested in watching TWO and also follows closely all the movements of the examiner. THREE has no inhibition in regard to the material, but makes no play response. When asked, "What do you do with the cup," she points to saucer and then places the cup in the saucer and then the spoon into the saucer in a very purposive and sensible manner. TWO watches THREE, duplicates the actions, and then pretends to drink.

On the multiple choice and command test, THREE without any error places the cube in box and cup and plate in turn; TWO likewise. THREE is more sedate in all these situations, TWO is more playful.

Both children simultaneously and without an imitation model begin to build a tower *when nine blocks are placed before each one*

262

of them. TWO builds a tower of four; THREE builds a tower of nine blocks. Following the tower THREE makes a horizontal row of nine blocks. THREE makes a good attempt at duplicating a *bridge from a model* but tries to put two blocks side by side on top of one, an impossible engineering feat.   TWO does not imitate either a train or a bridge but persists in building towers only.

THREE promptly adjusts to *performance box* and *places square* in rectangular hole; TWO makes imitative effort at putting square in all three holes but does not turn it adaptively on edge. When *shown,* she holds the block properly but persists in an effort to place it in the opening cornerwise. After second demonstration she still tries to put it in each of the two small holes but finally succeeds in placing it in the rectangular hole. On third trial she adjusts promptly.   It took TWO about three minutes to accomplish this reaction and it took THREE five seconds.

On *single paper fold test* TWO responds adaptively but makes multiple folds and begins at once to roll up the paper. THREE shows the same tendency but with more inhibition after the first crease. Neither child adapts to the double paper fold situation.

Drawing. When asked to copy a circle, TWO responds promptly with the scribble reaction but with no imitative response. THREE just as promptly makes a definite circular copy. Both children are much interested in the drawing tests and make prompt imitative effort to copy a *vertical stroke.* Both succeed. On the *horizontal line,* TWO persistently makes a vertical stroke with an unsuccessful lateral effort shown by an occasional oblique stroke. THREE without any error imitates the horizontal stroke and makes an adaptive effort at reproducing a *cross,* making two strokes; usually the second stroke is somewhat different from the first, but there is no successful reproduction of the cross. On imitation, TWO is able to make a crude circular mark which is different from either her scribble or her stroke.

Form-board. THREE puts blocks in form-board without any assistance. TWO does likewise but not as speedily as TWO. Having succeeded, she replaces blocks promptly without error. *When asked to put in the blocks in competition*, THREE more readily understands the instructions and works swiftly and places in the blocks ahead of TWO. It is clear that THREE has definitely more power to speed up.   Neither child adjusts to the first *reversal of the form-board*.

When given a recess at three o'clock and allowed to follow their own devices, THREE walks into the adjoining room and seats herself at a kindergarten *play table*.   TWO wanders about the room but stays much closer to her mother.   THREE comes back after a few minutes with teddy bear. Both the children take regard of each other but make no marked advances to each other. They seem to be content in playing, each by herself. TWO plays in combining manner with blocks and paper on one of the small tables. TWO shows more readiness to stay on lap; THREE is anxious to leave lap and play by herself at table.

Picture completion. THREE points out objects in *completed picture* but does not put the two severed halves together in an adaptive manner until she is shown the same picture colored and at the small table, when she puts together the two halves.   TWO cannot solve picture completion.

Independent play at small test table covered with play objects (as in comparison five). TWO takes up in turn, ball, doll, rattle, and bell and shows them to examiner. She plays with doll, then rings the bell, and she handles the crayon and then handles the ball for a few moments, then rolls it for a few moments. After dropping the crayon and rattle she picks them up and returns them to table. She carries on a little soliloquy describing the clothing, naming the hat and shoes and other parts of the doll, and brings it up to the examiner for inspection. She then takes up the ring, places it over the doll and then over the ball, and then takes the bell and rings it.

This is very characteristic of her type of attention. Her reactions are definitely above the EIGHTEEN-months level and express a higher degree of combining activity.

She stands the doll upright on the chair and then begins to transfer other objects to the chair and then takes them from the chair and brings them to the examiner. Having placed seven objects in his hands she then takes the seven objects and places them back on the table.

This is partly motivated by the fact that she wished to begin a game of *catch and toss* with the examiner. She throws the ball with good coördination and makes a gesture at catching but without success. In fact her catching becomes a form of batting because she does not inhibit her hands.

After the game she asks to see her mother. She played contentedly in the room for about fifteen minutes and might easily have been detained longer.

THREE *seats herself* with alacrity at *the test table* and takes up in turn rattle, ring, crayon, and bell. She scribbles a circular scrawl with crayon, rings the bell, and makes this remark about the rubber doll: "My father found one of these dolls on the hill."

The first reaction to the play material consists very definitely in trying out the different objects without bringing them into relationship to each other. She returns to the crayon and scribbles for a few minutes.   She makes doll whistle. She shows a desire to return to the other room. On leaving she makes a markedly more mature *reaction to the door knob*. TWO tried to turn the knob and was able to push the door open, THREE was fully able both to turn the knob and open the door.

When presented with one-ounce bottle and box of pellets, she takes pleasure in filling the bottle with pellets, one by one, breaking apart those that are stuck together. She also turns the bottle upside down when asked to return the pellets. Her attention in this is well sustained and when she has difficulty in pouring out the pellets, she shakes the bottle vigorously in an adaptive manner.

When THREE sees moist pellets adhering to the side of the bottle, she makes an adaptive effort to get them out with a little wooden rod.

TWO shows the same initial interest in putting pellets into bottle and even attempts to put them in before requested to do so. Her attention, however, is more readily distracted by the other objects on the table. When she drops a pellet, which is oftener than with THREE, she recovers it before placing the others in. Her co-ordination is accurate but it takes her much longer to place in the pellets. This slowness makes her movements seem more cautious whereas they really indicate less skill.

In taking the pellets out of the bottle she is also more awkward and spills them about more than THREE. When asked to take out the two pellets which cling to the side of the bottle she tries to thrust in her finger and to shake vigorously, and later thrusts in the wooden rod which is given to her but uses it much less purposively than THREE. Her pellets and bottle behavior, however, is definitely superior to that of the eighteen-months level. Later she begins to play with the pellets by putting them into the box instead of into bottle. In putting them into box she uses her whole hand; in putting them into bottle she uses index finger and thumb.

Reactions of children to each other. When THREE and TWO are both *brought* to the *small test table* and are seated at either end there is no conflict or dispute, but THREE at once seizes the two pellets and eats them, after which her interest soon declines. Both soon leave the table, but spontaneously return to the test table; and THREE initiates a game in which she pretends to feed TWO.

This final little scene epitomizes in a manner the difference between these two levels. Not only is the psychologist throughout the examination conscious of the greater maturity of social attitude of THREE when compared with TWO; but THREE, herself, recognizes TWO as her junior. In a similar manner, TWO yesterday treated EIGHTEEN as her junior and assumed a corresponding attitude of seniority.

CHAPTER 23

THREE YEARS *VERSUS* FOUR YEARS

Initial reactions. Both of the children entered the reception room without timidity and with very normal degree of restraint. FOUR is obviously more indifferent to the environment and takes off his hat and coat promptly and is immediately ready for the next adjustment.   THREE's reaction is somewhat more delayed and is a little more tentative. He takes off his hat alone. His mother helps him remove his sweater.   Both children smile responsively. While the examiner converses with the parents, THREE examines the swivel chair and FOUR investigates removable ink cell at the desk.

The children walk into the examination room in company with mother. Each child, without hesitation, goes to his mother's lap.

From their position they survey the toy cupboard on the opposite wall.   FOUR immediately asks questions about one or two of the objects in the cupboard.   They both turn their faces up toward mother as though to ask what is next. FOUR's attitude is very decidedly expectant and inquiring.

When spoon, cup, and saucer are placed before the children, each regards the other. FOUR sees no occasion for any response and THREE gingerly handles the spoon but makes no other response. Both listen for a while to the examiner's dictation, FOUR more than THREE.

When a *pile of ten cubes is placed before each child,* THREE promptly uses blocks for play purposes.   FOUR fumbles them, but not at first in any constructive manner. Without suggestion, however, he soon begins to arrange them in a row.   THREE takes a cue from this and does the same.   FOUR makes two equal rows of five and pushes one row with deft coördination across the table. THREE begins a simple block structure arranging four blocks in square.   FOUR also pushes one train of blocks backward.

He makes three or four new adjustments or combinations with the blocks while THREE is making one.   Basically the character of their responses is similar but FOUR is much more productive.

THREE finally arranges all the blocks in neat rectangular pattern and smiles with satisfaction at the result. He turns from time to time to look at his companion and examiner. He is definitely conscious of his social environment but not inhibited by it. FOUR finally arranges all the blocks in one long column which he moves back and forth.

Both *build bridge imitatively*. FOUR reacts and succeeds promptly.   THREE, at first, begins to build on the model and, having built the bridge, elaborates it by putting on other blocks, whereas FOUR builds an additional bridge out of his remaining material.

When they are *told to close their eyes and then to build the gate from a model*, there is a most obvious and significant difference.

THREE blinks his eyes coöperatively but does not manage to keep them closed.   FOUR closes them more effectively than TWO but there is some tremor and control is not fully achieved. THREE is unable to copy the gate construction.   FOUR inserts the keystone block. Before placing on the other blocks he delays and ponders but finally reproduces the model.

FOUR is much interested when the *color design blocks* are placed before him and says, "Look pretty."   THREE seems to have no conception of the problem of copying the design with his blocks; just as previously he rather readily lost his attention for the model of the bridge.   FOUR makes an effort to reproduce the design, but only partially succeeds.   THREE is not influenced at all by the problem but uses the card with design on it as part of a "choo-choo train."

Both the children are able to make *double paper fold in imitation* and both make creases in imitation of an additional diagonal fold. THREE, however, makes a straight crease, while FOUR imitates adaptively.

In *the drawing tests* in which a model to copy is presented there is a marked difference in the degree of general adjustment. THREE makes only a very partial adjustment to the situation and is more absorbed in his own drawing and makes only feeble relation of this drawing to the model. He makes a continuous circular movement in response to the circular model. He makes vertical strokes in an effort to copy the cross.

FOUR calls the cross a star and immediately makes an adaptive response. He makes an obvious effort to reproduce the corners in the triangle but does not make a triangle or square.

He makes a representative *drawing of a man*. The result is an elongated figure which he calls a "long man" and the appendages which he calls the "legs." When persuaded THREE also makes a responsive effort to the suggestions that he draw a man but the result is a few straggling strokes which, acceding to the suggestion, he calls "man."

There is a marked psychomotor difference in the coördination drawing test. FOUR takes definite and rather tense hold on the pencil and putting his whole mental and bodily adjustment into the problem he definitely traces two designs. THREE shows no such evident adjustment but holds the pencil at the end in a light manner and makes a wandering circular motion in feeble imitation, and this soon becomes a characteristic circular scribbling stroke.

The children, when asked by the examiner if they would like to do something more, both readily assent.

Picture completion reactions. They examine with interest the *complete picture* in completion picture test. THREE points to the dog and the shoe in the picture. FOUR names them.

In response to the *completion problem* THREE uses the two pieces for constructive play material. On persuasion he manipulates them about until he completes the picture, smiling with satisfaction, but his preferred interest is of a constructive kind and he again puts the cards on edge and builds a corner of them.   When the left half of picture was put in reverse position, THREE adapted in a very prompt manner.   FOUR fails to adapt on a colored version of same picture but makes a complete analysis, tracing outline of the incompleted half of the picture.

When presented with a *diagonally cut picture*, THREE adapts and readapts.   FOUR makes a partial adaptation and completes the picture verbally and with tracing, and after repeated trial completes it also in form arrangement. Imagery combination is if anything more developed than in THREE.

When presented with the *adaptation situation on picture completion*, he verbally solves the problem, saying, "This one should be over here and should be upside down," but does not execute his suggestions.

Both children show excellent *adjustment while being photographed*, although here again the quality of attention in FOUR is more fixed and can only be described as more mature.

Each readily *brings* his own *chair to a kindergarten play table*.

The children are not returned to mothers' laps but work at small, separate tables.

After demonstration FOUR fits forms discriminatingly on *form completion test*.   THREE responds, placing each card in turn, but not in a discriminating manner.

On *form matching test* THREE identifies one form, namely, the square.   FOUR identifies four forms.

On *color naming* response FOUR miscalls three colors but consistently names green, pronouncing it "dree."   THREE does not respond at first with color names but repeats, "This is yours and this is mine"; but he uses color names for three colors —brown, white, and red.

In *counting* FOUR counts 1, 2, 3, 4, 5 definitely.   THREE counts pennies, 1, 3, 5, 6; but in his answers to the question, "How many pennies are there?" when two pennies are placed before him, shows he has no number concept of "two."

In *practical number conception* FOUR gives definite evidence of having attained "two" because he consistently places two cubes in cup on command. It is clear from repeated tests that "three" is nascent but not established.

On the *cube commission test*, THREE apparently has a definite consciousness of "one" and places one cube in cup, but places several cubes when asked to place two.

On *the bubble number and relation test*, FOUR succeeds in placing one bubble under the chair and discriminates between in-front-of and behind but does not draw the accurate number of bubbles, drawing three instead of two.   THREE responds to the test in a nondiscriminating manner, merely making a characteristic circular scrawl around the picture.

FOUR *names incomplete man* a horse.   THREE calls it a chicken coop. Neither completes *the drawing* of one-eyed and one-legged man.   FOUR adds second ear but only after a suggestion. He then begins to fill in vacant places with scrawls.

By this time (*45 minutes have elapsed*), THREE shows a tendency to leave his chair and if left to his own devices would play in runabout manner, moving objects about.   FOUR shows no such restlessness but remains in his chair, ready for each new situation. In intervals he looks about, whereas THREE indulges in simple manipulation of the play material.

In the *puzzle box problem*, both children are interested to secure the ball.   FOUR promptly analyzes the problem and says, "I must pull this," pulling the string.   THREE tries first to pull the ball out. He does not succeed and soon gives his attention to the rod, making the remaining movements in a very adaptive manner but more slowly than FOUR. It takes him about twice as long to secure the ball. After securing the ball, he plays constructively with the box, apparently trying to restore it to its first state. He says he would like to keep the ball but surrenders it readily.

Free construction. Each child is presented with a box of free construction material. Both children are delighted with the material. FOUR exclaims over the flag and holds it aloft.   THREE also at first singled out the flag and held it up without saying anything. The second thing of dominant interest is the penny.

THREE then begins to take up various objects in turn and returns to the flag, although he has been urged to make something. He handles the material as individual units for the most part, taking the rod in one hand and tapping the floor with one of the wooden pins.

In definite contrast with this is the action of FOUR, who at once begins to combine the different materials. He places the rod upright in the timber with holes. At the end of three minutes FOUR has made three boats, one with three uprights and the other two with two uprights.

At the end of the three minute period THREE has simply piled four timbers on top of each other and does not answer to the question "What did you make?" He soon casts down this pile and begins to knock blocks together and to knock them about from place to place. He is much more controlled than any EIGHTEEN-months child, but the type of play is more akin to the earlier forms of manipulation.

FOUR'S play is more akin to constructive representation, with a larger element of imagination.   It would be wrong, however, to say that there is a complete difference in the two ages in this respect because in about five minutes THREE makes a definite portal out of three timbers and says, "See what I have made."

Summing up the differences in free constructive play one might say that there is much more evidence of guidance patterns in the play of FOUR.

THREE is not altogether free from such patterns, as he makes two rather distinct and neat piles of his material. (This degree of orderliness is not found in the eighteen-months level and is likely to be absent at the two-year level.) Although both children work independently there is more tendency on the part of THREE to refer to FOUR than vice versa.

After ten more minutes have elapsed THREE, like FOUR, places the flag in one of the timber holes and THREE moves it about singing "Choo choo" and calling it an automobile. He then places a wooden rod in a block in a similar manner and says "Another one, another one." Captivated with this idea he places other rods in the holes and his table begins to take on more resemblance to that of FOUR.

It is significant, however, that FOUR's immediate response to the material was in constructive terms, whereas THREE's response is in the nature of an exploitation of a somewhat accidental discovery.

THREE carries on a little chatter and sings as he works. FOUR makes spontaneous comments from time to time.

The superiority of motor coördination in FOUR is evident at almost every turn, in the manipulation of chair, in taking a sitting posture, in placing the rods into the holes.

The children have played (undirected) with great satisfaction and intentness with the free construction material for *eighteen minutes* and show no disposition to stop or evidence of fatigue. When asked whether they would like to continue to play, both children respond in the affirmative. *When told to replace the material neatly* into the box they pull the rods apart; FOUR assembles the material more rapidly than THREE, doing it in about half the length of time.

Both, however, have a sense of completion in the task, and THREE brings the filled box to the examiner.   FOUR would like to retain the flag. It is promised him later and he returns it to the box obediently.

On the *steadiness-fish test* THREE and FOUR both show profound interest and make a complete adaptation to the situation. The chief and most significant difference in the responses consists in the inability of THREE to inhibit the coöperative use of the free hand.

     FOUR almost immediately makes and maintains this inhibition and catches the fish in seven seconds in the second trial with the right hand.   THREE also captures the fish but shows marked tendency to use free hand.

The children have been under observation for one hour and three quarters. FOUR asks "What are we going to have next?" THREE responds readily to a verbal test, pointing out objects in pictures.

When asked to tell about the kitchen picture, THREE says "The girl, the cat, the lady."

On kitchen picture he says, "The boy is watching the fish."

The comparison at this level leaves the same general impression which develops in the comparisons made at lower levels. There is greater maturity of motor control, more *savoir faire* in the older child. In the present instance this difference holds for pronunciation as well as other specific acts of motor coördination. In spite of the excellent attack and attitude of THREE, FOUR was consistently superior upon every developmental item with the possible exception of the picture completion, and even this has a partial clinical explanation.

Both children are good examples of mental health and poise. To what extent temperamental qualities count for this we cannot say, but many of their reactions evidently reflect the result of wholesome training and home environment. Of all the comparative levels thus far studied the present pair required perhaps the least expenditure of managerial energy on the part of the examiner.

CHAPTER 24

FOUR YEARS *VERSUS* FIVE YEARS

Initial Reactions. FOUR and FIVE are brought to the clinic in an automobile and sit beside each other during the five-minute ride. Although they show no timidity, they maintain silence throughout the whole journey.   On leaving the car FIVE shows an almost condescendingly protective attitude by assisting FOUR out of the automobile. She also leads her by the hand up the stairs, and helps her take off her gloves, although FOUR is quite able to take them off herself. Nothing is said by either child until they are approached by the examiner. They answer his questions without hesitation.

The children take their places at the big examination table with alacrity and show no resistance. They walk in without being held by the hands, and then go to their mothers' laps. The children are somewhat amused and apparently a little perplexed to know why an *empty cup and saucer are presented to them.*   FIVE places the cup in the saucer and spoon in cup and begins to stir. FOUR does not react to the material.

When the blocks are presented, however, the children react without any delay.   FIVE at once begins to arrange the blocks in a square.

FOUR spontaneously builds them into a tower. FOUR builds two parallel towers of five blocks each.   FIVE builds two horizontal rows and then, apparently in imitation, also builds two parallel towers. The children frequently look at each other and also at their mothers.   FOUR and FIVE then take down their towers, FIVE leading; FIVE builds a wall.   FOUR this time takes her cue from FIVE and builds a similar wall.   Both

275

children are apparently interested in precision of arrangement as well as in carrying out a preconceived design.

There is no conspicuous difference in motor coördination. If anything FOUR handles the blocks more deftly. Although both are interested in the blocks, FOUR occasionally turns to her mother for approval.

The children are still playing spontaneously with the blocks when *five of the blocks are taken from each child.*

When told to *close* their *eyes for the gate-building test*, FIVE reacts much more promptly and adaptively.   FOUR has somewhat more difficulty in keeping her eyes closed.   FIVE at once builds gate in imitation of model.   FOUR continues to turn to her mother and gets her mother's encouragement. FOUR declares that she cannot do it.   FIVE asks her to do it and says, "Do it like I did; I copied it."   After two demonstrations but without further assistance FOUR also builds the gate.   FOUR is definitely more self-conscious while FIVE is independent and says, "Oh, that is easy!"

Children close eyes again while assistants build "memory steps." Neither child is able to reproduce steps built of ten blocks, from memory.   FOUR uses only eight blocks and makes two tiers and FIVE also makes two tiers, using ten blocks.   FIVE makes somewhat more comment than FOUR.   FOUR tends to talk in whispers.   FIVE talks with relative assurance.

In the *steadiness-fish test*, FIVE volunteers the imaginative remark that the fish almost bit her finger.   FIVE also remarks that she is in kindergarten, where she plays these kinds of games. There is no marked difference in the coördination in the steadiness-fish test; FOUR's attitude is more tense and serious than FIVE's.

No significant difference is revealed on *paper-folding test*. Both children make the double fold with ease and neatly. Both of them have comparatively more difficulty with the diagonal fold but their accomplishment is much alike.

A *fishing contest is improvised*. Both children enter into the game.   FOUR catches seven fish in the one-minute interval and FIVE catches nine fish. These numbers represent the number of successful coördinations made within the time limit of one minute.   FOUR is silent and serious throughout the contest. FIVE is jaunty and laughs and talks while she works. One of her remarks is imaginative in character. She says, "I am going to eat this fish when I get him home."

Children are released from mothers' laps and put at separate, small tables. Both children address themselves promptly to the construction material in the free construction test.   FOUR is somewhat distracted by the penny, which she brings to her mother, but soon begins to arrange the colored plaques and moves them about in an exploratory manner. At the end of three minutes she has piled several timbers, one upon the other, and added a shorter block and surmounted this with a yellow bead. Her interest is very evidently a constructive one, but she is unable to tell what she built. She is silent during the three-minute period.

FIVE, on the other hand, makes running comments as she manipulates her material. She gives her first attention to the colored blocks, arranging them in an orderly manner, bringing the triangular pieces of similar color together at their bases. She says, "I will make a design, blue design," and hums, "I try to make as good a design as I can." She picks up the flag and says, "Look," and then puts rods into the timber with holes. She places in four rods at the end of the three-minute period but does not name the structure. She has apparently more preperception of and interest in completed results. She asks for more time to finish what she is doing and when the photograph is being taken she wants to finish her construction before the exposure is made

Children are taken aside for photograph. The reaction of the children to the photographic situation was different from anything we have experienced at previous levels. There was complete coöperation. Time exposures could be made with facility and there was no inconvenience in arranging for the pictures. This silence and coöperation and poise were correlated with the higher level of development.

In the drawing test, the end results show a perceptible though not great difference in favor of FIVE. Her strokes are firmer and her drawing of a man is more highly elaborated, containing special strokes for teeth and eyebrows and a supplementary drawing of a girl who is with the man.   The greater maturity of FIVE is very definitely shown in *copying* a *cross*. The strokes of FOUR were wavering and on the first attempt four radial strokes were made by FOUR and on the second attempt three separate strokes were made, whereas FIVE said, "Oh, that is easy" and made two direct strokes at right angles to each other.

Both children are perplexed with the problem of *copying a triangle*.   The result in the case of FOUR is two long lines, joined together at the bottom.   FIVE delays some time before she makes an attempt to copy the triangle. She shows considerable auto-criticism and seems to be aware of her inability to make a diagonal stroke and says "It is an Indian wigwam" (probably a kindergarten association); but having made a right angle of two strokes she is unable to bridge the gap with one stroke but makes two strokes, resulting in a quadrilateral.

Neither child is able to solve the *patience test*, forming a rectangle with two triangular cards, but FIVE is able to complete a diagonally cut rectangular picture.

In *describing* the "*Home*" *picture*, FOUR simply enumerates objects, saying, "I see a girl,   her Mama,   pussy cat,   dog." FIVE says, "I see a boy washing his hair, a girl with a towel over her head. I see a girl with her shoes and stockings off. I see a girl coming in, another with a cat on the bed."

In the *four-part picture completion adaptation*, FOUR, after about a minute of trial and error adjustment, places together properly the two upper halves of the picture but fails to make any adjustment with the lower halves.   FIVE promptly brings the two upper halves together adaptively and after about three seconds on the lower half pieces puts them in proper position. In all tests of this character it is evident that FIVE is more consistently advanced in her preperceptive thinking.

Reaction of children to each other. In order to determine how the *children* react to each other both *are placed at one table, side by side, and given a box full of building blocks.* In the preliminary adjustment and throughout the experiment FIVE assumes leadership. FIVE assists FOUR to a chair and when the box is handed to the children, FIVE intercepts FOUR, takes hold of it, and appropriates the box Both take out enough material to begin building. There are no evidences of coöperation. They work for the most part independently, and FIVE appropriates the lion's share of material and playing space on the table.

FIVE dominates the play and erects a large fence or corral. She is much the more planful and, after several minutes, FOUR begins to hand her building material with which to carry out her (FIVE'S) building plans.

At the end of about ten minutes the children begin to play back and forth in a frolicsome manner but not with any common objective. At this point the examiner interrupts and asks them both to resume their positions in the chairs, with this question, "Now what are you going to do?"

FIVE answers promptly, "I am going to fix this for you," putting the material back in the box; and in reply to next question, "What is Betty (FOUR) going to do?" FIVE says, "She is just going to monkey around and drop them on the floor." This is descriptive of what was actually taking place at the end of the free-play period.

FIVE replaces the blocks very neatly in the box and FOUR hands the blocks to her.

Terminal reaction. On the return journey from the clinic the children again ride in the automobile. This time there is no discernible silence. The children "cut up" rather hilariously all the way home.

CHAPTER 25

The Comparative Aspect of Development

The foregoing is an account of what actually happened when sixteen average pre-school children, in eight pairs of ascending age, were brought into psycho-clinical comparison. Although the account must of necessity contain adventitious details, it plots in crude outline the general course of early development which is common to all normal children. The conditions of growth are such that no individual can at any stage be brought into immediate comparison with what he was or will be. We may, however, partially reconstruct the basic lines of his development from such typical cross-sectional views as we have sketched. We might even try to subtilize the developmental ghost of a generic individual from these sixteen seriate subjects, if we could dissolve away all the dross from our data. The paradigm of development can be ascertained by making more searching and more systematic comparative studies of the same individual and of pairs of young individuals.

A general retrospect of the eight comparisons reported in Chapters 17–24, suggests a few observations relating to the comparative aspects of development.

A law of contrast apparently governs clinical perception and clinical judgment. It is difficult to see and to evaluate symptoms of development as isolated phenomena. They take on definition and proportion only when seen in terms of a higher or lower level of development. In the series of simultaneous examinations above reported, many items of observation and many unrecorded impressions would have been denied us except for the ever present, stimulating standard of comparison.

The law of contrast works with real force. For example, when we compared the four-months and the six-months babies, the latter so fully outdistanced the former and built up (by contrast) such a strong impression of infantile perfection, that it was almost a surprise to find the tables so decisively turned on the morrow when Baby six, in turn, was brought into comparison with Baby nine. In the first comparison (four *vs.* six) it was the four-months babe that suggested an unstable sailor, while the six-months babe was all aplomb! But in the second comparison (six *vs.* nine) it was the six-months babe who became the wobbling sailor, and the nine-months babe who assumed the aspect of equipoise.

It cannot be urged that this law of contrast by distortion will lead us astray. On the contrary it will sharpen perception. In clinical work we are always dealing in some form or another with a series. A scientific use of the comparative method leads either to identification (matching) or to interpolation in a series. We get a true estimate of the developmental status of six by making two comparisons, and by interpolating six in its true position between four and nine. We deliberately make comparisons and then refine or correct them by a process of interpolation.

Mensuration is itself implicit comparison; but in the present imperfect state of psychometry, clinical judgment must place its chief reliance upon explicit, critical, comparative thinking. Ordinary "mental measurement" is not always as subtle or delicate as comparative perception. We have convinced ourselves of this fact, more than once, in studies of correspondence and disparity in "identical" twins.

Although simultaneous comparison accentuates the cleavage between adjacent developmental levels, it also emphasizes the community between these levels. In no instance did either child of a pair appear to be in an absolutely different category from his comparative companion. Even the four-months babe seemed on the whole to be near the verge of doing what the six-months babe could do, or he did in prophetic snatches what was the proper character of his senior. Likewise there was no impassable gulf between levels SIX and NINE. There were real scorable differences, but there were, also, many evidences that what NINE had attained was nascent or incipient in SIX. For example Baby NINE definitely looked for a fallen spoon. Baby SIX did not, but he was manifestly "conscious" (aware) of its disappearance. Prolong, project, and direct that "consciousness," and he too will look for the spoon. Indeed he doubtless looks for fallen spoons now, because it is about two months since we examined him. During this time and through some undefined process of organic concrescence in his nervous system and of accretion through experience, this particular form of "awareness of disappearance" has lengthened out into "looking for." This is development. In a somewhat similar manner, the *anlage* or rudiment of every item of behavior is anticipated just a little lower down. It is for this reason that our series of comparisons presented us with no abrupt or altogether astounding evidences of disparity. It was a gradual ascent; and we were scarcely aware of the distance we had climbed, until we looked back upon the long slope and the valley below. At the foot lay an inarticulate infant unable to pick himself up, unable to pick up a spoon. At the top there moved about a very articulate and very ambulatory young person, who can draw a picture, who can give a sprightly account of the many things she can do in kindergarten, and who helps her mother wash and wipe the knives and forks—and spoons.

At which comparison did the difference between the two adjacent levels seem most pronounced? This question is difficult to answer. The disparity between four months and six months was perhaps most marked, that between four years and five years least marked; even though the chronological interval in the former instance was two months and in the latter, one year. The difference between twelve months and eighteen months, also, was marked; probably because of the double accession of verbal language and of independent locomotion during that interval.   Expressed in arithmetical ratio the developmental disparity was at no time greater than .66⅔ or less than .80. It is therefore significant that our general clinical impression as to this disparity was not at variance with these ratios.

If we attempt to formulate the mechanism of development, in a few round phrases, we naturally turn to such Spencerian conceptions as differentiation, elaboration, and integration. In the spheres of relatively impersonal adaptive behavior, or general intelligence, these terms are broadly applicable. The "intellect" grows through the progressive acquisition of an almost infinitely increasing hierarchy of motor and psycho-motor adjustments, reflexes, habits, associations—adaptive behavior patterns. In this confessedly restricted sense mental growth is essentially quantitative,—the mere multiplication of modes of response—a kind of cumulative virtuosity.

First a neurone pattern (or system of patterns) for seeing the cube; another for seeing the red of the cube; another for clasping the cube; one set for the fingers, another for the thumb; another for thumb and fingers in conjunction. Then patterns for reaching, other patterns for releasing and for throwing; for placing the cube in the cup; for placing one cube on another, two cubes on another, three on another; for placing one between two, etc., etc., etc. In the progressive series of responses to a dozen blocks one can see prefigured, somewhat as in a crystal model, the lines of aggregation which are followed in the course of early intellectual development.

Does early personality development proceed in a comparable manner? This question begs a more important one. Do not personality factors condition in all sorts of ways the reaction of the children to such presumably "impersonal" stimuli as a set of wooden blocks? They undoubtedly do; but not in a wholly capricious, lawless manner. There are characteristic and prevailing tendencies in the overt responses to the blocks; and these responses are broadly conditioned by the maturity of the nervous system. Indeed the responses express this maturity quite as much as they do the individualized symptoms of personality make-up.

It is, of course, impossible, and even undesirable (except for purposes of practical or academic convenience) to separate intelligence from personality. The individual, of necessity, must behave as an integer. Even the operations of intelligence are limited and directed by the total, integral personality. The term personality make-up, however, refers not so much to the structure and caliber of intelligence, as to the emotive, volitional, and energy traits of the individual.

The development of personality make-up is infinitely more complicated and baffling than the development of intelligence (if we allow ourselves to make a distinction). In a certain sense, it is not so exclusively quantitative. It involves qualitative (instinctive) accessions throughout the whole span of immaturity. It is profoundly conditioned by metabolic and physiological factors and by racial and temperamental elements which are hereditary. But the personality is so dynamic, so reactive to all stimuli within its exploitation, so impressionable to stimuli beyond its control, that its structure and its overt actions reflect at every turn the influence of its social environment.

Our comparative cross sections were not designed to display the multiplicity and the diversity of personality traits, but they brought many such traits to light. A searching inquiry into the domestic and social behavior of our subjects would have added interesting local color to their portraits, and revealed more of their inhibitions, prejudices, motives, "drives," and personal idiosyncrasies.

Merely incidental inquiry, for example, revealed the fact that the three-year-old girl in the sixth comparative pair has a highly organized fear of rubber boots. The origin of the fear is unknown, but the fear has lasted for months and is sufficiently powerful to make her "tremble all over." This same girl is also subject to tantrums, during which she used to cast herself upon the floor and kick and scream. She still casts herself upon the floor and screams; but she no longer kicks; because she does not wish to awaken the baby who sleeps downstairs. She loves that baby very much!

In this web of anger, fear, love, unrestraint, and inhibition, one glimpses the complexity of the pattern of personality in a three-year-old child.

Personality develops at a very rapid rate during the pre-school years, and is more complicated and, in a sense, even more mature than we are accustomed to grant during these years. The gains in the sphere of personality are fully as striking as those in intelligence.

In every comparative examination the older child gave a convincing impression of greater maturity of personality make-up. Usually he seemed more serious, more sedate, more deliberative—adjectives which we ordinarily reserve for later life but which have a certain psychological validity when applied in a comparative manner to the period of infancy.

We are sure that this impression did not rest on the greater physical stature of the older child. His consistently superior motor control reinforced the impression but was not altogether responsible for it. In one instance the older child was obviously smaller and weighed less than the younger child, but the behavior of the larger child nevertheless appeared less mature.

The older child in every comparative instance appeared more self-contained, in the sense that he was obviously less at the mercy of the environment. The senior member of a pair showed a greater degree of reactiveness and appeared to be (always relatively) more self-conditioned than his junior contemporary. In this sense there is a quantitative increase in individuality. As the child grows older the external stimulus becomes less and less "the starting point of behavior." Even a six-months baby exploits his environment more than a four-months baby.

Part of the growing self-containedness, no doubt, is due to an increase in inhibition (and correlated integration). In countless details the child betrays the evidences of restraint and compromise with his environment as he grows older. The progressive inhibition of the hand-to-mouth reaction is one of the most palpable and instructive of such evidences. This reaction, which appears at the four-months level, may persist well into the eighteen-months level. At six months it may hold a dominating place in the field of behavior; but its dominance is gradually diminished by the appearance of competing drives or interests and the acquisition of new habits. At first the numerical frequency of the response alone is affected; later its intensity; and even when it is vigorous it suffers delay because of rival propensities. We describe the end result with the term inhibition, but the attainment of that inhibition cannot be explained in ordinary terms of voluntary control. The inhibition is the end result of a process of displacement through superimposed interests and acquisitions.

It would be instructive, could we trace the steady elaboration of the *consciousness of other persons*, which is correlated with the development of personality. This consciousness of others expresses itself at the four-months level in a responsiveness to facial animation and in an anticipatory adjustment to being picked up. At four years it is indescribably complex and expresses itself in the affections, fears, hopes, and suspicions which a child attaches to his superiors and in verbal questioning of a highly social import.

Accompanying this expanding and sensitive knowledge of others, there is a steady increase in the child's own private personality sense. His native docility, his imitativeness, the cumulative influence of suggestion, the inescapable weight of domestic tradition bring him to a state of relatively stable adjustment to his elders.

The last examination pair (four years and five years) were highly amenable children when compared with their early predecessors. They would do our bidding; they would sit when we told them to sit; they would await their turn; they would surrender even a coveted toy; they would remain quiet for a time exposure while being photographed;—what would they not do for us? We were left with a profound realization of their teachability.

This realization was, if anything, disquieting; it led us to think that we run a hygienic risk when the schools are permitted to over-exploit this very teachability which was asserting itself with such naiveté in the laboratory. In any event, it is certain that the child has by the end of the pre-school period achieved a remarkable degree of conformance and conformability to his elders.

The preordained importance of this conformability has been adequately recognized; but we have not paid equal respect to the child's own personality sense. This private personality sense undergoes a steady increase, while his sensitive knowledge of his elders is expanding. But he himself is an elder to those who are his developmental juniors; and it is delightful, not to say comforting, when we see the same outcrops of elderly condescension reappearing in his very infancy. Not one of our children behaved in violence to the rights of seniority. Our first two-year-old girl assumed "a little mother" attitude toward her eighteen-months companion, talked to her tenderly and tried to lead her by the hand. Our five-year-old girl assumed nothing less than a patronizing manner toward her four-year-old acquaintance; and this five-year-old child was by no means of aggressive temperament. Indeed her "playing up" to the four-year-old child, her efforts to amuse, her kindliness could not be described as aggression. It was a rudimentary form of benevolence, developmentally not unrelated to the parental impulse itself.

These interesting attitudes which children take toward their juniors are more than pretty bits of mimicry. They reaffirm the complexity and richness of the psychological development of the pre-school years. They also suggest a paraphrase of the famous dictum of Heraclitus who said "Nothing is; all is Becoming."

In development nothing is; but everything is comparative.

CHAPTER 26

Research Applications of the Comparative Method

In other chapters we shall emphasize the usefulness of the comparative method in clinical procedure. In the present chapter we wish to suggest several special applications of the same method to certain problems which have a research as well as clinical interest.

The comparative method is a method of approach which places a premium upon descriptive and interpretative analysis and which adapts itself to the problem in hand. We cannot, in the present stage of psychology, use an absolute, mathematically precise, and mathematically universal technique. We confessedly seek standards of comparison because of their efficacy in throwing into relief certain psychological phenomena which might otherwise remain obscure and which cannot as yet be measured with satisfactory, objective accuracy. Psychometric determinations are an invaluable aid to comparative investigation, but not a substitute. Clinical psychology, like psychiatry, needs to amass a vast amount of systematic descriptive data. Comparative analysis will aid in the accumulation and the evaluation of such data. Normative formulation will give them practical applicability.

In the field of pure science observations must and will be made for their own sake, because they may extend the boundaries of ascertained truth. In the field of applied and clinical science, observation of necessity is alloyed with a pragmatic prejudice. We watch, observe, and describe in order to increase our clearness of comprehension of problems which have at least potential practical import. Among the almost bewilderingly intricate phenomena of child development, we may well place some faith in the comparative method; for it can supply a broad orientation and can furnish us with a kind of dead reckoning. Comparative deductions will not have the precision of celestial observation, but they will none the less tell us something about where we are. Ultimately they may disclose dynamic units of measurement which will be appropriate to the highly dynamic character of the phenomena concerned.

In the following we suggest in a sketchy manner, several groups of psycho-clinical problems where the comparative method appears to offer a promising research approach.

1. *Developmental correspondence in twins.* This is essentially a comparative problem. The determination of mental and physical resemblances and disparities in twins provides a fertile ground for interpretative comparison. Among monozygotic twins we find graded degrees of developmental similarity, approaching complete duplication. The elucidation of these similarities and disparities offers a durable problem for refined investigation. Dizygotic or fraternal twins increase the range of comparison but at the expense of an increase in the complicating and indeterminable factors of differentiation. It is among true, monozygotic twins that we have in many respects the most favorable, because most controlled, conditions for analytic comparison. The subject is so full of scientific and human interest that we devote a brief preliminary chapter to it.

2. *Precocity and superiority.* This problem also has a highly comparative aspect. Superiority, of course, is largely a relative conception. It is a highly developed form of "normality," a kind of hyper-normality. To what extent it and, still more, genius and talent, are also conditioned by exceptional or unique factors can be determined only by thoroughgoing comparisons between the gifted and the normal or normative. In many respects the most favorable, because the most undisguised, period for such psychological comparison is infancy.

Likewise precocity. Precocity has to do primarily with rate and compression of development, and perhaps also with qualitative differentiations. In any event these differences can only be formulated in terms of what is accepted as "normal" or normative. The importance of clinical insight with reference to the problem of pre-school precocity is emphasized in a brief discussion in Chapter 28.

3. *Retardation and inferiority.* This problem is a converse of the preceding one. It involves an analogous, if not identical, developmental economy; only here there is dispersion instead of compression of development, with lagging instead of acceleration. Again the clue is comparative, and includes a formulation of the phenomena in terms of normative data. We discuss the problem at some length by means of a case study based on five periodic developmental examinations, with concurrent comparisons with·normal infants. Although inferiority expresses itself in many diverse patterns, the case presented appears to typify the basic relation which underlies developmental retardation and developmental deficiency.

4. *Developmental peers of incongruent age.* This presents a group of comparative problems which grow out of the laws of retardation and acceleration. In clinical experience we frequently find children who on a large array of tests and measures prove to be of almost equal developmental status. On as many as twenty out of twenty-five items they may score the same rating and yet they may differ chronologically by two, three, five, or ten years. Developmentally they are comparable peers; but they also present significant distinguishing personality traits and attainments which make them inviting subjects for analytic comparison. Their very equivalence emphasizes their contrasts and calls for an interpretation of these contrasts in terms of habituation, inheritance, environment. Such interpretative comparison should assist us in grasping the factors that determine personality differences.

In general, the younger the child, the less complicated and less encumbered the problem. Although the comparison of developmental peers is an interesting and rewarding effort at any stage of development, it is peculiarly challenging as a scientific problem at the lowest comparable levels. We refer to the comparableness of idiocy and neonatal infancy.

The lowest grades of idiocy fall below the four-months level of development and can only be described in terms of neonatal modes of behavior. The very profoundest cases of idiocy do not come to the attention of the clinician. We may infer that there are a small proportion of cases in which developmental arrest is so radical that it prevents the maturation of the neurophysiological mechanisms which determine the vegetative processes. Some of these undeveloped children are prematurely born or still born, and fall within the category of those idiots whose imperfection is so fundamental that they do not survive even on the vegetative level of behavior.

Above this zero line of survival there are numerous grades and variations of idiocy, presenting a wide array of clinical patterns. However untoward these embodiments of defect and deprivation may be, they merit and they repay our study. They fall completely within the scope of natural, lawful phenomena; and from the standpoint of clinical science it is necessary to inquire in what manner idiocy differs from the normal incompleteness of neonatal infancy. The correlation of our clinical findings with etiological factors and types is also a profitable field of investigation.

5. *Social and racial factors of development.* The psychological comparison of widely divergent social strata and races has somewhat recently become a subject of discussion. Mental measurement statistics and, to no small extent, speculation have been brought into play. The problem, of course, is one of vast dimensions and of great importance. Its solution, unfortunately, requires an equally vast scientific equipment. At present we can make only partial and piecemeal investigations. We can scarcely attack the problem from a strategic sector until we are ready to study the infant representatives of these social groups and races. The same is true of the related problem of sex differences.

6. *Increments of development.* We may never succeed even in inventing or discovering a static *unit* which will measure development as satisfactorily as the carpenter's rule measures the length of a beam. We are more likely to contrive a dynamic unit, but even this will probably be metaphorical in character.

By means of comparative discrimination, however, we can at least express developmental alterations in terms of more or less than some *thing* else or some *time* else. We can itemize the differences between a one-week-old baby and a one-month-old baby, draw a line under the column and try to add it up. In our effort to find a common denominator we may in time arrive at significant generalizations based upon comparative analysis.

In the foregoing instance we compared two contemporaneous babies of different ages in order to formulate an increment of development. We may also compare one baby with his former developmental self as summarized in a consecutive record or by successive, periodic examinations. In the neonatal period we might even undertake to record, systematically, the diurnal increments of development. One of my students has begun a series of weekly examinations of a six-months child and has demonstrated the feasibility of such investigation. Some of his observations are incontrovertibly objective, even though he happens to be the father.

This method of approach must be distinguished from the narrative, diary method so much in vogue in the early child-study movement. The diary method, although by no means sterile, was almost too comprehensive and too unselective to yield full fruit.

The comparative approach is deliberately selective and brings phenomena separated by time and space into juxtaposition for purposes of clarification. Although, like any method, it is subject to error and misuse, it is also to a considerable degree self-corrective. It helps us to focus both perception and judgment. For the same reason, it may be added, the comparative method has pedagogical importance both for clinical instruction and clinical demonstration.

7. *Conditioned development.*   Development does not pursue a completely preordained course. Even in the prenatal period it is modified by epigenetic influences. In the postnatal period it is constantly impressed and organized in terms of environmental and induced factors.

To a considerable degree the influence of these factors may be subjected to experimental and observational investigation. In the early months of infancy the method of the conditioned reflex can be used in manifold ways to display the operations of the conditioning process. In the space of an hour or half hour one may definitely and measurably modify an old response or establish a virtually new one. The strength, the persistence, and the educational significance of such induced responses constitute problems of fundamental importance.

Infancy is the golden period for the study of developmental mechanics. The learning process has become a central and almost staple problem in educational psychology. The bulk of the literature on the subject, however, is occupied with studies of specific forms of skill, and with achievements in the realm of the school curriculum. Much remains to be done in the investigation of the more fundamental and generic aspects of learning—the kind of "learning" which goes on hourly in infancy and is biologically bound up with the total phenomena of development. With the growth of psycho-biology, we may expect fundamental studies in animal and infant behavior which will illuminate the dynamics of personality-formation and the origin of emotional trend. A knowledge of these personality trends is infinitely more important for the understanding of human efficiency than any knowledge we may have regarding expertness and skill.

From the broad psycho-biological point of view "the learning process" is not preëminently a problem which pertains to school going, reading, writing, technical and academic behavior. It is a problem which is inherently bound up with development and can be best attacked by basic studies of those early stages of development which belong to neonatal and pre-school childhood. Ultimately many scientific methods will be brought to bear upon this problem. Physiological and biochemical research will probably figure preëminently. At present, simple comparative studies may do much to define vaguely recognized problems and to formulate new ones.

8. *Developmental symptoms of disease and disability.* We continue to use the term development, even in this context, with special reference to its behavior expressions. Rickets is being studied with detailed reference to its histological effects upon bones, and its chemical effects upon the constitution of the blood. These may, of course, be described as developmental effects, but we are using this term to denote the effects of the disease upon the behavior picture. Rickets unquestionably delays walking. This is a behavior effect; it would be scientifically appropriate to call it even a psychological symptom, or a neurological one, or a neuro-psychic one! It is a lawful (not capricious) accompaniment of the rachitic condition and as such comes under the head of symptomatology.

It is inconceivable that this should be the only behavioristic symptom of rickets, a disease which involves the whole body economy and includes the nervous system. It is even conceivable that there are behavioristic manifestations which are so early and so subtly characteristic that they might possess a diagnostic import. For this reason we cannot study too assiduously all the dynamic, behavioristic back strokes of both chronic and acute disease. Prodormal symptoms may be peculiarly important.

Here lies another open and almost untouched field of exploration, where comparative studies will again roughly chart the ground. A comparative, analytic study of both characteristic and atypical behavior symptoms of the ordinary diseases of childhood would be revealing. Clinical psychology and clinical medicine have a community interest in these problems. The practical importance of this fact is discussed in the chapter on Developmental Diagnosis in relation to medicine.

9. *Developmental sequelae of disease and trauma.* In the previous section we discussed the concurrent and frequently temporary behavior symptoms of disease and disability. In the present section we wish to mention the more permanent consequences and residuals of any abnormal interference of development.

The grosser and classical instances have, of course, been studied in considerable detail. The literature of mental disease and deficiency is full of case studies and clinical classifications which outline developmental defects. Much, however, remains to be done, both for medical and psychological reasons, in making these data more refined and discriminating. In the interests of neuropathology alone it is important that we should be able to furnish detailed behavioristic descriptions of the varied clinical cases of mental defect which come to autopsy. No adequate interpretation of the neurohistological findings is possible without a detailed developmental delineation, which may be correlated with the microscopic picture. It would be rather futile to give the neuropathologist an uninterpreted mental age or I. Q. Highly detailed comparisons, alone, can yield any productive results.

Beyond this particular field of inquiry, however, is a domain which is much larger and which borders upon normal psychology. The dynamic displacements which follow in the wake of prolonged invalidism and specific disabilities, have been frequently recognized by psychiatrists. These sequelae, if the bull may be permitted, should be more carefully considered while they are in the making. We shall then be in a better position to understand and to forestall them.

The child's psychology changes under the weight of handicap and physical depression. Why does he lose his *alter ego* for a new one? How does the psycho-morphosis take place? This is a problem in clinico-comparative psychology which presents itself repeatedly in hospital and home. Psychoanalysts have made much of certain adult abnormalities which trace back to trauma in early childhood. They arrive at this etiology through a process of retrospective deduction. Here, again, we ought if possible to study cases in the making.

Perhaps the importance of these infantile psychic traumata has been exaggerated. The normal resistance of young children to adversity also needs recognition and study. Adler's principle of mental compensation, through the intervention of the nervous system, has application to normal as well as abnormal psychology.

The phenomenon of compensatory physical growth is one of the most striking and interesting which has been uncovered in recent experimental studies of nutrition. The liberal margin of safety which nature has vouchsafed, at least to white rats, in the growth of stature is amazing. When certain inhibitions of growth have been removed even an old rat will begin to wax as though he were young!

To what extent do similar laws of latent compensation apply in the highly dynamic field of mental development? Though the question appears to be almost insolubly intricate, we may hope that a cumulative knowledge of infancy will shed light on it.

10. *Personality make-up*. This is a phrase which psychiatrists have conjured with, and which psychologists are no longer ignoring. Emphasis is being shifted from general intelligence to personality traits. Personality is a decidedly useful designation for the dynamic, integrated individual. And the psychology of personality, particularly on its emotive and volitional side, is unquestionably the most important from the standpoint alike of education and medicine.

How can this psychology be built up? By any and all methods which throw light upon the laws of human conduct. There has been some disposition to look for basic energic factors or attributes. But these attributes may prove to be as illusory as the reaction-time will-o-the-wisp. There is no reaction time as a *Ding-an-sich*.

There are only conditioned reaction times. Likewise, probably, personality traits.

Comparative descriptive delineations of personality in the same or different individuals through progressive stages of advancement offer the best hope for an elementary formulation of the subject. And if our approach must be comparative it will be genetic. We must begin with the neonatal child, when personality is all but wanting. When he is mature the glass through which we observe him is opaque. When he is an infant it is still somewhat transparent.

CHAPTER 27

Developmental Correspondence in Twins

Twins have always captured the curiosity and imagination of man. They figure in myths, traditions, superstitions, in art, in humor, and in advertising. They are written in the constellations. Recently they have become one of the problems of science.

For biologists, twinning has become a problem of central importance. Bateson has defined twinning as the production of equivalent structures by division; and emphasized its fundamental nature. Important studies in symmetry, asymmetry, teratology, sex, and heredity have been made in this field. H. H. Newman of the University of Chicago has made extensive studies of twin production, habitually exhibited in the nine-banded armadillo of Texas. He has also made a revealing analysis of the nature and causes of the twinning process through experiments on the eggs and embryos of the Pacific coast starfish. H. H. Wilder has reported in the *American Journal of Body Anatomy* studies of the physical differences in twins shown by skin patterns of soles and palms. Galton made a similar comparison of finger prints in twins. Baldwin has made a physical measurement of three pairs of fraternal twins and determined their differences in anatomical ages.

Of outstanding importance are Professor H. H. Newman's companion volumes on the *Biology of Twins* and the *Physiology of Twinning*. These two volumes and their accompanying bibliographies show with what industry and success biologists have investigated this central developmental problem. That a similar amount of psychological research in the same field would yield rich results can scarcely be doubted. The problem of psycho-physical resemblance and psychogenetic correspondence in twins is one of crucial significance. If we could solve it with any completeness, even for one pair of similar twins, we should thereby gain much insight into more fundamental problems of heredity, development, and education.

The question of correspondence and disparity in twins involves, of course, the deeper problem of the genesis of twins. It cannot be said that this problem has been solved. Biologists have for some time accepted a classification of human twins into two distinct types: (1) fraternal twins, who may or may not be of the same sex, who show ordinary sibling or fraternal resemblance, and are presumably derived from two separate eggs (dizygotic); (2) duplicate twins, who are always of the same sex, closely resemble one another, and supposedly originate from one fertilized egg only (monozygotic). The existence of both types of twinning has been indisputably established in the lower animals. There can be little question about the occurrence of dizygotic (biovular) twinning in the human family. There has, however, been some question in regard to the frequency of mono-zygotic twinning; and the possibility of reconciling specialization of resemblance and disparities in co-twins with this mode of genesis. Biologists and embryologists continue to recognize two distinct types of human twinning. Obstetricians have adopted the same distinction and maintain that it is usually possible by an examination of the placenta and foetal membranes to determine whether any given pair of twins was mono- or bi-ovular in origin.

Bateson has given us a very broad conception of twinning in his formula "the production of equivalent structures by division." He regards it as a fundamental manifestation of life. "When I look at a dividing cell, I feel as an astronomer might do if he beheld the formation of a double star; that an original act of nature was taking place before me." Cellular division, as such, is not twinning; but the tendency of the divided or repeated parts to assume symmetrical relations may be so regarded; and this tendency is an almost universal feature of biological mechanics. The fact that the experimental embryologist can bring about the growth of a paired structure by a simple scratch wound of a single limb bud reveals the fundamental nature of twinning. Newman insists, likewise, that wherever we have bilateral doubling, we have twinning in some form.

From this point of view every bilateral individual may be construed as being morphologically akin to twins. The human individual is undoubtedly derived from a single fertilized cell. He is monozygotic in origin. From this zygote, through a process of symmetrical division, develop all his right and left hand homologous organs and the right and left halves of his "unpaired" organs and structures. He is a product of developmental duplicity. Now in the case of true, complete, monozygotic twins, this process of duplication has been carried to such a degree that two offspring result from the single ovum. A perfectly symmetrical bilateral individual on the one hand, and a perfect pair of duplicated individuals on the other represent the ideal extremes of the process of twinning. Between these extremes there are many gradations and deviations, some of them benign, others monstrous in character.

Nowhere in the study of man do we find such complete duplications of individuality as among monozygotic twins. Here is an interesting and promising field for psychological comparison and for nice studies of developmental duplication and deviation. Being of highly similar genetic constitution, and being subject to highly comparable environments, the question of correspondence and disparity in co-twins becomes a well-defined problem for comparative investigation. Where else can we find an equally well-defined and simplified experiment for the study of individual differences?

The writer has elsewhere reported a study* of mental and physical correspondence in a pair of gifted twins, A and B. We became

* "Mental and Physical Correspondence in Twins," *Scientific Monthly*, Volume 14, pp. 305-322 and 415-429.

acquainted with these children when they were seven years old and we were first chiefly interested in their exceptionally advanced mental development. They were studied from this point of view at the outset but they proved to be quite as interesting from the standpoint of psychological comparison. Accumulating evidence convinced us that these two children presented a remarkable degree of correspondence in physical and mental constitution. (Figures 151, 152.)

Some twenty-five physical tests and measurements were made to determine the degree of physical correspondence between A and B. The results of this portion of the study are summarized in the accompanying table. An inspection of this table will show that in many items the correspondence amounts to complete identity and that in others it amounts to practical identity. Nowhere was a pronounced deviation revealed. The difference in standing height is one-fourth inch in favor of A. The sitting height shows the same difference.

Corresponding to this there is a difference of only one pound in weight. This disparity, however, is a variable one and sometimes B is slightly ahead of A in weight. The head girth shows a difference of but one-eighth of an inch and the cephalic index which represents the relation between width and length of head shows a difference of only 0.7. The cephalic width is only 0.2 mm. greater in the case of B and the cephalic length 0.1 greater in B.

A very interesting and tangible criterion of anatomical development consists in the degree of ossification of the carpal bones. These bones were compared by ascertaining the two major right-angle diameters of each bone with a millimeter rule applied to the X-ray plate. Four of the seven bones measured exactly alike. In the three other instances there was a disparity of one millimeter in one or two diameters. The similarity in these measurements indicates that there is a high degree of anatomical correspondence between the twin sisters.

FIGURE 151. TWINS *A* AND *B* AT SIX MONTHS OF AGE

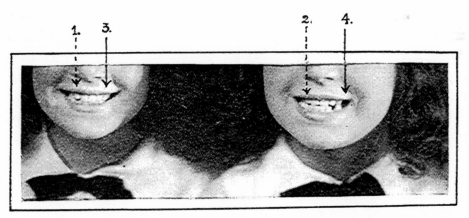

FIGURE 152. TWINS *A* AND *B* AT EIGHT YEARS OF AGE

Showing correspondence in eruption of right upper incisor (1 and 2), and in location of tiny pigmented mole near left corner of mouth (3 and 4).

PHYSICAL TESTS AND MEASUREMENTS OF TWINS, A AND B, AGE 9

Items Compared	A	B
Standing height (in.)	49⅞	49⅝
Sitting height (in.)	25¾	25½
Weight (lb.)	56½	55½
Head girth (cm.)	20½	20⅝
Head width (cm.)	13.4	13.6
Head length (cm.)	16.5	16.6
Cephalic index	81.2	81.9
Diameters of carpal bones (mm.)		
Scaphoid	5x10	5x10
Semilunar	7x10	8x11
Cuneiform	7x11	7x11
Trapezium	9x10	9x10
Trapezoid	7xca7	7xca7
Os Magnum	11x20	12x20
Unciform	8x15	9x15
Total exposed area	676	724
Friction skin patterns		
Right palm	9955C	9955C
Left palm	9955C	9955C
Blood pressure		
Systolic	95	96
Diastolic	65	70
Pulse (resting)	104	110
Blood agglutination group	II	II
Dynamometer		
Right hand	13	12
Left hand	12	11
Spirometer	78	80
Tapping rate		
Right hand	130	130
Left hand	127	118
Steadiness	14	17

There is no more interesting means of making a physical comparison than that reported by the friction ridges of the skin. These friction ridges are found only on the surfaces of the palm and the sole. According to the comparative anatomist they date back to an arboreal ancestry, when certain animals in their active life among the boughs were much aided by the non-skid qualities of such ridges. The ridges were coarser in those days; but we still inherit them in indestructible patterns which appear in the fourth month of intra-uterine life and which are carried to the grave.

Sir Francis Galton said "Let no one despise the ridges on account of their smallness for they are in some respects the most important of all anthropological data." Even in the ridge details there is absolutely no change in an individual from birth to old age. They furnish, therefore, a powerful aid not only for purposes of identification but for the comparison of individuals. A study of the palms and soles of A and B were made by Wilder's method. The right palms and the right soles were mapped out to indicate the major subdivisions of the skin patterns. A remarkable degree of identity was shown in both the palmar and plantar patterns (Figure 153). The formula for the palm patterns is the same for both palms of both individuals, namely, 9.9.5.5.c.

Dentition is of course related to development. The first dentition could not be observed, but when the children were 8 years of age, the right upper permanent incisor was in both children in a similar incompleted stage of eruption. This is shown in the accompanying photograph (Figure 152) and presents a rather startling indication of developmental correspondence. Finally may be mentioned one permanent indication of underlying identity of constitution. This is a tiny pigmented birth mole on the upper lip, situated a short distance from the left outer corner of the mouth in both twins. So here "the standard mole of the penny novelists" could not even be relied upon for the purpose of personal identification, because both twins have the self-same mole!

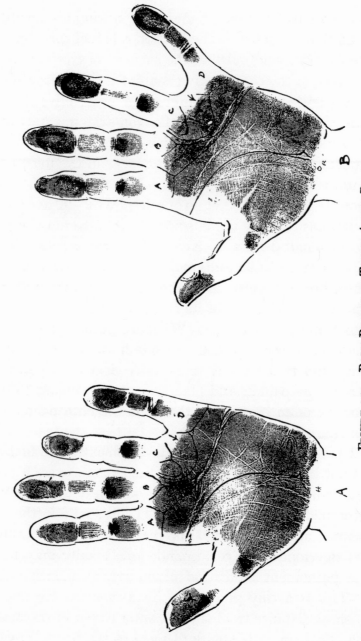

FIGURE 153. PALM PRINTS OF TWINS *A* AND *B*

Showing identity of skin patterns of right hands. Prints of the soles showed a similar identity.

There are several very tiny pigmented areas in the facial skin which are limited to one twin; and there are no doubt other physical deviations which minute study would disclose. Even two hairs, each but a half inch in length, taken from the same head, would, as Wilder says, prove to be "absolutely unlike if magnified sufficiently to show the epidermic markings that cover the surface with a fine tracery." By such ultrarefined standards, complete identity is a mathematical impossibility; but general coherent correspondence and absolute identity are two quite different considerations. Our data compel us to recognize a basic developmental and physical correspondence in Twins A and B.

We recently reëxamined these children at the age of eleven and we find the same striking physical correspondence. Alpha steps from the platform scales so that Beta may be weighed and the beam balances with only a tiny shift of the indicator. The mother immediately accounts for this negligible discrepancy in weight by a slight difference in the clothing of the two children! The incisors of A and B are now fully erupted and there is in both children a slight impaction of the two central incisors which was not present before. The right central incisor of A and of B is slightly askew as a result of this slight but shared anomaly. We were apprised of a new-found token of identity, a small mole hidden in the scalp in corresponding regions of the vertex.

Since the identity of these children has expressed itself in such structural details as teeth, skin-patterns, birth moles, and cranial and carpal bones, it is not unreasonable to suppose that there has been a basically similar developmental correspondence during the pre-school period when their nervous systems were undergoing fundamental organization.

The thorough similarity of this organization is amply attested by the psychological examinations which were made when the children were 7, 8, 9, and 11 years of age. The results of these mental and educational measurements are graphed in Figure 154.

Of particular interest are the results of the vocabulary test. This test Terman considers to have a far higher value than any other single test in the whole intelligence measuring scale. The

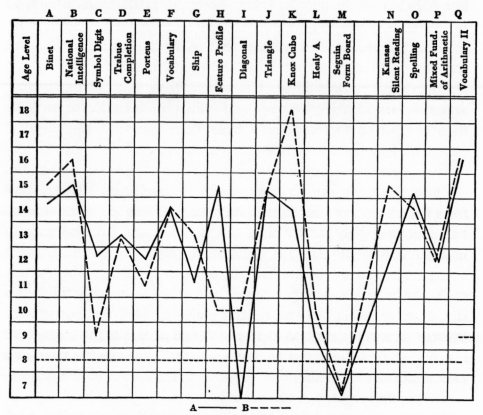

FIGURE 154

Graph showing correspondence in mental measurements of *A* and *B*. The results are plotted on the basis of mental age scores, the heavy straight dotted line representing the chronological age. The tests in order are: *a* Binet, *b* National Intelligence, *c* Symbol-Digit, *d* Trabue Completion, *e* Porteus, *f* Vocabulary, *g* Ship, *h* Feature Profile, *i* Diagonal, *j* Triangle, *k* Knox Cube, *l* Healy A, *m* Seguin Formboard, *n* Kansas Silent Reading, *o* Ayres Spelling, *p* Woody Mixed Fundamentals of Arithmetic, *q* Vocabulary II.

test consists of 100 words derived by random selection from a dictionary containing 18,000 words. An abbreviated series of 50 words of increasing difficulty ranging from *gown* and *tap* to *shagreen* and *complot* was given to both A and B. This virtually constituted a graded scale of 50 individual tests and revealed a startling degree

of resemblance; A failed on 16 of the test words; B failed on exactly
the same words, and on only one additional word, namely *harpy*.
The calculated vocabulary score of A at the age of 9 is 67 and for B
it is 65, a standard equivalent to the average adult level. At the age
of 11, the scores were, respectively, 71 and 68.

This degree of correspondence is truly remarkable when we
reflect that this searching test, in a statistical sense, compasses the
whole wide domain of the English language. Although we must
give due weight to the similarity of verbal and academic environment to which A and B have been subjected, do not the results of the
test testify even more eloquently to an underlying similarity of
nervous constitution and developmental determiners?

A comparative psychograph of the performances of A and B
in the Binet tests gives a graphical picture of the degree of intellectual correspondence of these two children at the age of eight. The
diagram is so drawn that success and failure are indicated in corresponding meridians on each side of the median column. All the
tests in the age level below twelve years were passed with great
facility and are not included. One half of the psychograph proves
to be almost a mirror image of the other. (See Figure 156.)

Such thoroughgoing psychological parity implies a high degree
of underlying developmental correspondence. How specifically did
this developmental correspondence express itself in infancy? We
raise a few questions and recur to them in the succeeding chapter on
precocity. Did Alpha and Beta attain postural control of the head
at the same rate and with equal coördination? Did they follow the
bedtime candle, pick up large objects, pick up small objects, look
for fallen objects, creep, talk, walk on practically the same dates?
A long array of itemized questions might be raised because of their
scientific and practical interest.

The tendency toward developmental correspondence asserts
itself not only in normal and superior twins but in retarded and
defective pairs. We have just compared co-twins A and B. We

turn now to X and Y, who are located at the other end of the developmental scale. For them we have also drawn up a comparative psychograph which may be readily contrasted with that of A and B. The ratings of X and Y on our developmental schedules are also indicated. It will be seen that this comparative diagram denotes a high degree of psychological correspondence.

The physical correspondence in these twins likewise is extensive and expresses itself in skin-patterns, cephalic diameter, and carpal development. The accompanying table of physical tests and measures summarize the details.

PHYSICAL TESTS AND MEASUREMENTS OF TWINS, X AND Y, AGE 6

Items Compared	X	Y
Standing height	41¼	42
Sitting height	22	22
Weight	38.14	39.5
Head width (cm)	12.4	12.4
Head length	14.5	14.5
Cephalic index	85.8	85 8
Friction skin patterns		
Right palm	11.9.7.5c.	11.9.7.5.c.
Left palm	11.9.7.5c.	11.9.7.5.c.
Blood pressure		
Systolic	90	100
Diastolic	60	60
Blood agglutination group	I	I
Dynamometer		
Right hand	3.5	3.5
Left hand	3	2
Dentition	=	=
Hair	=	=
Color of eyes	=	=
General appearance	=	=
Coördination	=	=
Posture and gait	=	=
Development of carpal bones	=	=

Twins X and Y are much alike in general appearance. This similarity is accentuated by the fact that they both have a markedly spastic gait which makes their motor carriage highly atypical and slow. In spite of the fact that their demeanor, posture, and general motor control are so peculiar, there is no great difference between the children in these respects. In fact the correspondence here is so great that it is inconceivable that the children came by their motor deficiencies as a result of natal cerebral hemorrhage. The length of the steps in walking is approximately the same. Y has somewhat less difficulty in running and apparently a slightly better control, but the motor correspondence is so great that it is altogether probable that the genesis of their paraplegic condition dates back to a germinal or early embryonic origin.

There is no marked difference in the control of speech apparatus, though X talks with somewhat more facility and assurance. The general parity of psycho-motor development is shown in their drawings. A rather elaborate series of drawings, both imitative and copied, were made by both children under identical circumstances and it is difficult to say which child shows a better accomplishment. Both of them have gone very little beyond the scribble stage and are about at the two-year level of development in drawing. They make only indifferent copies of vertical and horizontal strokes and neither of them can draw a cross. Neither of them can copy two dots. They recognize a drawing of a face. X called it a "hampelmann" and Y called it a "pumpkin," but neither could fill in eyes, nose, and mouth in a circle. (See Figure 155.)

Form discrimination is very poorly developed and their performances on the three-hole form-board, which consists of a square, triangle, and circle, were solved only when the blocks were put in close juxtaposition to the holes. When the order of the blocks was rearranged, both failed in the test. Likewise in the simple picture completion test, which required putting together two lateral edges of a bisected picture, both failed.

FIGURE 155

Drawings of twins *X* and *Y* at the age of six years. The drawings were made from the models shown in the left hand column.

The emotional and moral reactions of the children were much alike. Both coöperated well on their mental level. X is slightly more poised and self-possessed and placid. This emotional difference was brought out by their reactions to being photographed. Not aware of the fact that the children on a previous occasion had been seriously frightened by the grimaces of a too dramatic photographer, I proceeded with only ordinary precautions, but when the critical moment for the picture came, they simultaneously burst into tears and cries of fright. They surely looked like duplicate twins in the throes of this emotional episode. Y, however, was less easily quieted and less easily reassured. In fact, she had not regained her calm after about fifteen minutes. X cleared up more readily. The mother observes that this difference in emotional constitution shows itself in their home environment. In other respects, their deportment in the clinic was much alike.

The detectable intellectual differences are still slighter. Neither of the children has a fully developed number concept of *two*. X has an incipient concept of *two* but still confuses it with *several* and *many*. Y was barely able to recall three digits, which X failed to do in an equal number of trials. But X was able to tell us what she would do when sleepy, whereas Y failed on this simple comprehension question.

Enumeration of objects in three pictures showed considerable correspondence. For example, in describing the canoe picture, both of the children enumerated lady, motor boat, man, and stick—the stick being the paddle. They were tested independently and it was surprising that they should here use exactly the same words.

Considering the ordinary range and variety of individual differences among unselected siblings, these tests and measurements reveal a high degree of resemblance. The basic resemblance, indeed, is as thoroughgoing as that which has been described in the case of A and B. Compare the comparative psycho-graph of X and Y with that of A and B. (Figure 156.)

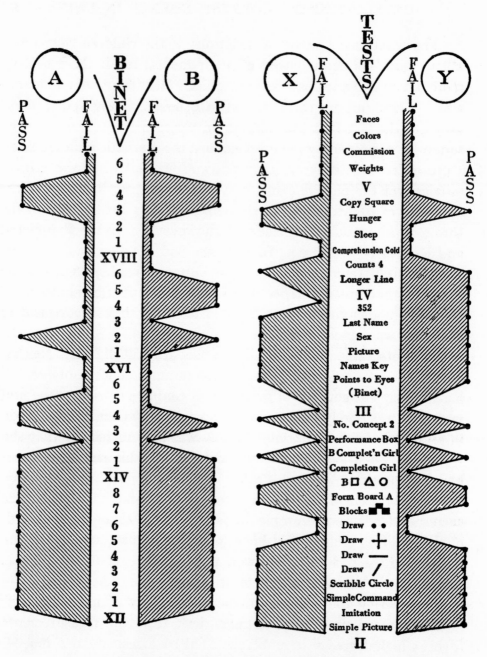

FIGURE 156. COMPARATIVE PSYCHOGRAPHS

Showing developmental correspondence in Twins *A* and *B* (age 8) and in Twins *X* and *Y* (age 6).

314

Fraternal or dizygotic twins conveniently widen within certain limits the scope of comparative inquiry. Fraternal twins are really contemporaneous siblings, born and bred together under the same roof. Unlike in genetic constitution, alike ordinarily in physical and social environments, they display the problems of developmental correspondence and disparity in a new light.

Triplets and quadruplets widen still further the range of comparative analysis. We have been fortunate enough to have the opportunity to study a set of quadruplets all of whom survived the first year of life. In spite of their extremely subnormal physical development, the individual differences in these children were observable at six months. On the basis of our findings the children were arranged in a rank order at that time. This rank order was confirmed at two successive examinations, at nine months and at twelve months. We may reserve the details for later report in connection with a more comprehensive study of the psychological aspects of twinning.

Developmental disparities in fraternal twins begin to assert themselves as early as the neonatal period. At four months they are unquestionably observable and sometimes well defined. For example, we have in our series a pair of fraternal twins, a boy (M) and a girl (F) who showed a considerable number of developmental discrepancies at four months. These disparities may be summarized as follows:

M and F look no more alike than ordinary siblings. F is of more delicate mold and comelier in features. She weighs four pounds less than her husky fifteen-and-one-half-pound brother. At birth she weighed four pounds; he weighed six pounds. The mother is sturdy and broad-shouldered, and nurses them both. She attributes their psychological disparity to the fact that her son, aged five, plays constantly with M to the exclusion of F, while her daughter, aged seven, shows a corresponding preference for F but cannot stimulate F as much because she, the daughter, aged seven, must go to school!

M nurses for twenty minutes, seven times a day. F nurses from ten to fifteen minutes, seven times a day.

M and F both sleep about fourteen hours a day; no difference noted here.

M tries to sit up, raising his head and shoulders; enjoys pulling at out-stretched hands so much that he frets with discontent if the game once started is stopped. F does not try to sit up.

M can stand by holding on mother's hand (a remarkable feat for the age of four months). F pushes moderately when feet are placed upon table but cannot stand even with support.

F vocalizes more in volume and variety.

M plays much more with his hands, but F began to play with her hands a week earlier than M.

M plays with paper, holding and waving it for a minute at a time. F promptly drops paper and does not exploit it as play material.

M can reach and grasp. F cannot.

F holds her head up much more effectively in the prone position.

In eye following movements M is distinctly inferior to F. His adjustments are coarser and he turns his head more. He does not respond as well in the upward following movements.

M is distinctly superior in his reactions to the table. M responded play-fully with the hands and picked up the spoon. F disregarded the spoon and exploited the table very little.

On the whole the qualitative differences in the developmental reactions are in favor of M. At nine months of age these twins were reëxamined and again the responses are qualitatively in favor of M. At nine months M weighed twenty-one pounds; F, 16 pounds. F was able to stand nearly twice as long as M. M was distinctly more vigorous in his efforts to seize a cube out of his reach.

The biological basis of physical and mental resemblances in dizygotic twins is in a sense more complicated than that of mono-zygotic twins. Dizygotic twins must be considered merely as two contemporaneous individuals. As a class such contemporaries doubtless show a higher degree of psycho-physical resemblance than non-contemporaneous siblings, but in any given pair we must be prepared to find ordinary fraternal differences. Indeed one twin may be mentally normal while the co-twin is backward or even feeble-minded. A few cases of twins have been reported in which one twin was normal and the other of Mongolian type of mental deficiency. Surprising as such disparities may seem to those who make twin synonymous with resemblance, it is natural that they should occur. Two separate ova are in these cases fertilized by separate spermatazoa. In one zygote both gametes are defective. In the other zygote only one or neither. There is no reason to expect duplication or identity under such conditions of conception. Or it may be that a second, potentially normal twin suffered a developmental damage previous to birth, during birth, or in infancy.

Pronounced disparity, however, is not limited to the fraternal type of twins. Although nowhere in the study of man do we find such complete duplication of individuality as among the monozygotic twins, nowhere also do we find such profound and monstrous individual differences as among twins of monozygotic origin. We are, therefore, confronted with an extraordinarily wide gamut of quantitative and qualitative diversities in the field of human twinning. The factors which bring about the diversities are not only germinal but also post-germinal and post-natal.

It is always important to recall Newman's general observation that in the human species, "twinning is by no means a fixed process but is highly variable, evidently beginning early and being more complete in some cases than in others." Newman holds that although every character has a genetic basis in the zygote, the exact expression of characters is dependent upon developmental or epigenetic factors that vary in each individual case. Furthermore the fact that developmental hazards are more numerous in cases of multiple pregnancy introduces another source of differentiation.

Notwithstanding all these influences which work in the direction of differentiation, there is no reason why instances of almost complete developmental duplication should not occasionally occur. The germinal and somatic determiners of development may be so nicely balanced, during the time of conception and cleavage, that we may have two persons who psychologically as well as morphologically stand for but one individual to the pair. Of the case of A and B, described in the foregoing pages, Shakespeare might again have said, "The apple cleft in two is not more twin than these two creatures."

CHAPTER 28

PRECOCITY AND SUPERIORITY

The problem of precocity is one of the most baffling in the whole field of development. To what extent precocity and prematuration should be made equivalent terms is itself a nice problem. Should prematurity denote untimely ripening and, by implication, unwholesome acceleration of development? Should precocity, on the other hand, indicate a form of forwardness, a state of being more developed than usual (or natural) at a given age? Perhaps the term natural is of doubtful value here, if we wish to suggest a distinction between precocity and prematuration; for precocity may be as natural as the usual; it may well be a normal form of advanced development.

We have in our files numerous instances of infants and school children who show pronounced symptoms of accelerated or advanced development, without conveying any suggestion of either unnaturalness or abnormality. Baby Number Thirty, in our four-month series, presented a clear case of generally advanced development. I examined him at a baby-welfare conference. He was not selected in any way; he comes from a home of average social and economic status. His developmental record at the age of four months, however, is sprinkled with double-pluses. He made a pronounced impression of "precocity." I could not elicit a reflex wink to a pencil, but on every other four-months developmental item he scored a definite success. He sat up with only slight support. He played with his hands; he played with a rattle; he closed in on a dangling object. He picked up a spoon from the table; he was more than ordinarily attentive to moving persons and other changes in his environment; he cried at the withdrawal of his toy; he reacted vigorously to the table edge. His mother declares he held his head up earlier and more vigorously than did her other children. Indeed she confessed, "I think he is too fresh for four months!"

A week later she wished us to examine the child again, for she knew he had made progress in the interval. This was no doubt a well-founded observation. Even ordinary four-months-old babies are undergoing such rapid development that weekly increments of this development are detectable. And if the child is truly precocious such an increment would be accentuated.

At the age of nine months this child was reëxamined by a clinical assistant, and again he made a pronounced impression of advanced development: His motor control, his alertness, his aggressiveness, his deftness and relatively intent adjustment to the situation before him were consistently above the normal nine-months level. He showed relatively mature restraint in the manner in which he handled the spoon; he made a persistent effort to hold two cubes in one hand. He used two words in addition to 'dada'; he made scribble marks definitely superior to the nine-months staccato dots.

How shall we interpret the case before us? We cannot cast a horoscope; but are we to dismiss the case as simply an idiosyncracy in the developmental rate? If the four-months symptomatology has proved prognostically coherent with the nine-months symptomatology, why may not the present reactions also have a broad import for subsequent nine-year-old and even nineteen-year-old characteristics? We shall watch the career of this child with more than ordinary curiosity. We may, of course, find that the acceleration that made him definitely advanced at four months and nine months will not project itself into his total ensuing development. We may be dealing with special forms of prematurity which have no significant relation to endowment; but we may also be reckoning with premonitory symptoms of real superiority.

It has been suggested on the evidence of Pearson's Biography that Sir Francis Galton, between the ages of three and eight years, must have had an intelligence quotient not far from 200. Terman, who makes the suggestion, adds, "The significance of this will be apparent when we say that after diligent search, . . . including many thousands of children in scope, the highest I Q we found is 170." In other words, even while he was a pre-school child, little Francis was betraying psychologically the signs of future intellectual eminence.

When it is recalled that he knew his capital letters at twelve months, both of his alphabets at eighteen months, and could read a little book and write his name before he was three years old, it is fair to inquire whether these signs of eminence were not potentially discoverable in his very infancy. We shall spare the reader any detailed elaboration of the suggestion. It has amusing possibilities, not to say pitfalls.

Mark Twain once exploited this field of psychological speculation in a characteristic after-dinner speech in which he referred in a eulogistic manner to a certain prophetic episode in the infancy of General U. S. Grant. This was but another of Mark Twain's jokes but, like many of his jokes, it had a grain of seriousness.

It is reported that Olerich at two years, eleven months, read with force and expression any reading matter and at twenty months knew the digits and nine colors; B.F. became interested in a type-writer at the age of three years, learning to type in three months and through her typing to read; Norbert Wiener at the age of six read writings of Ribot and Darwin; Heinrich Heinken was taken before the King at fifteen months and said, "Permit me, sir, to kiss the hand of your majesty and the hem of your royal garment." John Stuart Mill read in Plato, Socrates, and Herodotus before the age of eight. There is also reported a girl who at the age of five and one-half years consecrated her life to Jesus and who at six expressed a disgust with worldly affairs. Samuel Rzeszewski, the chess prodigy, learned to play at the age of four and won the first game which he played against his father; a gifted juvenile (reported by Terman and Fenton) began to walk about in her walker at seven months and at nineteen months spoke clearly and knew the alphabet, and at twenty-two months enumerated birds up to twelve in a picture; at thirty-three months she composed little jingle rhymes and made up stories about rabbits, frogs, fish, and squirrels. Martha S., according to her father's report, was given a book and pictures at the age of nineteen months, knew small and capital letters thoroughly at twenty months and after a few days' instruction at that time began to pick out simple words from a printed page, and at the age of twenty-four months had a reading vocabulary of over two hundred words. Mozart wrote music as early as the ordinary child begins to write letters. Thomas Arnold of Rugby, as an infant, made such a creditable record for scholarship that when he was three years old his father presented him with Smollett's twenty-four-volume history of England.

The above diversified list of evidences of pre-school precocity gleaned from various sources indicates how hazardous it must be to generalize on this subject. Whatever future research may reveal concerning the normal and superior tempo of development, we shall probably find that the problem of precocity and genius subdivides itself into numerous individual clinical varieties. It may be that the infantile developmental tempo sometimes bears no embryological correlation to the later stages and manifestations of maturity. It may be that there are late autumnal varieties of genius whose light will be altogether concealed to diagnostic perception.

The problem of precocity and superiority, therefore, will always need clinical approach and clinical evaluation. Even assuming that precocity most frequently has a natural and wholesome character, we must still be on the lookout for partial and unbalanced forms of precocity and for pseudo-precocity. Precocity by induction opens up not only vistas of human betterment but also possibilities of developmental detriment.

In last analysis, each individual case of precocity constitutes a problem of mental hygiene and we shall have to acquire considerable wisdom before we venture upon ambitious programs in the field of infant training. This old question of how much and how little stimulation a child should have during the first months of his existence is one of serious import and one on which we need more scientific information than we now possess. We find in actual practice two extremes with respect to stimulation. On the one hand, we have the inexperienced mother who has heard that babies should not be tampered with and who, therefore, goes to great lengths to surround her child with tranquility and repose. This mother may not play with the child at all or permit him even to crawl about on the bed.

On the other hand we have the child who is the center of family attention and is almost continually stimulated by the attentive ministrations of a mother, a grandmother, and an elder sister or brother. We have seen a child whose tenseness and excitability might well be ascribed in part to such excess stimulation. Between this extreme and that of relative deprivation by isolation lies a hygienic mean.

The mental hygiene of precocity must consider not only the laws of nascency and timeliness but also balance of development and abnormal forms of partial precocity or prematurity. Frequently lack of integration disturbs the developmental harmony. The idiot savant, certain forms of dementia praecox, freakish prodigies, cases of precocious pubescence and progeria, although they have widely different etiologies, show vividly the marked degrees of imbalance which personality and capacity make-up may assume. Paradoxically enough, in certain pathological instances like progeria, symptoms of infantilism and senility may be present side by side in apparently inconsistent admixture. If there are any dangerous tendencies associated with so-called normal precocity, they may well arise out of comparable though milder forms of imbalance and disharmony.

Mental hygiene insists upon the importance of fundamental symmetry and balance of development. Take, for example, the priggish form of intellectual precocity which sometimes shows itself in an "only child" who has become somewhat victimized by the over-zealous ambitions of his parents. Adolescence may find such a boy awkward, self-centered, persistent, argumentative, factual. Ordinary boys of his age may be scuffing up the grass, playing violent football, taking long hikes, quarreling, making boyish blunders. The "only boy" finds prolonged exercise a bore, football too rough; moreover he is unduly scrupulous about his school work and his music practice; he has less time to waste. The boys of his age, however, find him out of their sphere and even out of their sympathy; they discern that he is naïvely simple in certain spots and supercritical in others. With all his primness and intellectual advancement he is not an all-round boy and may not be an all-round man because of fundamental discrepancies between the development of his intellectual traits and of his personality traits. From the standpoint of mental hygiene the full development of personality traits in the sphere of personal and social conduct constitutes an indispensable basis for psychological wholeness and health. If we find such clinical cases of imbalanced development at adolescence it is fair to ask whether the danger of initiating such imbalance may not arise anywhere in the pre-school period from the first year of infancy on.

How infant prodigies are produced is a developmental question which has by no means been finally answered and which probably has varying answers for different instances. Don was a remarkable dog who was trained to "talk" and had an articulation vocabulary of several words which he repeated on the vaudeville stage for $1,000 a week. Here was a canine prodigy. We are by no means certain that this dog was remarkably superior to other members of his species, but we do know that he lived most intimately in the house of a forester and was virtually a member of this household. Since his master and mistress lived in relative seclusion in the heart of the forest, he undoubtedly received a disproportionate amount of human attention and became highly conditioned with respect to human stimuli. It, therefore, happened that his mistress one day was surprised to observe that he was apparently attempting to pronounce the word "Kuchen," while begging for a piece to eat. Utilizing this chance observation, she initiated a course of special training which resulted in this marvelous and interesting achievement of the "talking dog."

Human prodigies sometimes take form in a comparable manner. Samuel R. must be classified as a chess prodigy. He lived very intimately in a chess-playing family who played an inordinate amount of chess because of prevailing war-time conditions. Whatever hereditary basis there may have been for his amazing chess strategy, this predisposition was very early conditioned and was crystallized because of his intimate association with the game before the age of three.

It has been suggested that even ordinary children might attain extraordinary mental development were it not for an almost universal psychological tabu with which we surround them. If this tabu, which is but another term to express the weight of inhibitory tradition, could be replaced by an equally incessant and powerful set of positive stimuli of suggestion then would the reservoirs of potential development be unlocked! In other words, the recipe for increasing the number of gifted children consists in the removal of inhibition, the gratification of the sense of power, and the abolition of the psychological tabu which thwarts initiative and impedes the onward course of development in ordinary children. According to this interpretation the factor of hereditary endowment is of secondary importance.

But how safe are these suggestions? May not the psychological tabu constitute one of those beneficial mores which the race has acquired because of its protective value for childhood? Pry apart the eyelids of the newborn rat, let in the daylight and the retina will develop more speedily than if the lids had remained closed and allowed to open naturally. This is a tangible bit of evidence which demonstrates the pliability of developmental mechanics, but it contains no convincing argument in favor of pre-natural stimulation. Certain psychological arguments which have been advanced in favor of systematic intellectual training in infancy have a similar plausibility and need very cautious scrutiny. Dr. T. Williams has said, "Learning to like to think is of extreme importance in the attainment of genius known as precocity." Sidis has said, "The child is a thinking animal." "Learning should begin as soon as he learns to talk." "There is no danger of overtaxing his mind. The effect will be to develop and strengthen; it will be accustoming him to make habitual use of latent energy which most people never utilize at all."

These statements ought not to be construed too forcibly out of their proper context, but they reveal a philosophy of infantile education which is at variance with at least two of the maxims of Rousseau, who said: "The most important thing (in education) is to lose time, not to gain it." "A virtue prematurely taught sows the seed of a future vice."

G. Stanley Hall in equally skeptical terms has said "every encroachment upon the liberty of a child has a certain presumption against it, and the only justification lies in necessity." He has also suggested that there is a racial, if not an individual hazard in the policy of drawing too prematurely on the before mentioned unlocked reservoirs of latent energy. Burnham, with similar conservatism, suggests that the best guarantee of normal maturity is normal immaturity.

Being adults with imperfect, distorted, and frequently rationalizing memories of childhood, the presumption always is that we know more about maturity than we do about immaturity. In the intellectual and moral fields of development we have a clearer conception of what is normative and normal for the complete, matured stages than for the stages of immaturity. It follows that we ought to at least be extremely cautious in our philosophy of infant education. When we have more insight into the characteristics of immaturity our philosophies will have a sounder foundation; because, if in the name of education we do violence to the laws of immaturity, we endanger the normality of maturity itself.

The above comments on the pedagogical aspects of precocity do not pretend to deal comprehensively with the mental hygiene of this subject. They are offered by way of warning to suggest the risks that we take on the basis of our present inadequate knowledge. It would be misleading, however, to imply that precocity in itself is necessarily unwholesome or unnatural. It may be fully as natural and as lawful as so-called average development and may simply be one biological manifestation of an evolutionary prolongation of infancy. It may be that infancy is not only prolonged by a widening of the span of development, but also by increased concentration of development in the first portion of this span.

Instead of concluding with these general observations we shall summarize the evidences of superior and correlated precocious development in the pair of twins referred to in the previous chapter.

A complete family chart of the twin sisters A and B would show evidence of superior endowment in the immediate ancestry on both the maternal and paternal sides. Scientific and linguistic ability of high order and physical energy are some of the traits which are found in the two immediate generations. The trait of twinning also probably has a hereditary basis in this instance; for the mother also bore two boys, twins, who died in infancy.

Their sisters A and B were born six years later, by Caesarian section, somewhat prematurely, weighing respectively 4½ and 5½ lbs. They thus escaped some of the hazards and strains which may accompany birth.

Their prematurity did not hinder precocity. At any rate, they very early showed unmistakable signs of more than ordinary alertness and attainment. At six months A startled her mother by rising suddenly into a sitting position in the mother's lap. Very soon after this B showed the same capacity. At 11 months they had both begun to walk and talk; indeed they were talking in sentences, such as, "I see you, Auntie Tees." They spoke clearly with less than the usual infantile lisping; and, according to report, with more than the usual degree of purposive, voluntary speech imitation. In October, 1915, at the age of three they began the study of French, and in less than a year (by April 1916) they were reading elementary English, French, and Esperanto. Their mother was a very constant companion and stimulated this development by the aid of plays and games, but the children needed no prodding. They were distinguishing parts of speech with the aid of a Teddy Bear at the age of four. Formal arithmetic was begun at the age of six, and in less than a year they were solving, mentally, problems in fractions and percentage. They entered Grade III at the same age, and now (at the age of nine) they are in Grade VII, doing Junior High School work. They are not prigs; they are attractive, animated, sociable children, with a bubbling sense of humor. They are popular with their playmates. They can take charge of a gymnasium class, in which most of the members are two or four years their seniors, and preserve excellent attention and discipline. They speak mature but not pedantic English, and they speak French with the fluency of a native. They have read Genesis in Italian and are now speaking a little Italian. They have read the Book of Knowledge in its entirety in French; and a year ago embarked on Russian. They play duets on the piano; but not with rare distinction. They swim; they ride horseback; they write jingles, and they read by the hour. Their school work does not tax them; they do not worry about it; and they are far from fastidious in regard to the form of their written work.

In this brief general review of their developmental history it is impossible to make any noteworthy distinctions between A and B. They have been inseparable. They have also been abreast in their accelerated development.

A table of mental and educational measurements and a graph of these measurements indicate the relative superiority of both of these children. We first examined them at the age of seven years when both children had an intelligence quotient of over 180. This is a highly exceptional rating. They had just completed the pre-school period of their development.

One of the most tangible and significant items in their pre-school history is that which refers to their precocious language development. Their ability at the age of eleven months to articulate clearly and intelligently, "I see you, Auntie" is equivalent to eighteen-months-old maturity in this field of behavior. We would not venture to calculate an I Q on the basis of this one shred of evidence, but if we did we should derive a quotient not inconsistent with that which they earn at the age of seven and eight.

We reëxamined these children at the age of eleven years and find the same evidence of mental vigor and of accelerated development. We believe that their tempo will project itself through the adolescent period, and by a backward logical reference we conclude that this same developmental tempo had been established before school entrance and was perhaps detectable even in the neonatal period.

CHAPTER 29

RETARDATION AND INFERIORITY

This problem is the converse of the one just considered. Or perhaps it would be scientifically more appropriate to say that it is but another phase of the one central problem of development. According to the law of parsimony, reinforced by the concept of evolution, we may well believe that the fundamental biological principles of development are essentially uniform and universal. They apply alike to animals and man, to idiots and to geniuses. The end products are enormously different, but the mechanics of production are essentially the same; and so far as possible we should look for common characteristics among all the multifarious expressions and deviations of development.

We would, therefore, not exaggerate unduly the difference between the subject matter of the present and the preceding chapter. In the one we speak of acceleration, in the other of retardation; but these are always relative terms. We shall make frequent reference to the normal in order to emphasize this relative and comparative aspect. Although we must record the qualitative behavior differences between normal and inferior grades of infancy, we ought to be equally ready to record all similarities and equivalences which assert themselves.

To make our discussion as concrete as possible we shall center it around a report of Benjamin D., whose development we were able to follow from the age of six months to two years. He typifies a definite though not extreme form of defective development. We shall bring him into comparison with a normal boy, David N. of exactly the same age, who it happens on two occasions (nine months and eighteen months) presented himself for developmental examination on the very same afternoon that his inferior contemporary was examined. These two cases are, therefore, taken from real life, but we have introduced sufficient (though inconsequential) disguise to conceal their identity. We have also introduced into the report, to refine the grades of comparison, an intermediate case which came to the clinic at about the same time. This intermediate boy is Oscar S.

The reader can easily keep these three boys distinctly in mind without confusion if he will note that the initial surname corresponds to the clinical classification of each boy. D stands for defective; N stands for normal, and S for subnormal. The term subnormal is designedly vague because we wish to have it correspond in the reader's mind to a borderline grade of mentality.

The central character and point of departure for discussion is Benjamin D. A few excerpts from the clinical memoranda will serve as a convenient introductory summary. It should be noted that Benjamin D. came to our attention in the first instance as a clinical and not as a research case. Four follow-up examinations were made. We quote from the successive memoranda:

Memorandum 1. This child was examined at the XYZ consultation center at the age of six months. He presents consistent symptoms of mental deficiency and has not fully attained the three-months level of development. The outlook is doubly unfavorable because of the mother's mental status. We examined the mother on November 4, 1922, at which time the following report was made: "This girl has an intelligence age of only 9½ years and an intelligence quotient of 60. Although she is able to write a simple letter and shows some skill in arithmetical operations, she gives ample evidence of being defective in general intelligence. We diagnose her as being definitely feeble-minded. She will be able to carry on outside an institution only under very favorable circumstances of environment and supervision. She lacks sufficient mental competence to manage a home or to properly care for her child. She will undoubtedly come to grief again if she is expected to shift for herself. For her own safety and that of society, commitment to an institution should be considered."

Memorandum 2. This baby was brought to our clinic for developmental examination when he was nine months of age. We had seen him previously at the age of six months and had suspicions in regard to his mental status at that time. We find that these suspicions were justified because B at the age of nine months is unable to sit up without support. He does not maintain normal head posture; is lacking in normal leg reactions; does not reach for an object; and in most respects is at a developmental level of about four months. This represents a retardation of approximately five months which, at his tender age, is very serious if it is a constitutional form of retardation, as we believe. He is not likely to outgrow this retardation and, if he maintains his present rate of development, he may be fully four years retarded at the age of ten years. We would, therefore, diagnose him as being mentally deficient with an outlook similar to that of his mother.

Memorandum 3. Benjamin D. was reëxamined at the age of eighteen months. The results of the reëxamination confirm the diagnosis which was reported previously. We find that this boy is now developmentally at the nine-month level. This means that he has made consistent progress since we first saw him at the age of six months but this has been an absolute and not a relative improvement. He should be reëxamined next autumn when he is two years of age.

Memorandum 4. Benjamin was two years old today and reappeared for his fifth periodic examination. It is interesting to note that with each reexamination he seems more defective than he did before; but this is an illusion; for the rate of his mental growth is consistent. Developmentally he is now at the one-year level.

The result of the five successive developmental examinations indicated above are plotted on the accompanying developmental chart (Figure 157). It will be noted that there is considerable consistency in the ratio between the chronological age and developmental status ascertained at each examination.

The photographs, pages 343–51, furnish a basis for developing a concrete picture of the developmental progress of this instructive case. We introduce him as he was at the age of nine months. At that time he was a comely, smiling baby, apparently of a most amiable disposition. Dressed in his baby finery he made a very good impression and gave no obvious indication of his developmental deficiency.

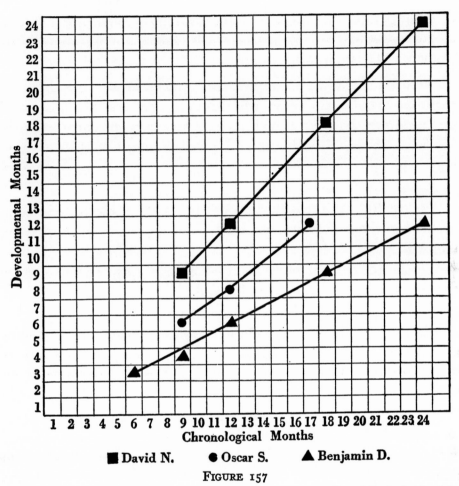

FIGURE 157

Chart showing the relative developmental status of David N , Oscar S , and Benjamin D., at 6, 9, 12, 18 mos., and 2 yrs. Five developmental examinations were made of Benjamin; three of Oscar; four of David.

The following paragraphs refer to the accompanying illustrations and will summarize better than extended description the changes in behavior which manifest themselves at nine months, twelve months and eighteen months. (Figures 158–191.)

Figure 158. This shows Benjamin D. in a dorsal position. The independent mobility of the index finger is nicely shown. He made gross random movements of the arms when the bell was offered to him but he did not make definite reaching movements. This re-action is really of four-months maturity and indicates the incipient eye-hand coördination characteristic of that level.

Figure 159 shows Benjamin D. propped up in sitting position and indicates that he will follow with his eyes a red rod which is moved up and down, back and forth, but he makes no reaching response. He reacts in this situation much as a four-months-old baby would react, though it must be remembered that he was nine months of age when the picture was taken.

Figure 160 indicates that he will not make a reaching response even when the rod is brought very definitely within his visual and motor scope.

Figure 161 shows, however, that he will grasp and handle the rod if it is actually placed in his hands.

Figure 162 clearly shows the defectiveness of his body-postural and head-postural control. He is manifestly attending to the en-amel saucer but in spite of its size and brilliance he does not seize it.

Figure 163. However, when he is held in the lap and brought near the table edge, he will lay hold of the edge of the saucer and rock it up and down with mild rhythmic motion. This response represented the acme of his behavior capacity at this examination.

Figure 164 shows his lack of reaction to a pellet placed before him.

Figure 165 shows that he makes a mild pushing response when his feet are allowed to touch the table surface. The picture, how-ever, reflects clearly the incompleteness of his neuro-muscular development when viewed in terms of nine-months maturity. The wobbly, yielding, molluscous impression which he made when he was carried in our arms reinforced this impression of immaturity and retardation.

*   *   *

Three months elapse, and Benjamin D. becomes chronologically one year of age. The scene changes and the next group of photographs faithfully portrays this improvement. He is now a vigorous, reactive baby and if one will generously forget that Benjamin D. is now one year old our subject will do admirably well for a six months old baby. The pictures speak for themselves but we add a few comments.

Figure 166 shows how well he now sits up. He maintains posture with slight support and can, indeed, sit alone for a moment if he is placed in a very favorable position. Note how definitely and vigorously he now reaches for the rod.

Figure 167 shows, however, that he will fall over in the sitting position unless he is propped or held.

Figure 168 shows a definite reaching response to the enamel saucer which previously did not stir him to acquisition.

Figures 169, 170, and 171 show how persistently he reaches when a coveted object is brought in his scope or threatens to be taken from him.

Figure 172 shows that he will even look for a fallen object which he can no longer see. It is evident that three months of time have added much to his capacity in the general field of prehension.

Figures 173, 174, 175, and 176 also show a comparable increase with respect to playful manipulation of an object. The object in this case is a spoon which he brings into exploratory use.

Figures 177 and 178 show how vigorously he crumples paper in his play.

Figure 179. He turns his head promptly and definitely to listen to the ringing of a bell.

Figure 180 clearly shows his ability to hold two cubes, one in either hand, with evident interest in a third proffered cube. His incidental attainment of thumb opposition is clearly shown in this picture. He presently drops one cube to attain the third cube, but this must be left to the reader's imagination.

Figure 181. The facial expression in this picture reveals the vitality and emotional vigor which the child had attained at this age.

Taken in the aggregate these pictures make a very favorable impression with respect to the reactiveness and adaptiveness of this child. Indeed, taken on their own merits they convey a consistent impression of normality, and the reader will be inclined to conclude that the child is in fact normal; but this assumes that the reader will forget Benjamin D.'s chronological age, and this is the very consideration which the reader must not forget. Developmentally Benjamin D. is approximately at the six-months level, but he is a year old.

*   *   *

The earth had completed half of its circuit around the sun before the next group of photographs was taken. At the age of eighteen months we note the following changes.

Figure 182. Benjamin D. now sits up without support.

Figure 183. He makes no effort to stand alone, though he can support his weight momentarily if he leans against a chair. The incompleteness of his postural control, which is but one gross index of his neuromuscular retardation, is clearly shown in this picture.

Figure 184 shows a lack of locomotor response when placed prone on the floor. He does not wriggle, crawl, or hitch.

Figure 185. He notices a pellet placed upon the table and is able to pick it up, but even in this reaction he has not attained complete nine-months maturity. His whole hand participates in the prehension. The response, however, is definitely above the six-months level and may be described as an imperfect nine-months response.

Figure 186. He still plays vigorously with paper but does not unwrap a cube.

Figure 187. He still bangs with a spoon.

Figures 188 and 189 indicate that he plays in a manipulatory manner with cup and cube.

Figures 190 and 191 show that his reaction to cup and spoon has lost some of its previous naïveté and that he will place either to the mouth in a manner which is eloquent of long previous training. He makes swallowing reactions when the cup is in his mouth although the cup is empty.

Again this group of pictures conveys a relatively normal impression, but the aspect of normality disappears when we are reminded that the subject is eighteen months of age. Perhaps he "seems" less normal than he did at twelve months; but that is only seeming. He is the same child.

* * *

On the very afternoon of the eighteen-months developmental examination there reappeared at the clinic a normal eighteen-months old baby, David N., whom we had seen under similar circumstances when he and Benjamin D. alike were nine months of age. On both occasions David threw Benjamin D. into dark shadows of contrast. At nine months when Benjamin D. was inert in the presence of toys David N. was active, alert, vigorous, engaging, and unquestionably normal. He (David) sat up without support and maintained an erect posture of the head while Benjamin D. was flaccid even in supporting hands. David N. was observant, eager, attentive, reaching for objects with directness, judgment, and persistence. He recovered a cube concealed under a cup. He picked up a pellet with fine prehension. He was emotionally well poised and showed excellence of personality make-up in his whole demeanor.

The best that we can say for Benjamin D. is that now at eighteen months he begins to approximate what David was at nine months and there perhaps we ought to allow the matter to rest. But when Benjamin was eighteen months old David N. also was eighteen months of age and, in justice, we must ask what was David doing *then?* He was walking all about the clinic, exploring its corners, exploiting its toys, placing geometric forms in a form-board, drawing vertical and horizontal lines, naming objects in pictures, beginning to build constructively with blocks and beginning to play dramatically with a clown-doll.

The developmental status of Benjamin D. and the developmental status of David N. are brought into parallel comparison in the accompanying tables. The accompanying photographs of David N. will help to personalize these data. (Figures 223–226.)

* * *

More briefly we wish to bring into this comparison Oscar S., whose developmental status at twelve months approximated the status of Benjamin D. at eighteen months. The photographs of this child at twelve months may be brought into comparison with those of Benjamin D. at the same age. Whether classified on the basis of developmental rate or attained developmental status it is evident that Oscar S. falls in an intermediate position between Benjamin D. and David N. (Figure 192–222.)

Oscar S. was examined when he was nine months, twelve months, and eighteen months of age. On the first of these examinations he secured a developmental rating of six months and on the second rating of nine months minus. We have a rather complete photographic record of this "improvement." Two series of photographs are assembled side by side so that Oscar S. may be brought into comparison with himself at these two ages. His developmental level at the age of nine months was six; and at twelve months it was nine. He is portrayed in identical situations and the reader can readily conduct his own comparisons. In three instances we have added for further comparison, pictures of Oscar S. at the age 18 months, when developmentally he was at the twelve-months level.

Oscar has a delightful personality, and we shall be duly cautious about specific prognostications. That we did him no injustice by rating him, when a year old, on a nine-months schedule is shown by the symmetry and the completeness of his "failures" when he is rated on a twelve-months schedule. Although it was supererogatory, we applied the latter schedule and secured

an almost unbroken series of failures. In only a few items did
he score a success. These failures are indicated in bold italics
on the subjoined schedule.

DEVELOPMENTAL SCHEDULE   YALE PSYCHO-CLINIC

Date............   TWELVE MONTHS   No.............

Name: OSCAR S. Age *12 mos.*

	Developmental Items	Rating	Responses and Personality Reaction
M15	Stands with help C; alone A.	**C**	Needs considerable support.
M25	Makes stepping movements C.	**C**	....
*M26	Walks with help B; alone A ..	**B**	....
M20	Can creep C; can climb B+.	**C**	Moved slightly backward in prone position on slippery table.
....			
....			
*L11	Says three words C; four B; five A+	**C**	*Dada* only.
			....
P41	Plays purposefully with cup, spoon, plate C	C	....
			....
P41	Plays with blocks B	**B**	Simple manipulation — no combining.
A23	Builds tower of two B+; three A	**B+**	No attention to model or demonstration.
*M35	Takes third cube without dropping B.................	**B**	Barely accepts 3rd on dropping.
M34	Inhibits hands to mouth B ..	**B**	....
A31	Secures covered cube C......	**C**	Attention to cup.
P41	Puts cube in cup (play) A...	**A**	....
A40	Puts cube in cup (commission) C	**C**	....
			....
A41	Cup or plate A+............	**A+**	....
*M40	Scribbles spontaneously A; imitation B................	**B**	Holds pencil and marks on paper merely result of manipulation.
A32	Unwraps cube B+...	**B+**	....
A18	Purposeful reaction to paper C	**C**	....
A15	Dangling object; pulls down C; uses string B	**C** **B**	....

DEVELOPMENTAL SCHEDULE   YALE PSYCHO-CLINIC—Continued

	Developmental Items	Rating	Response and Personality Reaction
A16	Reaches for string B.........	B	....
A52	Form-board; circle A; shown B	B	No combining of material.
M32	Secures pellet, fine prehension C......................	C	But by no means immediately.
	Picks up shot—puts in bottle (command) (imitation), removes imitatively	..	Definite interest and attempt to secure shot.
A21	Rings bell imitation B.......	B	....
A22	Hits rubber doll A	A	Simply squeezed.
A21	Imitates rattle of spoon in cup B......................	B	....
*A50	Performance box: rod in hole B	B	Interest in edge of box.
M34	Preference for one hand B	B	Right, but easily diverted to left. No protest if it is withheld.
P43	Plays with mirror image B. ..	B	Evident pleasure in image in mirror.
P31	Asks for things at table: pointing A; by name A+	A	....
L20	Adjusts to words C..........		....
P16	Inhibits on command B	B	....
P22	Bowel control A+...........	A+	Regularity increasing.
P23	Bladder control A+.........	A+	....
P35	Asks for toilet A+..........	A+	....
P20	Tries to put on shoes B......	B	....
P21	Uses spoon A..............	A	....

The three-column table on page 341 brings out an interesting developmental similarity between David N., Oscar S., and Benjamin D., when they were respectively 9, 12, and 18 months of age. Their successes and failures on the nine-months schedule are much alike. The failures are indicated in italicized letters.

It may be said that all three boys make a relatively good rating on this schedule. David shows no retardation; Oscar shows a retardation of 3 months; Benjamin, a retardation of 9 months.

Developmental Similarity of David N. (Age 9 mos.); Oscar S.
(Age 12 mos.); Benjamin D. (Age 18 mos.)

	NINE-MONTH LEVEL	David N. Age 9 months	Oscar S. Age 12 months	Benjamin D. Age 18 months	*=Ratings Equal
	Developmental Items	Rating	Rating	Rating	
M14	Sits alone C....................	C	C	C	*
M25	Makes stepping movements B....	B	*B*	*B*	..
M15	Stands with help A...	A	*A*	A	..
M26	Walks with help A	*A*	A	A	*
M20	Creeps or hitches A	A	*A*	A	..
P41	Pats table (prompt adjustment)..	B	B	B	*
A17	Exploratory manipulation: spoon	B	B	B	*
P41	Bangs spoon C..................	C	C	C	*
A16	Reaches directly: spoon C; string B	C	CB	C	*
A30	Fallen spoon: looks for C........	C	C	C	*
M35	Holds two cubes C; drops for third	B	B	B	
	B; accepts third A............	*A*	*A*	*A*	*
M33	Inhibits hand to mouth B+......	*B+*	B+	B+	..
A31	Lifts cup C; secures cube A.....	A	C	C	..
M34	Manipulates with one hand C. ..	C	C	C	*
P42	Puts cube in cup (play) A+.... .	*A+*	*A+*	*A+*	*
A40	Puts cube in cup (commission) A+........		*A+*	*A+*	..
M36	Releases cube in cup A..................		*A*	A	..
A20	Imitates spoon in cup A		*A*	..	
M40	Scribbles imitatively A+	*A+*	*A+*	*A+*	*
A32	Unwraps cube A+.............;....	*A+*	*A+*	*A+*	*
A18	Purposeful reaction to paper B ..	B	....	B	..
M32	Secures pellet C; prehension B ..	B	B	CB	..
A15	Dangling ring grasps above head C	C	C	C	*
	pulls down B; regard for string A;	B	B	B	*
	persistent reaching B	B	B	B	*
A21	Rings bell A............	A	*A*	A	..
P13	Reacts to mirror image B +.....	B+	A	..	..
L10	*Mama, dada,* or equivalent B....	*B*	B	B	..
L11	One other word A; two A+.....	*A*	*A*	*A*	*
L20	Adjusts to words B+	..	..	..	..
P14	Waves *bye-bye* B+; says *bye-bye* A+	B+	*B+*	*B+*	

The sceptical and the over-optimistic reader will insist that we raise a question whether the present retardation of Benjamin D. and Oscar S. will not be outgrown. If we raise this question we also ought to ask with equal seriousness whether the present wholesome normality of David N. will not, with the lapse of time, wither and fade. If developmental rate is a matter of caprice these are legitimate questions. If, however, developmental rate is fundamentally lawful we must conclude that the rate of progress which these infants have thus far shown is broadly prognostic of a rate and ratio of development which they will maintain throughout their infancy.

One other question remains for brief consideration. Is the actual chronological length of the period of infancy destined to be different for these three children? This question is, of course, too difficult to permit of precise answer. Studies of physical growth indicate that in general normal individuals grow somewhat longer, both from the standpoint of stature and of time, than do defective individuals as a group. It also appears that when large numbers are considered that the highest-grade defectives grow for somewhat longer physically than do the lowest-grade defectives, but the temporal differences in the length of the period of infancy do not appear to be nearly as great as do the psycho-developmental differences. In approximate terms, therefore, we may venture to believe that chronologically the duration of infancy will not be markedly different for Benjamin D. and Oscar S. and David N. The rates of development, however, within this chronological span of immaturity will be different because of the fundamental differences in endowment. There is approximately less necessity for nature to make haste in the case of Benjamin D. because she has bestowed upon him a smaller legacy than upon his more fortunate contemporaries. Even at eighteen months this discrepancy is palpably revealed. David N. has not only climbed higher but he has traveled faster.

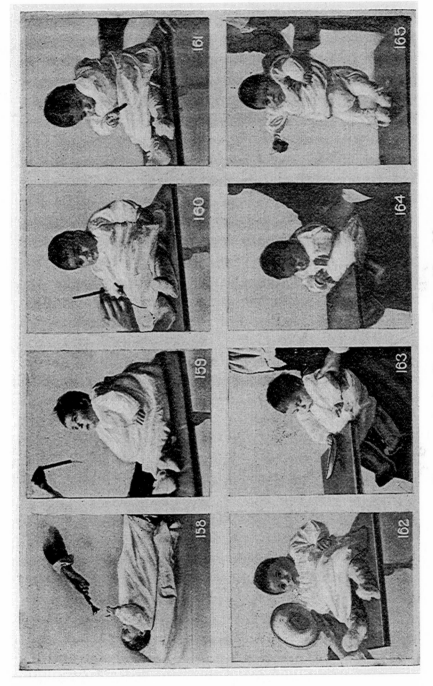

FIGURES 158-165. BENJAMIN D. AT NINE MONTHS
(For detailed comments on photographs, see text.)

343

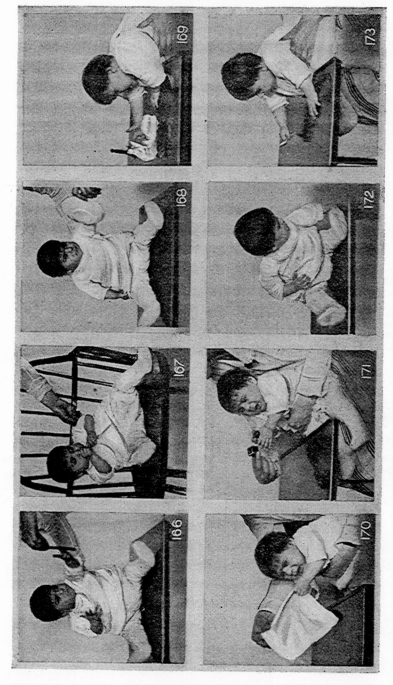

FIGURES 166–173. BENJAMIN D. AT TWELVE MONTHS

344

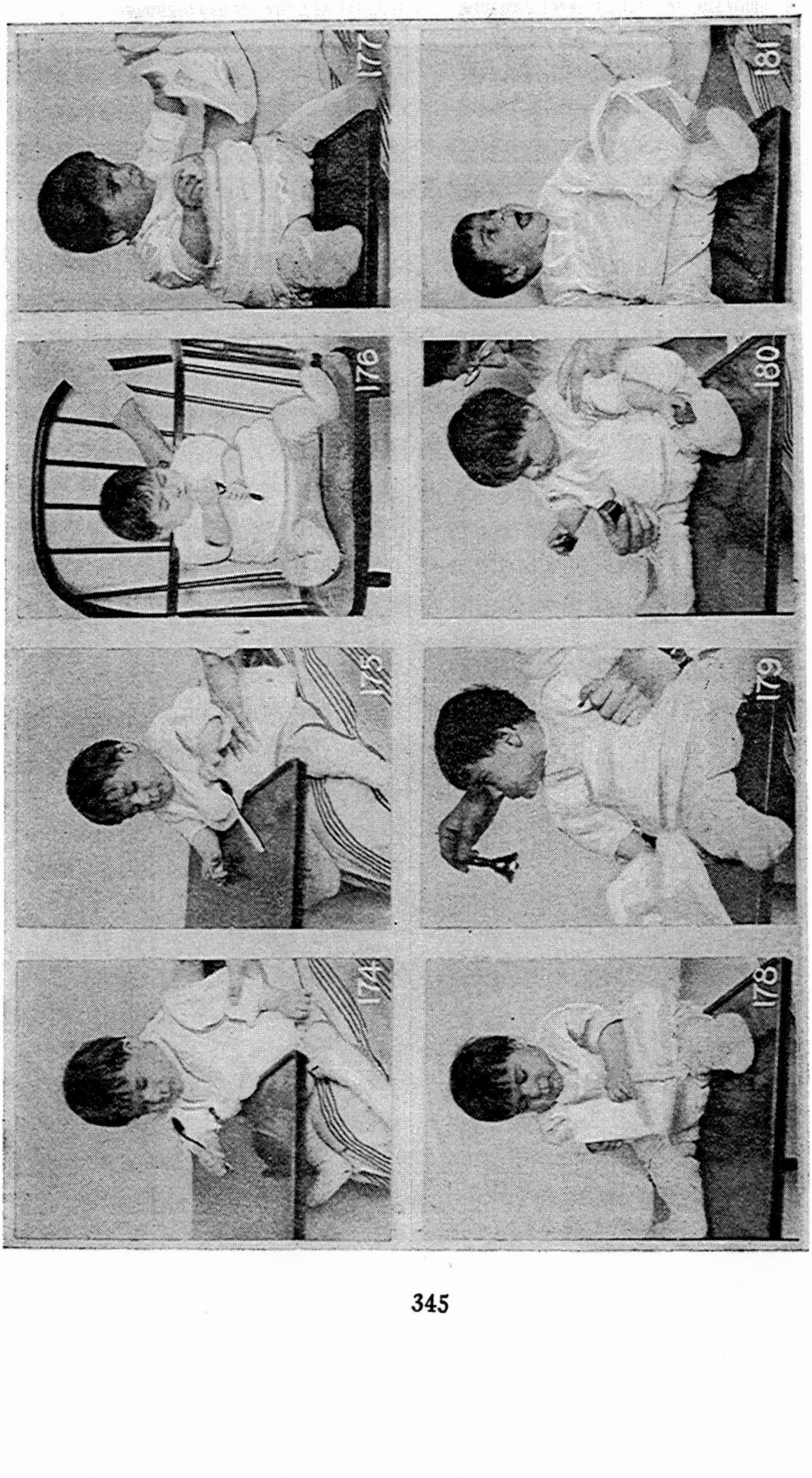

FIGURES 174-181. BENJAMIN D. AT TWELVE MONTHS

345

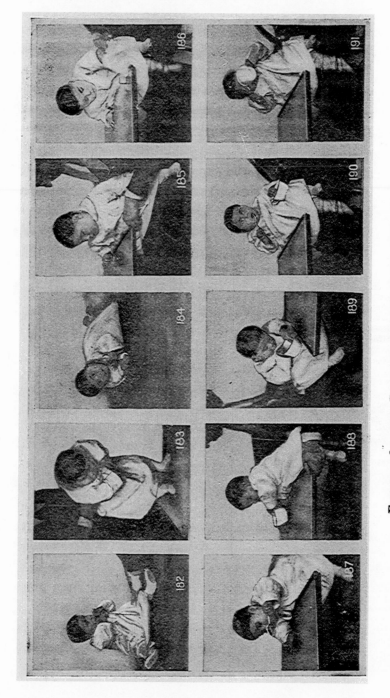

FIGURES 182–191. BENJAMIN D. AT EIGHTEEN MONTHS

346

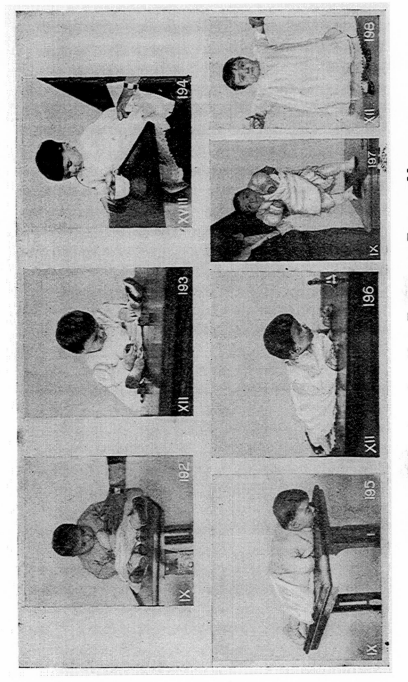

FIGURES 192–198.   OSCAR S. AT NINE, TWELVE, AND EIGHTEEN MONTHS

(The pictures are arranged to facilitate comparison of behavior at different stages.   The Roman numerals indicate the chronological age.)

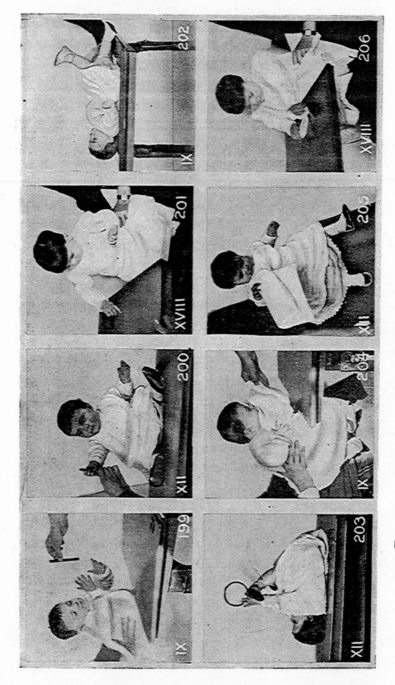

FIGURES 199–206.   OSCAR S. AT NINE, TWELVE AND EIGHTEEN MONTHS

348

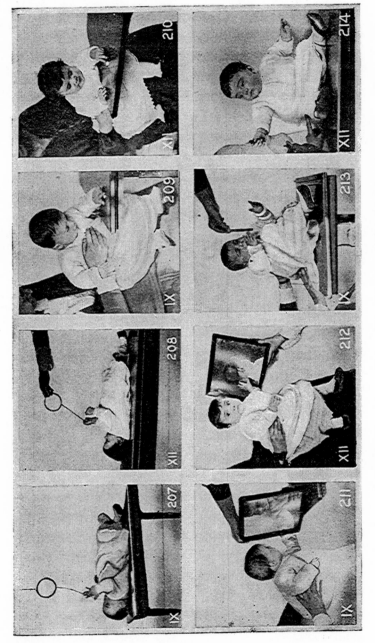

FIGURES 207–214. OSCAR S. AT NINE AND TWELVE MONTHS

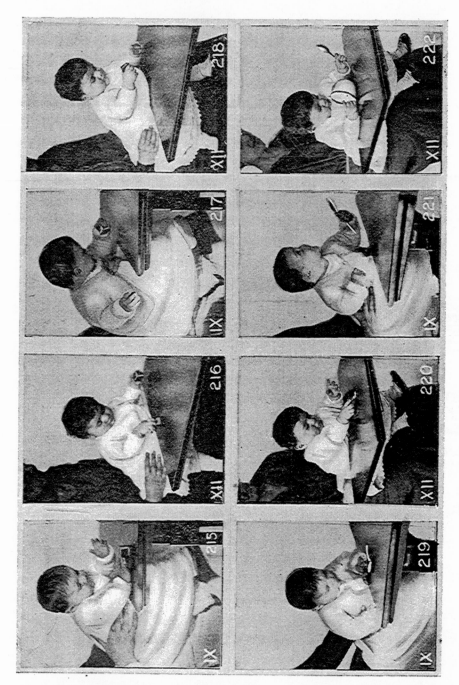

FIGURES 215–222. OSCAR S. AT NINE AND TWELVE MONTHS

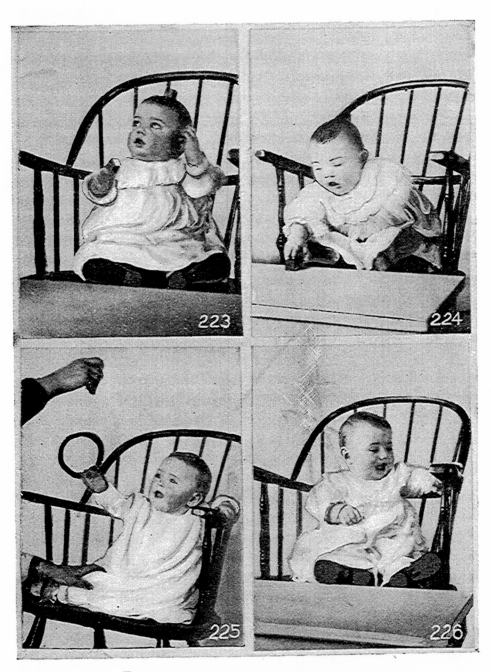

FIGURES 223–226.   DAVID N. AT NINE MONTHS

PART FOUR

DEVELOPMENTAL DIAGNOSIS AND SUPERVISION

CHAPTER 30

NORMATIVE AND CLINICAL PSYCHOLOGY

The concept of Developmental Level is a very ancient one. It is so ancient and commends itself so strongly to common sense that we may perhaps ascribe to it a measure of soundness as well as venerability.

In the scriptures it is told that the ear bringeth forth fruit of itself:—first the blade, then the ear, after that the full corn in the ear. But even before scriptural times the judgment of common sense must have recognized in a comparative way different stages of developmental maturity in children as well as in plants. It is very interesting to note how frequently untutored mothers, who have never heard of Binet and mental ages, will anticipate a diagnosis with some shrewd remark in which they say of a defective child: "He is still only a baby" or "He is no more than my two-year-old baby" or "She acts like a five-year-old child."

Custom, rites, tabus, common law, and statutory law specify in multifarious ways responsibility and privileges in terms of age. This specification involves a fundamental recognition of the concept of developmental maturity, and it would make a revealing research if some erudite person could make for us a critical survey of how the factor of age has figured in human institutions.

Some time ago, when looking through some very dusty reports of legal decisions bearing on criminal responsibility, I came upon a most interesting and lucid discussion of the problem of mental age. This discussion may be found in Volume 39 of *Connecticut Reports*, 1873, Hartford. It is contained in a charge made by Judge J. Seymour in the case of The State *vs.* Harrison Richards, from which a few quotations follow:

355

What degree of mental incapacity constitutes dementia and renders a person not criminally responsible for acts otherwise criminal?

Information for burning a barn; brought to the Superior Court for Windham County and tried to the jury, at its August term, 1873, on the plea of not guilty, before *Seymour, J.*

The defence was that the prisoner had not sufficient mental capacity to be criminally responsible for the act. The charge of the judge, which sufficiently states the facts of the case, was as follows:

JUDGE SEYMOUR'S CHARGE

The evidence seems ample to warrant you in finding that the burning complained of was caused by the prisoner. Your attention has been turned mainly to the question whether the act was done with felonious intent charged, and this question depends mainly upon another, whether the accused has sufficient mental capacity to warrant us in imputing to him a felonious intent.

That he is considerably below par in intellect is apparent to us all. This is indicated by his countenance and general appearance.

The same thing is indicated by his extraordinary conduct at the fire. As the flames were bursting out he was seen on all fours crawling back from under the burning barn, with nothing upon him except his shirt and trousers. The day was excessively cold. He remained some half hour, thus scantily clothed, gazing stupidly at the blaze, until ordered into the house. All this took place in broad daylight, in plain view of Mr. Gallup's house. . . .

He is not a mere idiot, nor does he appear to be a lunatic. He suffers from want of mind rather than from derangement or delusion, and the question is whether the want of mind is such as to entitle him to acquittal on the ground of what in law is termed *dementia.*

This enquiry is attended with inherent difficulties. Our knowledge of our own minds is imperfect; our knowledge of the precise mental condition of another is necessarily still more imperfect. . . .

Our principal embarrassment arises however from the want of a definite measure of mental capacity. Eminent judges and learned commentators have attempted to furnish rules and tests for the guidance of triers in cases of this kind, but upon examination these rules and tests turn out to be imperfect and unsatisfactory. . . .

And this leads me to refer to the rule adopted by an eminent English judge, Lord Hale. He reasoned that, inasmuch as children under fourteen years of age are *prima facie* incapable of crime, imbeciles ought not to be held responsible criminally unless of capacity equal to that of ordinary children of that age.

If this test be adopted the prisoner will upon testimony be entitled to an acquittal. The principal witnesses for the prosecution say that he is inferior in intellect to children of ten years of age, and several very intelligent witnesses for the defence testify that they are acquainted with many children of six years who are his superiors in mental capacity.

I am inclined to recommend Lord Hale's rule to your adoption, not however without qualifications which I think it important to observe.

And first, this test, like all others which I know of, is imperfect.

Probably no two of us have the same idea of the capacity of children of fourteen years of age, and then there is this further difficulty, that there can be no accurate comparison in detail between the healthy and properly balanced, though immature, mind of a child, and the unhealthy, abnormal, and shrivelled intellect of an imbecile. The comparison therefore is only of the general result in their respective appreciation of right and wrong and of consequences and effects.

This further consideration ought also to be borne in mind, that though in modern times persons under fourteen are seldom subjected to the penalties of the criminal code, yet in law children between seven and fourteen may be subjects of punishment if they are shown to be of sufficient capacity to commit crimes. In applying Lord Hale's rule therefore, the child to be taken as the standard, ought not to be one who has had superior advantages of education, but should rather be one in humble life, with only ordinary training.

And after all, gentlemen, you see that I can furnish you with no definite measure of mental capacity to apply to the prisoner. The whole matter must be submitted to your sound judgment. You will say whether the prisoner has such knowledge of right and wrong, and such appreciation of the consequences and effects of his acts, as to be a proper subject of punishment. Opinions on this subject have been expressed by most of the witnesses who have testified. These opinions depend for their value mainly upon the facts with which they are connected. You have the advantage of being able to compare with each other all the facts which have been brought to your notice bearing upon the prisoner's mental condition You will look carefully at all these facts. The history of the prisoner's life is somewhat significant. From early childhood it has been spent in alms-houses, subjected to constant constraint. In the most ordinary acts of his life he has been governed by the superior will of others to whose care he has been committed. He has, it appears, been seldom left to the free guidance of his own judgment. When so left, he seems to have acted without forecast, under the pressure of immediate wants and impulses.

If you acquit the prisoner on the ground of want of mental capacity you will so say in your verdict, in order that the prisoner may in that event have the benefit under our statute of a home where he will be kindly cared for, but kept under such restraints as to prevent his doing injury to the persons or property of others.

The jury acquitted the prisoner, stating in their verdict that the acquittal was on the ground of want of mental capacity.

If proof were necessary this interesting document would prove that the concept of mental age antedated Binet and the psychology of Binet. It was Binet's distinction that he laid hold of a concept which common sense (and common law) had already achieved, and refined it for purposes of scientific application. He created a method, but not a new idea.

The task of clinical psychology is to aid common sense, not to displace it altogether. Indeed, if a Connecticut jury were to pass upon a similar case involving criminal responsibility the court would still be under the necessity of submitting the whole matter to the "sound judgment" of the jurors. Psychometry has not yet attained that pitch of perfection and range of application that a mental measurement can be accepted or utilized without a qualifying judgment.

If psychometric determinations, including intelligence ages and intelligence quotients, were not so liable to misuse, strictures would be gratuitous. But these numerical indicators have actually been incorporated into legislation, and into administrative regulations relating to the detection and care of the feeble-minded. For this reason it is not superfluous to insist that there is a difference between a mental measurement and a mental diagnosis.*

---

*I may cite an instance which recently came under my observation and which illustrates well the difficulties and disadvantages of precise I Q regulations to determine assignment to special classes, institutions, etc It happens that two dependent girls, who were sisters, came to the clinic one morning for mental examination; one proved to have an I Q of 69 and the other an I Q of 70 The assumption that this

There are few diagnostic methods which operate automatically. There are blood pictures and cardiograms which deliver an instantaneous, unequivocal classification of a disease; but the rule in medical diagnosis is that all clinical evidence must be weighed and interpreted. Even in the field of syphilography, where the delicacy of the Wassermann test is at the disposal of the physician, his judgment not only qualifies but sometimes supersedes or foreruns the test. If this is true in physical diagnosis it must be true in mental diagnosis. It must be doubly true in the present stage of psychological technique.

For reasons of this character we are obliged to make certain distinctions between psychometrics and clinical psychology. Clinical psychology is a form of applied psychology which attempts, through methods of measurement, analysis, and observation, to arrive at a true estimate of the mental make-up of an individual. It aims to interpret human behavior and to define its limitations and possibilities in relation to practical problems which require responsible diagnosis and a degree of prediction.

As soon as the element of responsible diagnosis is emphasized in psychological procedure, mental measurement, as such, becomes of secondary instead of primary importance. The mental measures merely provide the points of departure or the foil for the development of a discriminating judgment. The clinical or diagnostic attitude requires not only precision of measurement but productive interpretation. For this reason the competent clinical psychologist must amass a great deal of first hand experience with both normal and exceptional individuals. He must also organize this experience into working concepts which he can bring to bear both on the case

difference of one I Q. point established a real differentiation between these two girls is, of course, absurd As a matter of fact, all things considered, personality traits as well as mental quality and mental level, the girl with the lower I Q is superior to the girl with the higher I Q Yet, if a recent regulation of the institution for dependent children, recommended for these girls, is strictly enforced, the girl with 69 I Q cannot be admitted whereas her sister may Irrespective of the fact that these two girls ought not to be separated, this distinction operates in a very undesirable manner The I Q does not have sufficient clinical validity to be made the basis of administrative regulations.

as a whole and on its specific aspects. He can exercise discriminating judgment in cases requiring differential diagnosis only if he can bring lifelike standards of comparison to bear upon the problem at hand. These lifelike standards of comparison can not be compounded out of multiple individual measurements but must be the end product of his accumulated experience.

Psychoclinical diagnosis makes a constant demand upon a normative, comparative kind of thinking. The term normative may be used to define that type of psychology which systematically creates both objective standards and descriptive formulations for the purpose of estimating in a comparative manner mental capacities and potentialities. Clinical psychology may be defined as a normative psychology applied to developmental or behavior problems requiring interpretative diagnosis. This application of the term normative helps to preserve a distinction between clinical psychology and psychiatry. It also serves to emphasize the distinction between purely psychometric procedure and comparative, interpretative diagnosis. Normative psychology attempts to be objective, systematic, and orderly but does not confine itself to mathematically exact devices.

As a scientific objective, statistical refinement and mensuration can not be pushed too far; but in application they may be pushed too fast. This is particularly true with regard to the clinical psychology of infancy.

We must in the present immature stage of applied psychology supplement psychometric procedure with broader normative procedure. This is particularly true in the fundamentally important field of personality traits. We must be ready to laboriously accumulate data for the delineation of normative portraits of personality. Unless a discovery of fundamental importance is made, we must paint these normative portraits in the language of common sense and in nontechnical descriptions of the reactions of children to the ordinary domestic and social situations of life. Such descriptive formulations of personality development and of attention traits are necessary for clinical procedure.   They are indispensable for the clinical, child psychologist because he cannot make reliable estimates or recommendations concerning mental development unless he is in possession of lifelike standards.

CHAPTER 31

Developmental Schedules

In this chapter are assembled in order the set of ten developmental schedules which comprise the system of developmental diagnosis. The average number of items which appear on one schedule is thirty-five. These items are all described in detail in the previous section on norms and procedure. The items are arranged in practicable order for administration. Each item is specified by its appropriate alphabetical and numerical classification. In addition a letter rating is assigned to each item. The letter rating is based on the frequency with which the given item was found in the group of normative children at the age level in question. A+ represents a frequency of 1 to 20 per cent; A, a frequency of 20 to 50 per cent; B+, 50 to 65 per cent; B, 65 to 85 per cent; C, 85 to 100 per cent. In general, therefore, *B* ratings show average or representative characteristics; *A* ratings may indicate advanced development; *C* ratings are not of much importance for differential estimate except in cases of retardation. The general method of application of these schedules will be described in some detail in the following chapter on *Differential and Descriptive Diagnosis*.

A schedule covering the neonatal period is included. This is not strictly a normative schedule and the ordinary letter ratings are therefore omitted. Approximate nascent dates are assigned, w standing for week, m for month. This particular schedule may be used when a descriptive record of the developmental status of a child less than three months old is desired. It is intended, chiefly, to increase the detail of observation and of record in cases of retardation where the infant falls definitely below the scope of the four-months developmental schedule.

In all the record forms, not only is a space left for the letter ratings but a broad column is provided for descriptive and qualifying entries. This column should be freely used not only for recording personality traits expressed in adjectives but for describing actual bits or episodes of behavior. Procrastination is a serious vice in record taking. It is well to make the entry or at least the jotting during or immediately after the examination.

It is our practice to record negative as well as positive results. Failures are indicated by encircling the appropriate letter rating with a ring. For typographical convenience these failures are indicated by heavy faced italics in the records on pages 339–41. The final estimate of the case is developed by inspection of the whole record, supplemented with comparison and interpretation. The general rating of developmental status is expressed by the age level, shaded when necessary with plus and minus signs. "Low nine months" indicates a low average. "High nine months" indicates a high average. "Sub nine months" is inferior; "Advanced nine months" is accelerated or superior. Descriptive formulations must, however, be added to these bare expressions. The general rating should rest upon a weighting of the concurrent individual ratings. Clinical judgment must always be used. The general rating is not to be calculated in any mechanical way by simple summing of scores.

At this point it is well to warn the lay reader who attempts to apply the items of a developmental schedule that errors of interpretation are easily made. A difference of two weeks or a month may make a great deal of difference in the score or "the showing," in the first year or two, particularly in the field of language responses. Delay in walking may be due to rickets, not to subnormal intelligence. Facility in words does not always augur satisfactory personal habits. Some children, perhaps, develop more by spurts than others. There always are individual differences. The estimation of the developmental status of children is open to the same errors which are commonly made in the layman's estimate of nutritional status.

In all cases in which reëxamination is contemplated, the results of the developmental examination may be plotted on a special consecutive-record form, as shown in Figure 227. We use a two-page folder for this purpose, devoting the blank space opposite the rectangular plot to our descriptive summary, recommendations, and notation of items of follow-up interest. Half of this form is reproduced in the accompanying illustration. The lowest rectangle on the page is used for the first examination. The developmental items are indicated by their appropriate numerals and successes are plotted with dots, failures with crosses. Separate estimates for the four subdivisions of behavior may be made.

It will be noted that all of the developmental schedules are nearly of equal length; and that the items are sufficiently diversified and graduated to make each schedule within its scope a sliding scale. Adjacent schedules may be brought into play when necessary.

From a clinical point of view, the diagnosis of development is equally complicated at all levels. Surely we should not invest twelve times more time in the examination of a four-year-old child, because he is twelve times older than a four-months-old child. We should be ready if necessary to spend as much time and pains in examining the latter as the former. For this reason our general clinical procedure is essentially alike for all the age levels.

No. 1684 Name Benjamin D.	M Motor					L Language					A Adaptive Behavior										P Personal-Social					Estimated Developmental Status (4, 4+, 4-, etc.)
	1	2	3	4	5	1	2	3	4	5	1	2	3	4	5	6	7	8	9	0	1	2	3	4	5	
Develp. Level [18] (mos.) A+																										Ht. 35
A																										Wt. 26
B+																										
B		X						X				X														M 12
C																										L 12
[12] A+																										A 12
A	X												X											X X		P 12+
B+												X	X								X					
B		X X					X	X X			X	X			X											Age 24 Mos. Date 6/10/24
C	X												X X													
[12] A+																										Ht.
A																										Wt.
B+																										
B																										M 9-
C																										L 9
[9] A+														X X										X		A 9
A	X	X X	X								X X X														P 9+
B+			X																							
B		X X					X				X X									X					Age 18 Mos. Date 12/20/23
C	X	X X										X X							X			X		
[9] A+																										Ht.
A																					X					Wt.
B+																										
B																										M 6
C																										L ?
[6] A+	X	X										X														A 6
A		X X X									X									X					P 6
B+	X	X									X															
B		X X X									X X	X							X			X X		Age 12 Mos. Date 6/6/23
C	X	X										X												X		
[6] A+																										Ht. 23 in.
A																										Wt. 9 lb. 9 oz.
B+																										
B																										M 4
C																										L 4?
[4] (mos.) A+		X									X															A 4
A	X	X									X													X		P 4
B+												X														
B	X	X X			X						X X									X					Age 9 Mos. Date 3/4/22
C	X	X										X												X		

FIGURE 227. FOLLOW-UP FORM

Shows record of Benjamin D on four successive developmental examinations The failures on various developmental items are indicated by a cross (x); the successes by a dot ( ) In practice, the identity of each item may be shown by pencilling in its proper numeral This form may be printed as the left page of a two-leaf folder, using the blank opposite page for interpretative comment and analysis.

NEO-NATAL PERIOD

DEVELOPMENTAL ITEMS

Ma	Quickening (note prenatal week)	Aa	Blinks at sound
Mb	Sleep (note hours and regularity)	Ab	Averts or lifts head when constrained; averts head from strong light
Mc	Pupils contract and dilate (1d)	Ac	Gropes adaptively on loss of nipple
Md	Reacts to contact stimuli taste, smell, touch (1d)	Ad	Fixes eyes on objects (2w)
Me	Winks on touch of eyelash (1d)	Ae	Puts hand to mouth (1w)
		Af	Makes defensive hand movements
Mf	Respiratory reflexes: cough, sneeze, yawn (1d)	Ag	Follows moving light (1m)
Mg	Lifts head when prone (1w)	Ah	Reflex inhibition of activity on tactile stimulus (1m)
Mh	Purses lips on contact (1w)		
Mi	Stretches (1w)	Ai	Recognition responses (mother, bottle, etc.) (1-2m)
Mj	Toe extension reflex (2w)		
La	Cry: hunger, pain, sleepiness, wet, handling (1w), tears (1w)	Aj	Specific conditioned behavior
		Pa	Random play (hands, arms)
Lb	Vocalization: (1m) a, eh, oo (3m)	Pb	Startled when blanket is lifted
Lc	Attends to voice and music (1m)	Pc	Startled by loud sounds (1w)
		Pd	Quieted by voice (1m)
Ld	Gestures of negation, withdrawal, pain	Pe	Quieted by caress (1m)
		Pf	Quieted by picking up (2w)
Le	Smile (2m)	Pg	Sleep habituations
Lf	Socially stimulated smile (3m)	Ph	Food habituations
		Pi	Reactions to bath
Lg	Emotional facial reaction (1-2m)	Pj	Reactions to dressing and undressing

FOUR–MONTH LEVEL

DEVELOPMENTAL ITEMS

P11 Selective attention to face B

M10 Holds head erect C

M11 Resists head pressure B

M13 Back resistant C

M14 Tries to sit up C; sits with support A

*M12 Lifts head prone C; chest B

M20 Crawling reaction C; side to back C; back to stomach A

M24 Pushes with feet C

*L10 Vocalization B

A10 Follows moving persons C plate B

*A11 Blinks at sound C; at hand B; at pencil A+

P42 Turns head to voice C; to bell A

*M32 Hands react to table B

A13 Regards spoon B+

A16 Reaches for spoon A+

A13 Regards cube A

M31 Clasps cube C; picks up cube A+

M30 Resists rod withdrawal C

M31 Thumb opposition partial C complete A

M33 Hand to mouth C

*A15 Dangling ring: reacts C; closes in A

A12 Paper on face: reacts C; defensive hand A

P12 Anticipatory motor adjustment B

* * * * * * * *

P40 Laughs aloud B

*P41 Plays with hands C; scratches B; plays with objects B+

P10 Adaptation nursing C; recognition C

P40 Enjoys bath C

M23 Kicks feet in bath C; splashes hands A

P42 Music: attends C; stops crying A

SIX–MONTH LEVEL

DEVELOPMENTAL ITEMS

M10   Holds head erect C

*M15   Sits slight support B+; alone A+

M22   Rolls back to stomach B

M20   Creeps or hitches A+

M25   Makes stepping movements A

*P11   Shows consciousness of strangers B

M32   Hands react to table C

P41   Pats table B

*A17   Manipulates spoon, cup, saucer B; exploratory manipulations A

P41   Bangs spoon B

A16   Reaches directly spoon B

M34   Inhibits head and one hand A; manipulates with one hand A

A11   Blinks at pencil B

P42   Turns head to bell B

*A13   Regards cube C; regards pellet B+

M32   Secures pellet whole hand A; fine prehension A+

M32   Picks up cube B

*A31   Lifts inverted cup B; secures cube A+

A30   Fallen object: conscious of B; looks for A

M35   Holds two cubes B; drops one for third B+

M36   Releases objects: throws to floor A; drops into cup (imitation) A+

*A15   Dangling ring: closes in C; clasps B; above head B+; persistent reaching A

M34   Preference one hand A+

A18   Paper: crumples B; purposeful reaction A

P13   Reacts mirror images A

* * * * * * * *

P11   Expresses recognition B

P40   Frolics when played with B+

P41   Plays with objects C

M23   Splashes in tub B

P41   Casts objects for noise A

P42   Reacts to music: stops crying B; coos A; smiling, laughing B+

P30   Takes bottles in and out of mouth A

L10   Says *mama, dada,* or equivalent syllables A+

NINE–MONTH LEVEL

DEVELOPMENTAL ITEMS

M14 Sits alone C

*M25 Makes stepping movements B

M15 Stands with help A

M26 Walks with help A

M20 Hitches or creeps A

P41 Pats table (prompt adjustment) B

*A17 Exploratory manipulation spoon, etc., B

P41 Bangs spoon C

A16 Reaches directly spoon C; string B

A30 Fallen spoon: looks for C

*M35 Holds two cubes C; drops for third B; accepts third A

M33 Inhibits hand to mouth B+

A31 Lifts inverted cup C; secures cube A

M34 Manipulates with one hand C

P42 Puts cube in cup (play) A+

A40 Puts cube in cup (commission) A+

M36 Releases cube in cup (imitation) A

A20 Imitates spoon in cup A

M40 Scribbles imitatively A+

A32 Unwraps cube A+

A18 Purposeful reaction to paper B

*M32 Secures pellet C; fine prehension B

A15 Dangling ring: grasps above head C; pulls down B; regard for string A; persistent reaching B

A21 Rings bell A

P13 Reacts to mirror image B+ plays A

* * * * * * * *

*L10 *Mama, dada,* or equivalent B

L11 One other word A; two A+

L20 Adjusts to words B+

P14 Waves *bye-bye* B+; says *bye-bye* A+

P40 Frolics when played with C; plays peek-a-boo, pat-a-cake B+

P30 Puts bottle in mouth

P42 Reacts to music: dances B; coos B+

TWELVE–MONTH LEVEL
DEVELOPMENTAL ITEMS

M15   Stands with help C; alone A

M25   Makes stepping movements C

*M26   Walks with help B; alone A

M20   Can creep C; can climb B+

*L11   Says three words C; four B; five A+

P41   Plays purposefully, cup, spoon, plate C

P41   Plays with blocks B

A23   Builds tower of two B+; three A

*M35   Takes third cube without dropping B

M34   Inhibits hands to mouth B

A31   Secures covered cube C

P41   Puts cube in cup, (play) A

A40   Puts cube in cup (commission) C

A41   Box, cup or plate A+

*M40   Scribble spontaneously A; (imitation) B

A32   Unwraps cube B+

A18   Purposeful reaction to paper C

A15   Dangling object: pulls down C; uses string B

A16   Reaches for string B

A52   Form-board: circle A; shown B

M32   Secures pellet, fine prehension C

Picks up shot: puts in bottle (command), (imitation), removes imitatively

A21   Rings bell (imitation) B

A22   Hits rubber doll A

A21   Imitates rattle of spoon in cup B

*A50   Performance box: rod in hole B

M34   Preference for one hand B

P43   Plays with mirror image B

* * * * * * * *

*P14   Waves *bye-bye* B; says *bye-bye* or *hello* B+

P43   Plays *peek* or *pat-a-cake* C

P31   Asks for things at table: pointing A; by name A+

L20   Adjusts to words C

P16   Inhibits on command B

P22   Bowel control A+

P23   Bladder control A+

P35   Asks for toilet A+

P20   Tries to put on shoes B

P21   Uses spoon A

P42   Reacts to music; vocalization B

EIGHTEEN–MONTH LEVEL

DEVELOPMENTAL ITEMS

M26	Walks alone C		M42	Imitates vertical line A; horizontal A+
M20	Climbs stairs C		A50	Performance box: square A
P34	Climbs for objects A			
*L11	Says five or more words B		P22	Hits doll imitatively B
P31	Asks for things at table C; by words A		M36	Throws ball in box B
			L21	Pictures: points to 1 or 2 A; more A+
L14	Two or more words together A+		L12	Names one A; two A+
P41	Plays with cup and cubes B		L30	Picture II, names one object A+
*A23	Blocks: tower of 3 C; 4 A		A60	Names watch 4th view A+
A24	From model B; builds bridge A+		*P51	Points to one part of body B; two or more A
M25	Accepts fourth cube B			* * * * * * * *
A41	Places cube in cup, plate B+ box A		L40	Repeats things said A
			P14	Says *hello, thank-you* B
*A52	Form-board: circle B+; shown B; triangle A+; shown A; adapts circle A		*P16	Habitually inhibits certain acts B
			P49	Looks at pictures B+
M32	Picks up shot; puts in bottle (command), (imitation); removes pellet from bottle (imitation)		P44	Listens to stories with pictures A
			P52	Counts to two or three A+; part of alphabet A+
A27	Folds paper once A+		P22	Bowel control B
*M40	Scribbles spontaneously B; imitatively B		P23	Bladder control A
			P35	Asks for toilet A
M41	Imitates stroke B; differentiates A		P20	Puts on shoes A+
			P21	Uses spoon well B

TWO-YEAR LEVEL

DEVELOPMENTAL ITEMS

L14	Speaks sentences B
L15	Pronouns, past, plural A+
P17	Tells experiences B
P31	Asks for things at table by name B
	Plays with blocks
*A23	Builds tower of four B more B+
A24	Bridge A
*A41	Puts cube in cup, plate, box B
A70	Number: "just one" differentiated A
*A52	Form-board: solved in time B; no errors A Adapts: in time B+; no errors A+
M32	Shot in bottle: (command) removes from (imitation)
A27	Folds paper once B; square fold A+
*M43	Drawing: copies circle A+
M42	(imitatively) vertical B; horizontal A; circle B+; cross line A+
*L21	Picture cards: points five to seven B; over B+
L12	Names five B; nine A+
L13	Names five familiar objects B
A50	Names watch: 2nd A+; 3rd A; 4th B
P53	Tells name B; full name A; sex A
L22	Prepositions 2B; 3B+; 4A+
P56	Uses color names A Names one color A+

* * * * * * * *

P45	Plays imitatively B
P44	Listens to stories with pictures B
P15	Shows affection B
P22	Bowel control C
*P23	Bladder control B
P20	Puts on shoes A
P21	Uses spoon well C
P42	Asks for tunes by name B

THREE-YEAR LEVEL

DEVELOPMENTAL ITEMS

L14 Speaks sentences C
L15 Uses pronouns, past, plural B
Plays with blocks
*A23 Builds tower, more than four B
A24 Bridge B
A27 Double folds paper B+; diagonal A
*M43 Drawing: copies circle B; cross A
M42 (Imitation): vertical C; horizontal B; circle C; cross B
M46 Traces diamond A
*A61 Picture completion I B; adapts B+
A62 Picture completion II A; adapts A+
A34 Removes ball from box B
A63 Form completion 2 of 5 A
M45 Aligns card B
A60 Names watch 3rd B; 2nd B+
*L12 Picture cards: names 7-9 B
L31 Enumerates 3 objects in picture C; 4A
L32 One or more descriptive words A+

A53 Discriminates lines B
*A57 Matches 4 to 10 forms B; 7 A
A54 Makes aesthetic comparison A
P56 Names one color B; two A
A55 Discriminates weights A
A71 Counts four pennies A
P53 Tells sex B+
L42 Repeats 6 syllables C
*L22 Prepositions: 3 B ; 4A
A42 Performs three commissions A

* * * * * * * *

P52 Knows a few letters or rhymes A
P45 Play: pretends B
P44 Likes stories B
P17 Tells stories B
P20 Puts on shoes B+
P36 Goes on simple errands (outside) A
P39 Crosses street alone B+
P37 Trusted with breakables B
P26 Puts away toys B
P42 Recognizes favorite tune B

FOUR–YEAR LEVEL

DEVELOPMENTAL ITEMS

A25	Builds gate from model A		L32	Uses one or more descriptive words B
*A25	Builds gate imitation B+			
A70	Puts 2 blocks in cup B; 3 B+		*A43	Comprehends 2 of 3 questions B
A58	Four block design B			
A26	Builds memory steps A+		A44	Comprehends: lost A; street A
M47	Steadiness fish test B			
A27	Folds paper diagonally B		A45	Comprehends 2 of VI questions A+
*M43	Drawing: circle C; cross B; square A; triangle A		A42	Performs three commissions B+
M46	Traces diamond B cross B+		P56	Names 2 colors B+; 4 A
P46	Draws man (head, legs) A		A54	Makes aesthetic comparison A
*A66	Names incomplete man B			
A67	Draws 3 completions B; 5 A		L16	Defines by use A
A65	Completes rectangle A		P51	Distinguishes right and left A+
*A64	Completes patience picture B		P54	Names coins A+
A57	Matches 7 forms B		P54	Knows money is for purchase C
A63	Completes two forms B; 3 B+; 4 A		P47	Uses building material constructively B and A
A68	Supplies missing parts A		L46	Non-infantile articulation A
*A70	Counts 4 B+; 10 A; 13 A+			* * * * * * * *
A73	Applied number concept 2 A; 3 A+		P36	Goes on simple errands (outside) B
A72	Draws 1 bubble C; 2 A; 3 A+		P45	Plays constructively C
L23	Obeys 4 prepositions B+		P25	Washes self B
A55	Discriminates weights B		P24	Buttons clothes B
A56	Selects 2 of 3 humorous pictures B		P20	Laces shoes B+
P38	Resists suggestion B		P21	Uses knife B+
L44	Repeats 4 digits B+; 5 A+		P25	Brushes teeth B
L43	Repeats 12 syllables B			

FIVE–YEAR LEVEL

DEVELOPMENTAL ITEMS

*A25	Builds gate B		P51	Distinguishes right and left B+
A26	Builds memory steps B+			
M47	Steadiness fish test 4 B+; 3 B		A68	Supplies missing parts B+
A27	Folds paper diagonally C		A71	Counts 10 pennies B+; 13 A; (6)
*M43	Copies square C; triangle B; diagonal B; hexagon A		A45	Comprehends VI questions B+
M46	Traces cross with coördination C		P54	Names 4 coins A (6)
A35	Threads garden maze B		P55	Distinguishes A. M. and P. M. B+ (6)
*A63	Completes 3 forms C; 4-5 B; 6 B+; 7 A; 8 A+		A74	Tells number of fingers A+ (7)
*P46	Draws recognizable man B		L33	Describes picture A+ (7)
L34	Interprets humor B		P20	Ties bow knot A+ (7)
P38	Resists suggestion 4 times A; 3 B		L36	Gives differences A (7)
*L17	Vocabulary index 3-8 B; 8-12 A		M44	Copies diamond, ink A+ (7)
L41	Repeats 4 digits B; 5 A (7)		A42	Performs three commissions B
A55	Compares weights B		P26	Orderly placement in box B
P56	Names 4 colors B		P25	Washes self B
A54	Makes aesthetic comparison B		L46	Non-infantile pronunciation B
L16	Defines by use B		P20	Laces shoes B
*A65	Completes rectangle B		P47	Uses building material in IV A construction B
P53	Tells age B			

CHAPTER 32

NORMATIVE SUMMARIES

These summaries are condensed, tabular characterizations of the ascending developmental levels from four months to the age of six. They are intended to serve as thumb-nail sketches. The strokes in these sketches are too few and too short to make a symmetrical picture, but the delineations are concrete and objective, and it is hoped that they will fill their purpose, which is clinical rather than aesthetic. They are called normative because they are to be used as standards for orientation.

The summaries for convenience follow our adopted classification of four rubrics of behavior:—motor characteristics, language, adaptive behavior, and personal-social behavior. It is, of course, recognized that there are no corresponding cleavages and that the personality must behave as an integer; but the separation into these divisions is clinically serviceable.

The normative summaries are purposely brief. It must be recognized, however, that they are cumulative and that each level presupposes what has gone before. The normative three-year-old child has not only achieved the behavior items outlined in the three-year summary, he also incorporates and embodies all that has been ascribed to his predecessors at the neonatal, six-months, nine-months, twelve-months, and other levels.

To offset any undue impression of simplicity or uniformity which may be derived from the unqualified summaries, we have added for each level a list of individual traits and deviations. These specific items will add local color to the normative picture and should build up a valid impression as to the psychological diversities and interests of each age level. Even the four-months-old child appears to have his individualities and idiosyncracies. Indeed almost every infant is likely to have some trait of character, some trick, habit, achievement, or peculiarity which expresses this individuality and which occasionally may be symptomatic of a defect, weakness, or excellency. As the age levels mount it proves that some of these signs of individuality have a practical mental-hygiene significance.

The normative summaries, themselves, are intended to serve a double purpose. Primarily they are drawn up in condensed, tabular form to delineate prevailing differences between the various developmental levels and as a guide to general orientation. They will help to give the examiner his bearings in approaching a case.

Secondly, it is hoped that the summaries will serve as a frame work around which the student may organize his experience with children into working clinical concepts. One reason why we fail to make more effective use of our experience is the fact that we neglect to organize it about nodal points.

That the amateur at least may benefit by such apperceptive use of the normative summaries was strikingly illustrated by a recent experience with a small group of graduate students. I brought a well nourished, attractive-looking baby before the group for demonstration. No introductory remarks were made. I simply carried the baby into the room and holding her in my lap allowed her to play spontaneously with a cup and cube. The estimates of this baby's age ranged from two months to two years!—Yet I doubt not that one or two of these students made "intuitive" judgments as to the child's normality by watching her behavior.

But normative judgments are much more trustworthy than intuitive ones. As a matter of fact the child was a physically well developed, normal looking, but not altogether unambiguous baby. She was exactly nine months of age, and on the developmental schedules she rated consistently at the six-months level. She gives no promise of achieving average mental maturity; she will be inferior, possibly defective. Diagnosis and prognosis alike depend upon the considered use of normative criteria.

The following normative summaries, in a measure, are abridged developmental schedules. They may therefore be utilized as cues for preliminary clinical orientation, and even for rough, approximate classification in cases of retardation.

FOUR MONTHS

Motor Characteristics

> Prefers to lie on back
> Tries to raise self, lifting head and shoulders
> Can roll from side to back (or back to side)
> Holds head erect when carried
> Lifts head when prone
> Pushes with feet against floor when held

Language

> Coos
> Smiles
> Laughs aloud
> Makes several vocalizations

Adaptive Behavior

> Notices large objects
> May notice spoon on table
> Hands react to table

Personal-Social Behavior

> Shows selective interest in animated face
> Makes anticipatory postural adjustment on being lifted
> Not much affected by strange persons, new scenes or solitude
> Turns head to voice
> Plays with hands

Six Months

Motor Characteristics

Prefers to sit up, with support
Can roll from back to stomach (or stomach to back)
Uses hands to reach, grasp, crumple, bang, and splash
Opposes thumb in grasping cube

Language

Coos to music
Articulates many syllables in spontaneous vocalization
Frequently laughs at sights and sounds
Is responsive to animated facial expressions

Adaptive Behavior

Notices small objects on table like cube
Picks up objects from table
Bangs spoon
Clasps dangling ring
Shows varied selective attention to environment

Personal-Social Behavior

Plays actively with rattle
Expresses recognition of familiar persons
May show consciousness of strangers
Enjoys presence and playfulness of persons

Nine Months

Motor Characteristics

Sits up without support
Makes stepping movements when feet touch floor
May creep or hitch
Opposes thumb in picking pellet

Language

> Says *dada* or *mama* or equivalent
> Makes simple adjustments to words
> Makes rhythmic movements to music

Adaptive Behavior

> Manipulates spoon and saucer
> Exploits paper
> Looks for fallen object
> Reaches with marked persistence

Personal-Social Behavior

> Restores bottle to mouth
> Likes persons as well as toys
> May know a trick or two like Peek-a-Boo

TWELVE MONTHS

Motor Characteristics

> Stands with support
> Creeps or hitches alone
> Walks with help
> Shows a preference for one hand in reaching
> Scribbles imitatively with a crayon

Language

> Comprehends simple verbal commissions
> Says two words besides *mama* and *dada*
> Can wave *bye bye* and often can say it

Adaptive Behavior

> Places a cube in a cup on command
> Recovers a cube concealed by a cup
> Retains a cube in either hand and takes a third
> Puts a small rod in a half inch hole

Personal-Social Behavior

    Plays with or reaches for his mirror image
    Coöperates while he is being dressed
    Holds a cup to drink out of and may use a spoon
    Plays with blocks but not very constructively
    Inhibits simple acts on command
    Imitates simple acts like scribble and spoon rattle

EIGHTEEN MONTHS

Motor Characteristics

    Walks alone
    Climbs chair or stair
    Throws ball into box
    Scribbles spontaneously

Language

    Says five or more words
    Comprehends simple questions
    Points to nose, eyes, or hair
    Says *hello, thank you,* or equivalent

Adaptive Behavior

    Accepts fourth cube and retains three
    Builds blocks in tower, imitatively
    Places circular block in form-board

Personal-Social Behavior

    Uses spoon without much spilling
    Bowel control practically established
    Shows dramatic mimicry in play
    Habitually inhibits certain acts
    Tries, definitely, to put on shoes
    Plays combiningly with cup and cube

Two Years

Motor Characteristics

Draws a vertical stroke imitatively
Plays simple catch and toss with ball
Can operate a kiddy car around a chair

Language

Uses simple sentences and phrases
Names familiar objects like key, penny, watch
Distinguishes *in* and *under*
Points to seven of ten simple pictures

Adaptive Behavior

Builds a block tower of three or more
Places three blocks in form-board
Folds paper once imitatively

Personal-Social Behavior

Bladder control established
Listens to stories with pictures
Tells experiences
Asks for things at table by name
Likes to play in sand, filling and emptying

Three Years

Motor Characteristics

Draws a circle from copy
Draws a horizontal stroke imitatively
Creases a piece of paper neatly
Aligns a card to an edge

Language

> Uses pronouns, past and plural
> Names three objects in a picture
> Can tell simple stories
> Distinguishes prepositions, *in, under, behind*

Adaptive Behavior

> Builds bridge imitatively
> Builds block tower of four or more
> Discriminates between two short lines
> Combines two parts of severed picture

Personal-Social Behavior

> Can open door
> Can carry breakable object
> Asks questions of elders
> Puts on shoes

FOUR YEARS

Motor Characteristics

> Draws cross from copy
> Traces diamond path
> Hooks fish in 15 or 30 seconds with right or left hand

Language

> Distinguishes four prepositions
> Uses descriptive word with picture
> Repeats twelve syllables

Adaptive Behavior

> Folds paper diagonally
> Draws three completions in incomplete man
> Completes patience picture
> Puts two blocks in cup

Personal-Social Behavior

>   Uses building material constructively
>   Buttons clothes
>   Goes on errands outside of house
>   Washes self

FIVE YEARS

Motor Characteristics

>   Draws triangle from copy
>   Draws prism from copy
>   Hooks fish three times in one minute

Language

>   Defines words by use
>   Knows three or more words in vocabulary list
>   Interprets humor
>   Speaks with noninfantile articulation

Adaptive Behavior

>   Builds keystone gate
>   Completes four of eight forms
>   Discriminates weights
>   Performs three commissions

Personal-Social Behavior

>   Draws recognizable man and tree
>   Laces shoes
>   Puts on coat and hat alone
>   Uses play material with advanced constructiveness
>   Replaces material in box neatly

Individual Traits and Deviations
Four Months

B1   Holds spoon and regards it for one minute.

B3   Tries to put hand in mouth when about to go to sleep. Scratches pillow at night. Takes evident satisfaction in being handled and talked to. Stops crying on hearing phonograph.

B4   Starts to cry on hearing phonograph. Has habit of scratching face.

B6   Puts hands to bottle when placed in mouth.

B9   Very playful. "Doesn't want to sleep as much as he ought to." Sleeps only from twelve to thirteen hours a day.

B12   Usually goes to sleep crying. Sucks at nipple when nothing in bottle. Description of behavior strongly suggests underfed baby.

B16   Given a finger for support, can raise himself to sitting position (without further assistance). (Born 3 weeks prematurely.)

G18   Watches hand as she moves it back and forth on table.

G19   Has a habit not of sucking, but of biting. Blows bubbles. Likes attention.

B20   Mouth opens on sight of bread. Jumps at sounds, even in sleep.

B21   Has vigorous leg thrust, almost pushed self off scales when being weighed. Turns completely over from back to stomach. Gives definite clinical impression of advanced if not superior development.

G23   Likes to pull at sleeve for play.

G24   Smiles on being picked up.

B26   Has habit of sleeping with hands over head. Cried with fright when sister spoke in squeaking voice to amuse him.

G28   Has begun to play with feet.

B30   Definitely plays with rattle and cries on withdrawal of rattle. Maintained good head posture as early as one month. Plays *peek*—draws blanket over face and pushes it back.

B31   Has just begun to play with his knee.

B33   Makes *ah ou* sound. This is increased in "responsive" intensity as soon as mother talks to him.

G37   "Holds" nursing bottle.

G38   Used to cry regularly when clock struck. Does so no longer.

B40   Very pronounced, recurring, hand-to-mouth reaction. Cries consistently when laid on back; but stops when put in prone position.

B&G41 Twins of fraternal type. B can stand up when holding mother's hand, a remarkable feat. G pushes but cannot stand. G vocalizes much more than B. B plays with his hands much more than G. B reaches and grasps, G doesn't. B distinctly inferior in eye following movements; but superior (advanced) in table edge reactions. B picks up spoon; G disregards spoon.

G45 Definitely pats table in play.

G46 Persistently reaches for cube. Regards spoon intently and is apparently conscious of its sudden disappearance.

B48 Grabs for a suspended ball when lying in cradle.

B50 Makes persistent rhythmic rocking movement with whole body, while seated in mother's lap. Is very alert and alive to persons in environment, conditioned if not increased by the abounding attention which he gets from affectionate aunts, parents, cousins, etc., of all ages, in a populous household.

INDIVIDUAL TRAITS AND DEVIATIONS
[SIX MONTHS]

G4 Excellent emotional tone. No timidity or irritability even when sleepy. Good poise.

G9 "Sings" when mother sings.

G10 Able to play *pattycake*.

G16 Laughs when father speaks to him.

G26 Takes pleasure in stepping movements.

G27 Looks toward door at feeding time in anticipation of bottle.

G27 Is a very active baby. Took great pleasure in pushing up body vigorously when held so that toes touched lap of father. Repeated this pushing reaction by actual count 250 times in succession, when the father feared to continue the game.

G31 Wakes at 3:30 A.M. and sleeps very little after that.

B34 Gets very angry when things are taken away from him, while G37 permits you to deprive her of things good-naturedly. G31 cries when she fails to get an object just out of reach.

G40 Pulls out hair when angry.

G41 Shows definite fear of strangers. Corners of mouth go down.

G46 Shows the quality of alertness to a marked degree. Coos interest when reaching for desired object. Can almost pull self up to standing position. In posture, eye expression and decisiveness of response she makes a definite clinical impression of superiority the validity of which subsequent reëxaminations confirmed. [Sat up at five months; stood up at seven months.]

G47&51   Cry when they see sterness or hear scolding.

G51   Showed surprising persistence in pellet test.

G53   Makes a sort of leaping reaction of delight on the approach of her father. Also plays *peek-a-boo*.

INDIVIDUAL TRAITS AND DEVIATIONS
[NINE MONTHS]

G3   Can whistle very clearly.

G5   Peevish when object is taken from her.

G12   Puts cube No. 2 in mouth in order to take cube No. 3.

B14   Cries when measured for height, but regains calm promptly.

B16   Plays harmonica.

G18   Sat up at 4½ months and makes a marked clinical impression of superior persistence and emotional control; also very observant of slight sounds.

G19   Pulls table cloth in order to draw objects near to her.

B20   Hides face when spoken to sternly. Tries to imitate when mother clucks to horse.

B27   Puts paper and all in mouth after candy has been wrapped up.

B30   Can drink out of a cup, holding it by the handle.

B32   Does not solve coördination test, but is interested in small hole in performance box and puts finger in it.

B38   Plays the piano. Winks reflexly when she drops a toy which falls with a bang; also winks when it falls on a soft surface (self-conditioned reflex).

B39   Shows great pleasurable interest in dog.
Also reputed to have a very bad temper.

B42   Solves third object problem by bringing two hands together to clasp third cube, retaining the other two in hand.

G45   Showed significant difficulty in placing a cube in a cup. She pounded and banged: the pounding was clearly the result of her effort to release the cube. She finally succeeded. Waves hand back and forth when asked "How do the trees go?" Sometimes shows "obstinacy."

G46   Cries at disappearance of cube in inverted cup test.

G46   Has almost acquired bladder and bowel control. Makes desire for
       evacuation known by facial expression and grunt.

B48   Pulls off shoes and stockings.

G50a   Shows interest in string when pulling down dangling ring. This baby
       also showed remarkable poise and adaptability when laid on the
       table to be measured for her height. Her face expressed wonder-
       ment, but there was no protest.

G52   Said *all gone* at nine months, before she could say *mama* and *dada*.

Individual Traits and Deviations
[twelve months]

B2   Is impatient of interference in his play, but is very sociable and does
       not object to handling.

B4   Shows with hands "how big is the baby"; also pretends to smoke.
       Gives evidence of having a rudimentary sense of humor; does
       not laugh merely from imitation.

B6   Has strong likes and dislikes; refuses to go to certain people. Shows
       displeasure when mother pretends to cry. Also holds breath and
       turns blue when something he much likes is taken away from him.

B8   Is full of energy and overflows with animal spirits.

B9   Makes a perfect series of arcs when scribbling with a crayon.

G13   Cries abnormally hard when she doesn't get what she wants; shows
       temper, throws things.

B14   Was sick when examined and did not show much vigor; but re-
       sponded to tests nevertheless and played constructively with
       blocks.

B16   Covers cube again after uncovering it.

B18   Is manifestly nonplussed by third cube dilemma; but he reads *ABC*
       from the newspaper.

B19   Shows sympathy for mother when she is hurt.

B21   Folds a piece of paper imitatively; throws paper in wastebasket;
       "combs hair."

B36   Carries sweater to mother to suggest going.

B39   Has bottle filled with water left beside him at night; finds it himself
       when he wants it.

G41   Scratched sister's face when sister was taken on mother's lap.

G42   Is the only girl out of fifty who definitely recognizes and points out
       pictures like a shoe and a man.

G45   Imitates coughing and spitting. Can turn on gas jet.

G49   Was much frightened by cousin who came into room dressed in black.

G50   Trembles when she gets excited or delighted.

B51   14 months, is a good-natured happy-go-lucky boy; but casts self on floor, face downward, in despair and tearful grief when older sister says sharply "Bad Bobby!"

G52   Has been taught how to hold a pencil and approaches Spencerian perfection in her writing or scribbling posture.

INDIVIDUAL TRAITS AND DEVIATIONS
[EIGHTEEN MONTHS]

B2   Has a violent temper, is reported to be stubborn, and is emotionally very excitable.

B3   Is reported to be much interested in machinery! Comes from machinist family.

G7   Pretends to read paper.

B9   Knows most of letters of alphabet.

G14   Is jealous and pushes father away when he approaches mother.

G18   Is irritable and petulant and insists that grandmother should solve certain tests (like the form-board) instead of herself.

B18   Drools, but this is variable and seems to be associated with dentition.

G20   Is jealous and dislikes to see mother pick up another baby.

B21   Is beginning to use a spoon and spills some; but won't let mother feed him.

G26   Is showing evidences of unpleasant disposition; sulks, throws things down, and calls for candy in very cross tone.

B28   Above average in achievement; but superior excellence of personality especially notable. Attention quality is markedly superior for his age; he is extremely well poised. He was bashful at the beginning of the examination, but readily and completely overcame this.

G29   Was examined at the ages of six, nine, and twelve months. At twelve months she made such a favorable impression in personality symptoms that she was recorded as being poised and amiable. Now she makes whining noises when given something she doesn't want; gives evidences of negativism, pushing things away from her. These traits reappear when she is reëxamined at two years.

B34   Calls a picture of a flag *hurrah.*

B43   Showed anger when unsuccessful with the performance box test; struck at the block.

G50   Is apparently more interested in the examiner than in the test material.

INDIVIDUAL TRAITS AND DEVIATIONS
[TWO YEARS]

G1   Showers her father with questions all day Sunday, when he is at home. Is very advanced in conversation. Can carry on a pretty prolonged conversation with an adult.

B2   Has memory for events which occurred day previous.

B2   Can catch a ball with ease, his father having taught him. Uses a catching glove.

G3   Makes friends very easily. Attempted to barter away all her toys for form-board.

B4   Speaks with perfect pronunciation.

B5   Has number concepts up to four. G8 has concepts up to six.

G6   Admires herself when dressed, in the mirror.

G8   Has a very hearty laugh and a constant smile. Can sing five nursery rhymes.

G12   Refuses to concede that she can be bad.

G13   Recognizes at random twenty letters of alphabet. Can lower needle and start phonograph. Is far more talkative than three- or four-year-old children of neighbor.

G16   Smiles when she is praised.

G17   Was bashful for a whole half hour before she coöperated satisfactorily in the examination.

G18   Was "stubborn" for a full hour before the examination could proceed. (Practically all of the other children responded rapidly and often spontaneously.)

B23   Will go off and cry himself to sleep if he gets a bad scolding. Hides toys so girl upstairs can't have them.

G25   Bangs her head when in a temper.

B28   Ran away recently and went a distance of several blocks.

B29   Doesn't mind a scolding at all.

G38   Has been taught to cross herself and to kneel in prayer.

B43   Can throw a ball straight up into the air.

G45   Can tell her full name, street address, and town.

B50   Is very particular about keeping his hands clean, the least speck must be washed off. He also tries to walk like the old man across the street!

Individual Traits and Deviations
[three years]

B5   Stuttered so seriously at two years and ten months of age that he was brought to our clinic. In two months, without special treatment, no trace of his defect remained.

B6   Showed an unusual degree of coöperativeness and (social) attentiveness which in an older person would be called courtesy.

B7   Is a bright boy with good judgment and well poised; he makes a practical common sense approach to new situations. He will probably succeed well in school and in his social relations.

B8   Can go to the grocery store to bring home a quart of milk and can buy things without a note. He does not like to have his sister use his things.

G9   Is very fond of music and carries a tune exceedingly well for her age.

G10   Is a twin sister of G9 and has very similar traits, though she is apparently more impulsive and aggressive. Both of them have the same number of teeth, recognize exactly the same six letters of the alphabet (and no more), both count to 5, and both said *chocolate* as their first word.

G14   Is an only child and much lacking in self-reliance and independence, probably because mother has done everything for her.

B18   Is another only child who has for that reason been "taught" a great many things. Though he recognizes only a few letters of the alphabet, he can spell his name and address.

B20   Has a great dislike for green vegetables and will always spit them out. [But B12 is reported to be extremely fond of lettuce!]

G25   Seldom plays with other children.

B29   Is interested in colors; can name and identify nine.

G33   Is the only girl in a family of ten children and is much petted by her numerous brothers.

B35   Is an overindulged only child.

B36   Screams and kicks when crossed.

B51   A bright boy. Wanted to impress mother that it rained hard, so he said: "It rained so hard I saw two green fishes swimming in the rain."

G52   Distinctly shows recognition recall (with identification) of chimes heard for first time ten months previously.

INDIVIDUAL TRAITS AND DEVIATIONS
[FOUR YEARS]*

B1   Has gone on errands to the store, four blocks away, since he was two and one-half years old. Can keep a tune very well. Is learning to print. (Drew superior man.)
Wets bed. Usually sleeps soundly but, if suddenly awakened, trembles. (Prefers to sleep in dark room.)

G2   Can dance on tips of toes. Goes to Sunday School alone, across the car tracks several blocks away. Went to store, grocer said he could not send order, insisted on carrying home by self three grapefruit, large steak, and loaf of bread. "I stopped on every step." Plays with one thing almost all day—paper dolls, cuts them out and makes dresses, sews (?), and irons. Much afraid of fire, having seen garage burn near house, but when matches blazed up in a match box made her sister (older) march in back of her out of the house as she had heard about school fire drills. Has an imaginary friend called "Naris" who plays with her while sister is away, sends her home when she hears sister coming back from school as sister has a scornful attitude toward "Naris." Can print name.

B3   Anxious to do everything older brother and father do; wears man's neckties, won't wear anything considers like a girl's, also hates to wear old clothes. Plays by hour with same toy; if wants something when he goes to sleep, wakes up with same demand. Can print name rapidly, but usually starts to print in "mirror" writing. Admitted that he had written with pencil on the beds; when father scolded him said, "George's father didn't talk that way when he told the truth"; uses this method to avoid scolding.

G4   Very irregular schedule; not hungry for breakfast; does not eat anything until she has played first; has to be coaxed to eat. Can be trusted to stay on sidewalk, even if ball has gone into street;

*These four-year children are arranged in the order of their intelligence, the brightest heading the list. Their individual traits and deviations are reported at somewhat greater length to show the frequency and wide distribution of mental hygiene problems.

does not want to play alone. Is afraid of old men; won't go to bed without someone in room and insists on having light left on.

B5   Can put a picture puzzle together made of 150 pieces.

Has a sense of humor in contrast to older sister; enjoys and takes part in father's joking, tells long tales about what has happened but is ready to admit that he was "fooling," makes jokes, e. g.: Mother said "That man's name is Mr. Fisher." Thought himself humorous when he replied, "He fishes all the time." Frightened by a thunder-storm, but not excessively. Sucks thumb.

B8   Tells long fantastic stories, e. g.: "Had a new suit for Christmas and it didn't fit, so Mother rolled it up and tossed it up the chimney and Santa Claus caught it and then Father threw Mother out of the window into the snow and a policeman came along and picked her up and brought her into the house. Wasn't that a funny thing?" Fun in mimicry. Looking over his shoulder at his new suit, "Am I all right in the back, I can't see."
Slightly afraid of thunder-storm (frightened by maid).
Is coaxed slightly to eat, particularly at breakfast. Will not eat spinach (ate some that was gritty a year previously).

G9   Makes all designs with color cubes for past year. Sews outline stitch designs on cloth. Runs away from dogs, but no excessive fear. Has sung in tune for over a year.

G10   Very fond of stories, dramatizes them. Does not like vegetables, but eats them pretending that they are desert. Very good sense of rhythm.

G11   Has known all letters for about four months; insisted that father teach them to her as he read the paper. Can print her name and any word spelled to her.
Vomits if forced to eat what she doesn't like; consequently mother places on table only such things as she thinks child would like. (Marked domination by child in many instances.)

G13   Does not like vegetables and is not coaxed or forced to eat them. Only difficulty reported by mother in regard to going to bed. Plays, sings, protests until parents are ready to go. Has always protested against going to bed. Was rocked when a baby. (Younger sister, not rocked, gives no trouble.)

G14   Afraid of feathers and pieces of cotton; formerly afraid of fur. Otherwise not timid.

G15   Afraid of dog (mother says she was always afraid of dog, too).

G16   Won't go to bed until someone else goes.
　　　　Afraid of drunken men (conditioned by conversation heard).

G21   Can sing several verses to a song in tune.
　　　　Afraid of "Old Man Nubby" (conditioned by children in neighborhood).

G22   If she eats oatmeal, an eruption appears on her face. (Likes oatmeal.)

G23   Knows all her letters by sight and prints A, B, C, E.
　　　　Before almost every new test situation, said in low tone, "I don't think I can," or "If I can." Covered her drawing with her hands. Able to make a "B plus" man, but could not be persuaded to do so until end of examination when left by self. (Not defiant in resistance.) Same initial difficulty in drawing copy of circle. Excessive dislike of nurse who had used needle on child's arm in hospital.

B26   Excessively shy before strangers, face flushed, head down, spoke in whisper; but adequate reactions. Went to party among strange children; did not leave mother's side. More than occasional bedwetter. Wets self twice a week when playing. Won't go to other children's houses, but they come to see him.

B27   Boy cried excessively, hours at a time, when sister went to school; mother, fearing child would be ill, permitted sister to take boy to school giving age as four when only $3\,4/12$. At present not particularly anxious to go; irregular in attendance.

G29   Dressed self entirely, even buttoning back buttons when mother was ill in bed. Puts her money in a bank and will not spend it, though brother tries to persuade her to buy candy.

B31   Afraid of dogs, screams in terror; when eighteen months old a dog licked his face, formerly had played with him.

G32   Speaks both Italian and English equally well.
　　　　Afraid of rag-man ("Puts bad children in a bag!").

G34   Won't touch potatoes. (Ate them while she was in the hospital.)
　　　　Has tantrums. (You can't reason with her until they are over.)

G33   Frightened by a cross rooster that came running toward her.

B36   Very much interested in automobiles. Favorite pastime with toy autos, garage, etc. Watches autos for an hour out of window. Runs to window if he hears car making "a funny sound."

B38   In a musical family, beats time on drum with Victrola or piano.
　　　　Very imitative and dramatic in his pretence of doctor, musician, grocer.

B39   Tantrums. (If he gets to crying you can't divert him as you can the other children.) Cried while waiting after examination.

G40   Cross when she wakes from nap; cries for half an hour.

B41   Talks both English and Lithuanian.
       Cries if someone hits him, but not if he hurts himself. (Cut his finger with a knife and did not cry.)

B43   Lively imagination. Fed a wooden cow and then complained that his hands were sticky from "feeding that animal." Watches men building a garage by the hour; men occasionally speak to him.
       Until recently wet bed, reconditioned by "gold stars" as reward. Used to take cotton to bed with him and then would cry if he lost it.

B45   Very irregular schedule. Eats and sleeps when he wants to. Tantrums. ("Makes him worse if you hit him".) Wets self day as well as at night. Has light in room when going to sleep. Talks a little in sleep. Habit of grinding teeth.
       Mother claimed he was very destructive and would never play for more than few moments with any toy. (Sat contentedly throughout whole examination period, about fifty minutes, and continued to play with free construction material during interview, another half hour.)

B46   Child goes to movies almost every afternoon. Afraid of dark. Goes to sleep with light in room; is often very restless at night, wakes up screaming.

B47   Cries very easily, with impatience, when slightly hurt. (Not uncontrolled tantrum but peevish whining.) Used to refuse cereal. Cried from nine to eleven before it was eaten, but mother insisted. No difficulty now. Also remains quiet Sunday morning while father and mother sleep late. (Dominates other situations by fussing.) Mother doesn't read to him because he asks so many questions. Likes to take carts apart. Took all the screws out of the piano. Hits father, if father puts arms around his mother.

B48   If children tease him starts crying and cannot stop him, two to three hours at a time. Also great difficulty in adjusting to new places. Cries while waiting before examination.

B50   Cried when urged to persist with fish steadiness test, but was easily diverted. (Only child who cried during examination.)

INDIVIDUAL TRAITS AND DEVIATIONS
[FIVE YEARS]

B2   Is afraid of nothing, but his brother, aged four, is afraid of many things.

B4   Prefers drawing to any other form of amusement.

B5   Has had a nurse who trained him to be self-reliant. He can dress himself entirely alone.

B7   Talks delightfully, showing excellent poise, sociability, and intelligence. Can also play by himself contentedly by the hour. Has never been punished or frightened. Markedly non-nervous and comfortable personality qualities. Adaptable and trustful. Went to hotel several weeks ago and slept in room while parents went downstairs.

B9   Is the dominant twin and imposes on brother and keeps house upset.

B10   Shows collecting instinct; has two drawers in which he accumulates papers, nails, tin boxes, etc.

B16   Wakes every night at one.

B18   Showed originality in the way he built an auto out of screws and washers.

B19   Is bed-wetter. Mother and father also both had enuresis.

B24   Disliked school in . . . when there was no kindergarten; and he was not equal to Grade I. He likes the kindergarten here.

G26   Will not eat vegetables. Is violently affectionate. Has a tornado temper, a lively sense of humor, and an I. Q. of 138.

G33   Talks very little. Is reported never to talk in the kindergarten (Cf7).

G34   Is very sociable and imaginative. She said spontaneously to E: "Do you know what I dreamed about last night? An elephant sailed in a sailboat and banged it and had no more trunk and blood all came out of the big hole."

G35   Is of very happy disposition; sings constantly.

G43   Is a great help at home and takes considerable responsibility in the care of the baby.

G44   Is an only child and very shy about playing with other children. Said "I don't want any brothers and sisters because I'd have to dress myself."

G45 Has excellent poise; sat for hour and a half at her little table at home, getting up only once to perform the commissions given by the examiner.

G46 Is very different from her sister who is nervous and worries. Readily forgets and is content even when denied.

G50 Has snapping black eyes. She is rather spoilt. Does not mind well. Is constantly active and a "chatterbox."

CHAPTER 33

General Clinical Procedure

INTRODUCTORY

Specific procedures for the application of diagnostic tests and items have been detailed in a previous section. It is important, however, to emphasize certain general differences between clinical work with children of pre-school age as compared with children of school age. The task of applying mental tests and measurements to school children is enormously simplified by the fact that these children have had experience in a school room. They, therefore, yield with comparative readiness to the conditions of an ordinary psychometric examination. This examination takes on the guise of a modified recitation in which there is considerable conversation between subject and examiner. And the organized docility of the school child makes this type of approach not only possible but effective.

When, however, we are forced to deal with relatively untutored and highly independent subjects, like a mercurial, eighteen-months runabout, the clinical situation is different. It may also be more interesting because of the tax which it makes upon the examiner. If he is somewhat irritated and mortified by the apparent nonconformance and nonconformability of his subject, he has not acquired what may be called a completely impersonal and truly clinical attitude.

Pre-school clinical situations require patience and versatility of approach. It would be clearly unscientific to make any fundamental distinction between clinical pre-school and clinical school psychology. Practically, however, the problems peculiar to the pre-school age are so diversified and present themselves in relation to such different social situations that it is not unlikely that the developmental diagnosis of pre-school children will in time separate itself as a specialized field.

CLINICAL DIFFERENCES BETWEEN AGE LEVELS

It is extremely difficult to generalize in regard to clinical procedure because of the very wide range of development. In a chronological sense the pre-school span is narrower than the elementary school span, but from a developmental point of view it is vastly wider. At one end of the span we have the four-months-old child who can not even sit up and may not even turn his head to a spoken word. At the other end of the span we have the school beginner.

These age level differences are so great that the examiner must make certain broad differentiations of clinical approach with reference to them. The manner in which he greets the mother; the manner in which he makes his first contact with the child; the promptness with which he begins his examination; the directness with which he approaches the child; the physical arrangement of his apparatus; the position which he takes at the table, etc.,— these elements in examination are subject to significant tactful adaptations in conformance with the emotional maturity of the subject.

The four-months-old child may be approached with a certain impunity, whereas the four-year-old child may demand very delicate deferences to his personal make-up. Even the highly mobile eighteen-months and two-year subjects may demand such deference, although here a certain kind of clinical diplomacy and managerial foresight come into requisition. For example a highly attractive toy, like a pull-around horse on wheels, thoughtlessly left in the corner of the examining room may seriously upset the intended course of the examination in the case of an eighteen-months-old child.

We have unconsciously made frequent reference to the eighteen-months level. This is only natural because this age presents outstanding complications. It is the runabout, fugitive, flighty, mercurial age when the attention (and the child!) darts from one point to another with such facility that a false impression of instability is imparted. I might cite the confession of a sensible and very competent mother of twins who steadfastly asserted that two contemporary infants were as easy to take care of as one until these infants attained the age of eighteen months, when the opinion was frankly revised. This is a trying age for a tired mother and may also tax a psychologist who attempts to harness that mobile attention too tightly to some device or test. The examiner must resort to quick ruses and flashes of surprise in the presentation of his test material in order to get a response. This is not an unnatural or distorting modification of procedure. It is a clinical recognition of the type of attention with which the examiner is dealing. Emerson said that education begins with respect for the child. Clinical examination begins at the same point. If the examiner makes this mode of attention his ally instead of regarding it as a perplexity, the eighteen-months-old child becomes a possible clinical subject. Indeed, if the clinical examiner will consistently assume this respecting attitude as a matter of professional course, he will find every age of childhood interesting and challenging.

APPROACH AND RAPPORT

The importance of rapport in psychological examinations has been consistently emphasized in the literature. Rapport is essential in the conduct of an ordinary psychometric examination of a school child; it also contributes to the success of the developmental examination of pre-school children at the higher age levels. At the lowest age levels the term is scarcely applicable, if it is made to carry a connotation of mutual understanding.

When does rapport become an important factor in the examination of infants? An interesting question. The four-months baby is not highly sensitive to the presence, absence, or peculiarities of persons. We do not deny that he himself has a rudimentary personality, but observation of him is a relatively objective proceeding.

Not so, however, with the twelve-months child. Even at six months there is a discernible consciousness of strangers and an elementary social susceptibility. Just to that extent there is an interaction between observer and observed, and just to that extent we have to reckon with the maintenance of rapport. Or if the term rapport is not applicable to so callow an infant, let us use the next French word in the English dictionary,—*rapprochement!* Certain it is there must be an appreciable drawing together, and an establishment of a state of cordial relations, even at six months.

Confidence in young children can not be established by conversational persuasions and verbal commendations. The examiner must rely upon more primitive forms of reassurance. Or, what is still more important, he must avoid all primitive forms of alarming and disquieting. He must not peer with piercing eyes (although the piercing eye is popularly associated with diagnostic penetration); he must not talk too loudly; he must not look too serious or act too aggressively.

Putting all this in positive language, we may say that the essential thing is to disarm and not to dominate the young subject. You cannot hypnotize him by intently gazing at him. Indeed the most effective thing you can often do when he comes into the room *is not to look at him at all.* Once he thinks that you have no designs upon him, he becomes your diagnostic prey. Indeed the establishment of controlled freedom is the ideal basis for optimum clinical observation.

For all these reasons *approach* is a more important consideration in pre-school procedure than is *rapport.* The child is something of a diagnostician himself; he enters the room in a questioning, unsettled attitude; he makes very prompt observations and appraisals of his own. Let him, if possible, sense nothing which is disturbing. An occasional and sometimes a patent smile on the part of the examiner will help to remove initial apprehension. In difficult cases rely on methods of nonaggression. Apparently disregard the suspicious client. Offer him an enticing toy, but do not thrust it upon him. Leave him to his own devices and by indirection rather than by frontal attack enable him to develop an attitude of trustfulness. He will, of course, have to make the adjustment himself; you can only supply the conditions which will facilitate the adjustment. Pretty soon he may walk up to you on his own initiative; but even then do not impose upon his confidence.

Again we have particularly the eighteen-months to twenty-four-months age group in mind. The two-year-old child is considered to be the most resistant of all children to psychological examination. We ought not, however, to give too much recognition to *resistance* as a clinical obstacle. Rather, we should regard resistance as a symptom of our failure to devise the right technique and to find the right clinical approach. Resistance is not a specific personality trait. Is it not a mildly rationalizing designation of a failure of clinical rapprochement?

There are no insuperable obstacles in the examination of infants and pre-kindergarten children. There are exceptions, however, which might be advanced to prove the rule. One of our resistant children was an extraordinarily fearsome, deaf, mentally deficient, mute, and colored boy of three. The other was a shrinking, negative, and also subintelligent boy who had been conditioned into an abnormal form of clinging dependence by a feeble-minded mother with a mental age of six. We also confess to a somewhat stormy session with a pair of non-English-speaking twins, who frequently reverted to simultaneous weeping. But between the squalls they coöperated sufficiently to furnish us with a relatively complete record. Another pair of twins, aged three, reacted very satisfactorily on all performance tests, but maintained unassailable

silence until just at the close of the examination. It should be added
that the refractory colored boy above mentioned finally responded
after two visits to his home, and that the shrinking boy became
approachable after separation from his mother.

GENERAL CONDUCT OF THE EXAMINATION

Assuming satisfactory approach and rapport, the success of an
examination will depend considerably upon the skill and executive-
ness with which the examiner handles the psychological material.
This should be kept in the drawer of the examining kit with some
orderliness, and should not be spread out on a table. So far as
possible, when he is attempting to create a controlled test situation,
the examiner should exclude competing external stimuli and confine
the child's attention to the immediate situation.

The psychological deck, therefore, should be clear. Irrelevant
stimuli like the examiner's watch, or scarf, or paper weight should
not be too near the zone of action. The influence of the mother also
is a factor which must be kept under some control (we shall discuss
this presently). The arrangement of the furniture and toys in the
room, likewise, should be taken into account. As we improve our
clinical technique we shall probably make more systematic effort
to standardize and to control this physical part of the clinical situation, because it is very important in the case of young children to
observe the nature of their adjustment to the total room situation
as well as to the stimuli immediately within their reach.

The order of procedure in the examination should, so far as
practicable, conform to the order indicated in the diagnostic schedules reproduced in the preceding chapter; but there are so many
variables in the clinical situation that this order should not be
pursued in any dogmatic or arbitrary manner. Frequently the child
will, himself, create a favorable situation for observation which the
examiner should exploit rather than thwart. For example, if a two-
year-old child should suddenly rise from his chair and run to the

window to see what is happening in the street, the examiner may be able to make significant observations as a result of this episode and bring the child back to the table without any prejudice to the examination.

In this sense the examination must represent a kind of working compromise between the child and the examiner. Although we believe procedure should be standardized in detail and should so far as possible be uniform, the stage of the psychological examination is in such a state of unstable equilibrium that it would be unscientific as well as impracticable to attempt to make the examinations rigidly standardized. By admitting a judicious amount of flexibility we create a situation in which the child displays characteristic behavior and our major objective should be the observation of behavior which is truly representative of the child. This does not leave us at the mercy of pure impressionism, but it does avoid faulty psychometric determinations at the expense of considered clinical judgment.

No hard and fast rules can be made with respect to the duration of the examination at any age level. Much depends upon the personality of the child and upon the happiness of the initial approach. Much also depends upon the liberality with which we allow the child to take the lead. The examiner must always have due regard to fatigue symptoms, but in our experience the factor of fatigue is of relatively small importance. If the child has not had his accustomed meal or his accustomed nap he does not make as favorable a subject for examination, but it is gratifying to note that moderate fatigue, convalescence from illness, and a minor lack of well-being do not seriously distort the behavior picture. Occasionally the fatigue may be so extreme that the child refuses altogether to respond to situations, but such complete refusal appears to be a more characteristic fatigue reaction than deterioration of response. Even severe illness does not mask completely the capacity and the developmental status of the child. The examiner should, therefore, be somewhat conservative in attributing failure and defects of response to physical factors. In spite of all the above qualifications, it, of course, remains true that the child appears at his best when he is rested and well nourished.

The duration of the examination need not be conditioned altogether by the age of the child. It will be noted that there is no great difference in the length of the nine diagnostic schedules which are used at the ascending age levels. To be sure, a four-year-old child is more highly organized than a four-months-old child, but it does not necessarily follow that we should spend a larger amount of time in making a developmental examination of the older child. From a strictly clinical point of view a four-months-old child is just as complicated as the four-year-old child and presents an equally difficult and significant problem of diagnosis. If we expend less time in examining him, it is probably because we have not acquired the methods for making a longer examination. The factor of fatigue should not enter as a serious deterrent because the infant has self-protective mechanisms to meet the danger of being overtaxed. As a matter of fact, we may observe with profit the behavior of a four-months-old child for a period of forty minutes or one hour without inflicting any hardship whatever upon the child.

From the point of view of developmental diagnosis, all levels are on a par with respect to their intrinsic importance and our diagnostic technique, and even the investment of our time should not give undue preference to any particular age level.

THE MOTHER-CHILD RELATION AS A CLINICAL PROBLEM

In the psychological examination of school children the approved rule is: Examine the child alone. Terman, for example, in his general instructions for using the Measuring Scale of Intelligence, says, "At all events the presence of parent, teacher, school principal, or governess is to be avoided. Contrary to what you might expect, these distract the child more than a strange personality would.

Their critical attitude toward the child's performance is very likely to cause embarrassment. If the child is alone with the examiner he is more at ease for the fact that he does not feel that there is a reputation to sustain."

As soon as we shift our developmental examination down to the infant and pre-school levels the problem becomes somewhat different. The infant at least has no conscious reputation to sustain and it is possible that we have sometimes gone too far even with older children in insisting upon isolation during examination.

In our own work with pre-school children, both in the research and practical clinical applications of this work, we have adopted the view that the mother-child relation is a natural one which should not be avoided but which should be reckoned with clinically. We have, therefore, permitted our youngest subjects to remain in their mothers' laps during the examination. This has, if anything, favorably conditioned the responses of the child. There are no great difficulties in adjusting the posture of the child and preventing undue physical interference on the part of the mother. Although the child is no doubt psychologically conditioned by this proximity to the mother we are interested to watch his reactions in this situation. This does not mean that the child must, during the whole examination, remain in the mother's lap. For some of the diagnostic items he may be taken out of the mother's lap; he may be taken to a small table or he may be put on the floor; but up to the eighteenth month we tolerate the mother's presence and capitalize her cooperation. This situation makes it possible to preserve a natural unstilted atmosphere and to intersperse the tests with interview inquiries. It helps to maintain a natural atmosphere of confidence in which the child is more likely to display himself characteristically.

No hard and fast rules with respect to the mother's presence can be made for the age levels from eighteen months up to five years. Our experience has shown that the solution of this problem must be adjusted to meet individual situations. Ordinarily we begin the interview and examination with the child and mother in close contact. After approach and rapport have been established it is possible to work somewhat more independently with the child. Sometimes he can be taken into a separate room with the door closed. A very good arrangement for most children is a separate room with the mother seated in an adjoining room. The mother need not be in plain view, but if the child shows timidity he may be reassured by occasional journeys to his mother's side. Sometimes the intervening door may be closed if the child hears his mother talking in the adjoining room, but if he senses a long ominous silence he may rush to the door in mild panic which is speedily tranquilized by a reassuring sight of her when the door is opened.

The description of these various difficulties should not be allowed to build up in the reader's mind a false impression. The difficulties are by no means insuperable. They simply call for sympathetic, practical, common-sense adjustment and they do not by any means destroy the feasibility of developmental examination. They make the examination more interesting and challenging.

We ought not to strive to isolate the child simply on theoretical grounds. The mother is, after all, a rather prominent and normal factor of a pre-school child's environment, and our clinical procedures should exploit and not ignore this fact. The intimate relation between developmental diagnosis and parental guidance is another reason for constructively approaching the mother-child relation as part of the total clinical problem. It is not only our business to estimate the child as a detached individual but to estimate his behavior in terms of his natural dependence upon his mother.

CHAPTER 34

DIFFERENTIAL AND DESCRIPTIVE DIAGNOSIS

The system of developmental diagnosis based upon the fore-going schedules and norms frankly places a premium upon descriptive diagnosis. It is our desire to avoid the misuse of absolute psychometric determinations, and to utilize the advantages of a comparative technique. What our method may lack in apparent precision is offset by the clinical concreteness and the clarification which go with descriptive, comparative formulations. It is hoped that the necessity of making comparative estimates, rather than automatically deriving scores, will foster the exercise of interpretative, clinical judgment. The comparative approach will make it incumbent upon the examiner to bring his previous experience to bear upon the problem in hand; and it should also help to organize his experience as he accumulates it.

In previous chapters we have indicated the possibilities of the comparative method both in clinical and nonclinical situations. In the present chapter we attempt to specify how our norms and schedules may be used in the actual task of developmental diagnosis. The procedure will in one respect be the same for all types of cases, whether normal or subnormal or superior, young or old,—it will be comparative.

The normative summaries and developmental schedules as drawn up are designed to serve as instrumental aids in arriving at comparative judgments. These judgments may be of a broad and approximate character or they may be analytical and refined, depending upon the time which is expended in the examination and depending upon the experience of the examiner. The very simplest use which may be made of the normative summaries may be in-

408

dicated by the following illustration. A kindergarten child with a serious history of retardation is brought to a physician for examination and advice. We shall assume that the physician has had no psychological training and that he is not ready to undertake a thorough developmental examination. However, after a half hour's conversation with the mother and casual observation of the child, he arrives at some facts concerning the child's developmental status. On the basis of these facts he may risk the popular formula that the child is doing pretty well and (being so young) is likely to outgrow his backwardness. On the other hand if the physician will do no more than refer to the series of tabular normative summaries, he may in an approximate manner at least determine how seriously his little client is retarded. He may try on each successive normative pattern to note which appears to fit the child best. If the physician is not misled by some specious form of "brightness" (like repeating a poem), he is not likely to make any egregious mistake in using any of the simple normative summaries as standards of comparison.

The procedure outlined above is not, of course, recommended as ideal practice. It is simply suggested that even this use of normative data is far better than a complete lack of formulation and orientation.

The above illustration indicates the most rudimentary and crudest use which may be made of our normative data. The illustration also reveals the working principles of the comparative method. If we carry further a similar process of comparison, matching, rectifying, and checking, we can build up an interpretative judgment of the clinical case in hand. We wish to repeat that the normative items are not to be used in a mechanical or purely psychometric manner. We must not simply measure the child; we should try to apperceive him in an interpretative manner and the items on the developmental schedules should be considered as so many tools for sharpening perception. Critical examination of the action photographs may also help toward a classification of the case under consideration.

We now describe the manner in which the developmental schedules should be used in actual clinical practice. Our description of procedure will be based upon our own experience with the methods as applied to both normal and problem children. If the child is presumably normal, the schedule which is appropriate to his chronological age should be tried out first. It is desirable that such child should be presented for examination at an age which closely corresponds to one of the age developmental levels. If his age falls between two levels, the level which is nearest to his age should first be used. If there is any marked discrepancy between his age and the level, this fact must be considered in weighing the final judgment. When work is done on the appointment basis there will not be much difficulty in arranging for an examination at a time which coincides with one of the developmental intervals. Indeed the periodic or birth day placement of the examination increases the interest and coöperation of the parent.

Record of the child's responses is made during the course of the examination and descriptive jottings relating to the character of his responses should be entered in the space set aside for this purpose on the developmental form. Each schedule is sufficiently rich in items and sufficiently extensive to permit a wide range of examination. The final estimate of the child's developmental status is determined by a judicious consideration of the number and character of his successes and failures. The estimate should not be built up in any mechanical manner by simply adding and classifying the letter ratings, but by a process of inspection and evaluation in terms of the total behavior picture and the examiner's own normative standard of the given developmental level.

The basis of the final clinical estimate must, of course, be objective; but we shall never be able to get away from subjective impressions in clinical work. Our task, then, is not to suppress them altogether, but to regulate them strictly in terms of objective evidence. The impressions will then tend to become valid judgments. The process of developmental diagnosis, therefore, becomes a combination of objective observations and controlled, comparative evaluation. If the clinical judgment is not kept under objective control the subjective element in the judgment becomes a source of error. If on the other hand it is kept under control it becomes a source of correction.

In order that the clinical conclusions may not be made too sweeping and generalized in character, our record forms provide for separate developmental judgments in the four major fields of behavior, namely, the motor, language, adaptive behavior, and personal-social behavior fields. For each of these subdivisions the examiner finally determines whether the child is at a given level, below the level, or above the level. His deviation whether upward or downward may be indicated by a single plus or a single minus or a double plus or a double minus. Sub nine months and advanced nine months are sufficiently descriptive terms in many instances.

When the child referred for developmental diagnosis is obviously not normal, a modified procedure must be followed in the application of the developmental schedule. We have seen this very morning a seven-and-one-half-year-old boy who was referred for diagnosis. Physical examination showed definitely that he presented a case of mildly defined mongolianism. His deportment on entering the clinic definitely presented a subnormal behavior picture. The question then arose, "On what developmental schedule shall he be examined?" We took him to the blackboard, in which he was interested, and he drew a rough rectangular figure for a man. He copied with fair facility a right-angle cross. He copied also a circle but he was unable to copy imitatively an oblique cross. We gave him the pile of red blocks and he built a bridge from a model. He was unable to build a gate from a model. On the basis of this preliminary evidence we decided that the three-year-old schedule was appropriate to him. Actual examination showed that this was the proper schedule for recording his present developmental status.

Further diagnostic questions concerned the quality of his performance on this three-year-old schedule.

Every item on the schedule was applied. We find that there are
failures on A 27 (second part), on A 61, on A 62, on A 34, on L 32, on
P 53, on P 44, on P 17, and on P 26. It is apparent from the record
that a two-year-old schedule would have been much too easy and
that the four-year-old schedule would have been too hard. He
makes a moderately good showing on the basis of objective scoring
on the three-year-old schedule. The quality of his responses, his
general demeanor, his use of sentences and pronunciation, his emotional development, the type of dependence displayed toward his
mother and father who accompanied him, the liveliness of his emotional responses, etc., are highly consistent with the three-year
developmental status. His pronunciation is more infantile than we
ordinarily find at three years, but we should rate him in all the four
rubrics of behavior (motor, language, adaptive, and personal behavior) as being at the three-year level.

The developmental prognosis in this case can be formulated
with safety and in some detail. This child will never get much
beyond the upper pre-school level of development. In personality
traits he is favorably constituted. He will not become a social
problem. He is affectionate and amenable and has responded very
satisfactorily to domestic training. The normal average three-year-
old child can be trusted with breakables for short periods in the
house. This boy has learned to wash the dishes and to dry them.
This practical achievement is an earnest of future attainments but
does not by any means promise that he can ever maintain existence
independently of external support. Comparison with normative
three-year-old characteristics might be carried out into considerable
detail, but it is unnecessary in this instance. The developmental
diagnosis is definitely established and the general limits of development are clearly forecast by the present ratio of three years: seven
and one-half years.

To further illustrate the application of the schedules let us assume a more difficult case for diagnosis, a so-called border-line case. Our general approach to the problem of differential diagnosis would be the same. We should get our first broad orientation with reference to the case by means of the tabular normative summaries. Our next step of orientation would be a tentative application of one or two of the first diagnostic items in the developmental schedule selected. We might have to shift from one schedule to another, but we should not consider this a waste of time nor a fault in the technique because this very process of selecting the proper schedule is a process of conscious matching and identification which should intelligently direct and define the final clinical judgment. Even after the selected schedule has been applied in its entirety in a given case it is sometimes desirable to bring out the adjacent lower schedule or the adjacent upper schedule or both of them and to use them as touchstones to determine whether we have indeed made a proper selection in choosing the intermediate schedule. This tentative reconsideration of the schedules will either correct or fortify our judgment. In the conduct of our own clinical work we try to make it a rule to do as much comparative thinking as the place and time permit and not to make a decision until the evidence and conclusions of this comparative evaluation are in.

We must further assume a small group of cases in which even then we are unwilling to come to a decision but are ready only to formulate a descriptive and provisional diagnosis. In these instances the child must be put on the books for a follow-up reëxamination. An interval of time is allowed to elapse, supplemented perhaps by some directed observation, in order that we may increase the range of our diagnosis and bring the child into comparison, not only with an immediate normative pattern, but into comparison with his former status as summarized in the previous descriptive diagnosis. We thus introduce an additional comparative aid and safeguard into our diagnostic procedure and may then be in a position to make a definite diagnosis. In some instances there should be several such follow-up examinations before a final opinion is reached. Pre-school developmental diagnosis may have many difficulties, but it has one fundamental advantage; follow-up examinations accrue at a rapid rate and it takes only a few months or at most a year to place important additional developmental evidence at our disposal.

In all this comparative evaluation we constantly bring various aspects or items of behavior into juxtaposition. In this way we are able to build up an analytical estimate. Most problems require differential diagnosis. However, we are obliged finally to arrive at a kind of composite evaluation and to determine whether the maturity of the personality and the "general quality of attention" (which also is chiefly conditioned by maturity) conform with the general personality demeanor and attention mode of a normative developmental level. To arrive at this summary conclusion it is always necessary to refer to the normative portrait which we have acquired as a result of previous experience with normal children.

Occasionally it is helpful and desirable to bring a subnormal case into interpretative comparison with a clearly defined clinical record of another comparable subnormal case. In these instances we reinforce our clinical decision, not only by comparison with a normal standard, but with a subnormal standard. The application of the subnormal standard, however, is purely accessory and the chief reliance must always be placed upon the regular normative summaries.

If the reader has unassailable convictions with respect to the necessity of uniform, invariable, psychometric determinations, he may look askance at the suggestions which we have made which apparently endorse subjective impressions. There is, of course, a factor of danger in this direction, but we are assuming an intelligent and responsible diagnostic attitude and we would emphasize the fact that the comparative method as outlined above is in considerable measure self-corrective if the standards of comparison are used with scruple.

The character of the diagnostic problems which arise in the pre-school age is such that we need a flexible instrument for observation, testing, and descriptive record. It is hoped that our schedules will prove, in this sense, to be serviceable.

RECAPITULATION

1. Developmental diagnosis ought not to consist solely in the determination of a series of items by test and measurement. It is not purely a process of induction by enumeration.

2. Developmental diagnosis as outlined in this chapter becomes a form of comparative appraisal, using objective norms as points of departure and of orientation. It is synthetic as well as analytic.

3. This system of developmental diagnosis is sufficiently flexible to permit varying degrees of refinement in its application:

(a) The bare normative summaries aided by the photographs may be used as patterns for rough classification.

(b) A complete schedule furnishes items for the formation of separate estimates with regard to motor development and to language, adaptive, and personal-social behavior.

(c) These separate estimates may be shaded with plus signs and minus signs, determined by the examiner's familiarity with the characteristics of normal and subnormal children at the various levels.

(d) The estimates may be readjusted or confirmed by partial tryouts on adjacent developmental schedules.

(e) The estimates may be synthesized in one single estimate of general developmental status shaded with plus and minus signs and qualified with descriptive comment to indicate how completely or incompletely the child's status approximates that of the given level.

(f) Provisional estimates, both specific and general, are recommended in all instances where the examiner's judgment is not assured.

(g) The tentativeness and doubt in these instances should be removed by one or more reëxaminations after an appropriate interval. The original and the follow-up examinations should be plotted with interpretative comment so that their comparative significance can be studied.

4. The developmental schedules are so ordered that each level makes with the succeeding level a developmental ratio of two-thirds or three-fourths (and in one instance four-fifths). If any child, on two or more periodic examinations, approximates consistently the developmental level which is one full interval below his normal level, there is a presumption that he is retarded, subnormal, or deficient. Contrariwise he may be advanced if the reverse relation should be approximated, or if he makes a consistently and repeatedly high score on his proper schedule.

5. The terms retarded, low average, average, high average, and advanced should be used unless contributing clinical evidence warrants a more definite judgment.

The problems of pre-school development are still so undefined and so complicated with possible medical factors that considerable clinical caution must be used in applying norms and standards.

6. Caution becomes constructive when it expresses itself in significant descriptive comment and in comparative formulations.

7. Items, tests, and measures furnish the objective basis for comparative appraisal. The developmental schedules will furnish a developmental rating; but a diagnosis in the true sense of the term must rest upon a critical and responsible interpretation of evidence from various sources.

CHAPTER 35

PERSONALITY RECORD AND THE PARENTAL INTERVIEW

Developmental diagnosis is interested in all manifestations and evidences of maturity. It is not, of course, limited to a measurement of intelligence. It is concerned with all symptoms which relate to the attained status of the nervous system, as expressed in motor coördination, language achievement, adaptive performance, or personal and social behavior. Behavior symptoms of maturity in all these fields can be observed and recorded.

The synthetic, dynamic aspect of the behaving individual which we call personality also comes within the scope of observation. We cannot, however, measure personality traits with precision. We can scarcely define what we mean by personality, but from the point of view of developmental diagnosis we are obliged to reckon with the make-up and the maturity of personality.

In certain clinical cases involving imbalanced precocity or behavior disorder the distinction between maturity of general intellectual behavior as compared with maturity of personality may be a crucial consideration. In school administration and educational classification intelligence is taken as the factor of primary importance. In the field of mental hygiene, however, personality becomes the factor of central significance.

As part of the developmental examination, therefore, a deliberate effort should be made to record all personality reactions which are observable in connection with various test situations. These personality reactions include attitude, attack, and attention.

Personality and behavior are, of course, inseparable. The behavior episode expresses the momentary sum of the emotive elements and drives of the personality. These elements and drives are

417

part of the equation but we arrive at them by the route of inference. There are many pitfalls along this route. Our only secure footing is in the domain of the overt behavior. Our primary task, therefore, is to detect and to characterize the behavior itself. Granting all this we are nevertheless interested in personality traits and think it worth while to attempt to describe the personality factors and symptoms correlated with the maturity of personality in common-sense terms of expression when technical terms are not available.

On each developmental schedule record form we have, therefore, left a broad column for entering a record of personality reactions relating to attitude, attack, and attention as evidenced during the course of examination. To facilitate a record of these reactions we suggest a brief code made up of the following abbreviations:

*Al Al*ert—attends immediate attack. *Resp s Resp*onsive smiles. *Spon Spon*taneous. *Spon*taneous smiles *l*aughs. *C*onversation, comments, expressions of pleasure. *Ps.* Passive—grave or serious, unresponsive to examiner and material, indifferent to success or failure. *T.* Timidity; inhibited behavior; reluctant to enter room; over-anxious about total situation. *Inh.* Inhibited by consciousness. *Ann.* Annoyed at removal of material. *Imp.* Impatient with lack of success. *Dep.* Depressed by failure. *Asst.* Wants much assistance. (Looking or asking for help—not self-reliant.) *Dis.* Distractible; attention easily diverted. *R.* Restless; moves about room or handles material. *Agg.* Aggressive; demands material. *F.* Fatigued. Direct, *pf. p*urposeful, or *c*ritical, *d*eliberate (painstaking). *Hes,* hesitating (timidity). *sl* slow, *cl* careless or superficial. *Ply. p*layful. *Ps* persistent, *vps* very persistent.

The above list of personality items is offered chiefly for its suggestiveness. It is not good practice to use these descriptive designations too freely or in a manner which implies that the qualities indicated have a self-subsisting reality. To counteract this tendency it is well for the examiner to get into the habit of describing the total personality response so far as possible in terms of the specific behavior. He then has an objective record of actual occurrences which convey a definite impression of personality traits without ascribing to these traits undue psychological independence.

In the present stage of psycho-technology we have scarcely any means of objectively measuring personality traits. We have not even worked out a satisfactory descriptive technique. Different writers mean different things by such an apparently definite term as aggressiveness. The problem is indeed a most complicated one. From a small pocket dictionary containing 23,000 words I was able to compile a list of single adjectives, describing personality traits or symptoms, so lengthy that it covered four closely written pages. When classified the adjectives fell into relatively even-sized groups under the headings suggested by Hoch, namely, (1) traits indicating intellectual characteristics; (2) traits indicating amount of energy; (3) traits indicating reactions as a member of a social group; (4) traits indicating degree of independence and responsibility; (5) traits indicating prevailing mood and emotional control; (6) traits indicating development of moral sense. Even with all these headings at our disposal there was a small group of adjectives which could not be classified. To simplify this complicated field of personality, psychology presents an extremely difficult task.

It is possible that the normative approach may be of some value even in this field. Until we acquire some basic psycho-technical method we shall be compelled to use the empiricism of common sense. After all it is the task of clinical psychology to systematize and refine common sense. It is possible, therefore, that by means of descriptive and comparative procedures psychologists may be able to build up verbal working sketches which will delineate characteristic personality reactions and will enable us to estimate more precisely the maturity of a child in terms of personality adequacy and of character formation. However sublime the fatuity of such an undertaking may seem to the pure psychologist, it represents a basic clinical task in the mental diagnosis of young children. Meanwhile it may be profitable to continue the formulation of representative items in the field of personal-social behavior because many forms of behavior in this field have a high correlation with the maturity of personality. Supplementing the developmental schedule we have one other promising field of inquiry for the discovery and estimation of personality traits. We have the mother, and sometimes an observant father, brother, or sister can contribute. We ought to assume that even the mother of moderate intelligence has some significant knowledge in regard to her child. She has had unusual opportunities to observe him and can furnish not only interesting sidelights but substantial behavior items relating to the child's character and social capacity.

If the child is in any way subnormal or above normal it becomes important to learn all we can about his previous development both from the standpoint of his medical and his behavior history. The trustworthiness of the detailed testimony furnished must, of course, vary with the mother's intelligence or temperament and will always be subject to the examiner's discount. Nevertheless the analytic parental interview has many possibilities as a source of information of clinical value. In connection with our research work on the developmental norms we used the analytic interview as a method for securing a behavior register of the child at various levels; and although we were fully aware of the limitation of this method we were also convinced that when the interview is conducted with discrimination and in relation to a carefully conceived plan it can be made to yield valuable results.

The parental interview schedule which is appended to this chapter is an adaptation of this same behavior register to meet the needs of ordinary developmental examination. This form permits a compact record of significant personality traits and mental health items. Information on these items must be secured by means of the analytic interview. No effort is made to formulate the items into uniform questions, because the questions must of necessity be varied to suit different ages and must be adapted to the intelligence of the informant. The questions should not, of course, be too suggestive. In the case of problem children certain items must be followed up with considerable detail. For example, the item relating to the child's habits of eating and sleeping may be extremely significant. The genesis of these habits should then be sought out so far as possible, not only in the child, but in the parent. The analytic interview is then used not only as a means of interpreting the personality make-up of the child but also that of the parent in relation to the child.

Even in its present sketchy state it is apparent that the parental interview device may be systematically exploited as a form of mental-hygiene supervision. By means of such an analytic interview in the hands of either a physician or a trained examiner we may hope to secure data significant in the understanding and control of behavior in young children. The interview may then not only be used for immediate diagnostic purposes but associated with the developmental examination as a kind of mental-health inventory which will serve to disclose special achievements, excellencies, and peculiarities and also the habits or weaknesses that need guidance or correction. If the usefulness of this type of inquiry can be established and if a workable technique can be perfected, the parental interview may be used to effect a policy of developmental supervision and parental guidance. The possibilities of such a policy are discussed in one of the succeeding chapters.

The condensed parental interview blank is reproduced on the following page. Figure 228 is a reproduction of a specimen record form with the entries made in a developmental examination of a (normal) eighteen-months child.

PARENTAL INTERVIEW

Interview with............by..........Date........Case No. ....
Child's name. ....Sex.........Born........Where......Race....
Father's name.......... Address............Occupation ....
Brothers (note ages and normality) . ...
Sisters.... ....Elders at home . ...
Exceptional home conditions.. ....

A *Development*. 1 Birth? 2 Nutrition? 3 First teeth? 4 Sat up? 5 Rattle?
6 Walked? 7 Said *mama* or *dada?* 8 Other words? 9 Use spoon? 10 Keep
dry? 11 Keep clean? (bowels). 12 Entered kindergarten? 13 Serious
diseases, accidents, convulsions?

B *Personal Habits*. 14 Eating? (control, fastidiousness). 15 Dressing?
(fussy, neat). 16 Cleanliness? (washing, handkerchief, things out of mouth).
17 Sleep (quickly, soundly, dreams). 18 Toilet? (regularity, soil or wet
bed). 19 Sex behavior? 20 Speech? (articulation, stuttering).

C *Social Behavior*. 21 Like to play? (hard, alone, with others, age). 22 Like
pets? 23 Favorite pastime? 24 Sociable with other children? 25 Get
along? (quarrelsome). 26 Affectionate and sociable with parents? 27
Sociable with strangers? 28 Adjusts well outside of home (party, picnic,
doctors, Sunday school, etc.). 29 Obedient? 30 Obstinate? 31 Deceptive?
32 Sensitive? 33 Jealous? 34 Need any special discipline? (what?). 35 Responds to discipline? 36 Is he sensible, reasonable about things? (sense of
value). 37 Sense of humor? 38 Cry easily? 39 Tantrums? 40 Moody?
41 Babyish? 42 Timidity or fears.

D *Independence and Self Reliance*. 43 Can he play contentedly by himself?
How long? 44 Does he lead other children? 45 Stand up for his rights?
For his possessions? 46 Can he take responsibilities at home? 47 Errands?
48 Money? 49 Very selfish or self-centered? 50 Lack self-confidence?
51 Suggestible? 52 Show initiative, originality, imagination, concentration?

E *Special Traits*. Note any special achievements, excellences, or distinctive
characteristics. Also any peculiarities, habits, or weaknesses that need
guidance or correction.

F *Hereditary Factors*.
(Carry extended entries with numerical designation to reverse side or
additional sheet.)

DEVELOPMENTAL SCHEDULE-YALE PSYCHO-CLINIC
EIGHTEEN MONTHS

Date _6/9/23_

Name _Gertrude R._ Age _18 mos. + 1 wk._ Born _12/15/21_

ATTITUDE: Poised+ unstable   initial timidy   recurring timidity   sociable +
co-operative+ indifferent   painstaking   goodnatured   grave+ negative
inhibited   EXPRESSION: Face mobile   fixed   ordinary   CONVERSATION: Spontaneous   restrained   meager   inflected   ATTACK AND ATTENTION: Alert+ dull
persistent + labile   aggressive   self-reliant   wants help or approval
purposeful ✓ mature   superior   immature   defective   ordinary ✓
Physical defects or deviations _right internal strabismus_
Height _32¼_ Weight _23½_ Teeth _16_ Nutrition _3_ Measures A B C D✓ E

DEVELOPMENTAL ITEMS	SCORE	RESPONSES AND PERSONALITY REACTION
M26 Walks alone C	C	'Very fond of it'
M20 Climbs stairs C	C	
P34 Climbs for objects A	A	
*L11 Says five or more words B	B	Vocabulary, 20 (see mother's list)
P31 Asks for things at table C	C	
by words A	(A)	
L14 Two or more words together A+	(A+)	"all gone" "all done"
P41 Plays with cup and cubes B	B	sp. has blocks at home
*A23 Blocks: Tower of 3 C 4 A	A	
A24 From model B builds bridge A+	(A+)	
M25 Accepts fourth cube B	B	puts 2 in each hand
A41 Places cube in cup, plate B+ box A	A	good adaptation
*A52 Form-board: Circle B+ Shown B	B	
triangle A+ shown A	A	
Adapts circle A	(A)	persists in trying O in □
A27 Folds paper once A+	A+	definite effort but very crude sp.
*M40 Scribble spontaneous B imitatively B	B	
M41 imitates stroke B differentiates A	(B)	
M42 imitates vertical line A horizontal A+	(A)	Says "all done"
A32 Unwraps cube C	C	
A50 Performance box square A	(A)	p++
A22 Hits doll imitatively B	B	
M36 Throws ball in box B	B	
L21 Pictures: points to 1 or 2 A more A+	A+	"bow wow"- sp.
L12 Names one A two A+	A (A)	
L30 Picture II, names one object A+	(A+)	
A60 Names watch 4th view A+	(A+)	
*P51 Points to one part of body B	B	responds by facial movements eyes & mouth
Two or more A	A	
**********		
L40 Repeats things said A	A	but only single words
P14 Says hello thank-you B	B	TaTa for thankyou
*P16 Habitually inhibits certain acts B	B+	
P49 Looks at pictures B+	A	
P44 Listens to stories with pictures A	(A+)	Beginning to like mother Goose
P52 Counts to two or three A+	(A+)	
part of alphabet A+		
P22 Bowel control B	B	regular - has regular att.
P23 Bladder control A	A	
P35 Asks for toilet A	(A)	
P20 Puts on shoes A+	A+	++ interested
P21 Uses spoon well B	B	very nicely (mother)

FIGURE 228. DEVELOPMENTAL RECORD FORM WITH ENTRIES
The subject was a normal child of eighteen months. (The circles indicate failures.)

CHAPTER 36

CLINICAL PHASES OF CHILD ADOPTION

Adoption at its best represents one of the finest human adventures in altruism. Adoption is called a legal function, but it is a social reality which goes back to remote antiquity. In a partial sense it is scarcely less significant than marriage. Indeed the probate law provides that the child in adoption shall be "as though born in wedlock." And, like the rite of marriage, adoption is something which should not be lightly entered upon.

Instinct enters profoundly in adoption as it does in marriage. Adoption, however, usually has a psychological setting which permits foresight and rationalism to come into freer play. It makes men and women look searchingly into the future as well as the present and this consideration for the future is so wholesome that purely impulsive adoption should be systematically discouraged. The best practice and the best legislation require a probationary period of at least one full year.

There are few situations which place upon us more exacting demands for prediction. The difficulties of prediction become greater the younger the child and the more definite the specifications of the adoptive parents. These difficulties cannot well be evaded nor should we seek to evade them. The impulse to adoption comes to its most vigorous and characteristic expression with reference to infants. It may be the very childlessness of the parents which makes them fasten their desire upon a small baby. This is an instinctive, racially engendered, preferential regard for infancy and, other things equal, the adoption of young children should be preferred to the adoption of adolescents. At least a certain social premium should be placed upon the adoption of very young children if we can adequately protect both child and foster parent.

424

The intelligent foster parent is entitled to at least reasonable assurance as to the health and developmental potentialities of the infant. Can we supply this assurance? We can at least reduce the risk. An exhaustive medical examination, including a thorough developmental diagnosis, can be made in all cases of prospective adoption. This initial thorough examination can be further safeguarded by successive follow-up examinations. If necessary the probationary period should be prolonged for this purpose. The difficulty of making precise predictions in early infancy is fortunately somewhat reduced by the rapidity of growth at this time and a probationary period of one or two years should make possible a reasonably definite prognosis in ordinary cases.

Clinical regulation of adoption procedures will prevent hasty and ill-advised legal action. Tactful but complete frankness with regard to the educational and developmental outlook of the child can do no harm during the probationary period preceding adoption. The prolongation of the probationary period also is usually beneficial. There are instances, however, in which it is unwise to attempt to dissuade parents from adopting a child who has been diagnosed as being mentally defective or hereditarily handicapped.

Because of its clinical interest, it should be said that some of the best laws on adoption contain a provision concerning annulment. The Minnesota statute, for example, provides:

> If within five years after his adoption a child develops feeble-mindedness, epilepsy, insanity, or venereal infection as a result of the conditions existing prior to the adoption and of which the adopting parents had no knowledge or notice, a petition setting forth such facts shall be filed in court which entered the decree of adoption, and if such facts are proved, the court may annul the adoption and commit the child to the guardianship of the state board of control. In every such proceeding it shall be the duty of the county attorney to represent the interests of the child.

The necessity and even the desirability of such an annulment provision may be questioned in many cases. Surely this provision

ought not to be invoked except in very exceptional instances and
annulment of adoption ought to be at least as difficult as proceed-
ings for marital divorce. The possibility of such annulment is no
sound reason for neglecting adequate clinical control of child
adoption. A brief reference to a few of the child placement and
adoptive cases which have been referred to our clinic may serve to
illustrate some of the problems involved.

One foster parent, having made preliminary inquiries in regard
to the importance of inheritance and the possibility of bringing up a
child so that he would not be parasitic after the age of twenty-one,
indicated the following specifications: He wished to adopt a boy,
say six months of age, because the adoptive mother definitely
preferred a young baby and this boy must be such that he might
be put through college! Here we have a case which required a
considerable degree of prediction. Put in diagnostic terms the
problem is to ascertain college educability in a six-months old-baby
who is not yet ready to sit up without support. It would be pre-
sumptuous to suggest that such a selection could be made with
absolute certainty in this early period of infancy. However, even
college educability is governed by lawful factors and wherever there
is law there is at least the theoretical possibility of prediction. All
diagnosis deals with probabilities. In simplified instances the probabilities are 100 per cent and we have complete certitude. There is
a diminishing series of gradations below this 100 per cent grade of
certitude and it is far from impossible that diagnostic procedures,
aided by observational opportunities, will some day be able to meet
with a high percentage of certitude the exacting problem of prognosis
embodied in the above adoption specifications.

The improving standards of child placement work throughout
the country are placing more and more demands upon psychological
and developmental predictions. For example, the report on the
mental examination of the child required by the Bureau of Child
Welfare in Connecticut demands, in addition to ordinary data, a

definite answer to the following questions involving not only immediate diagnosis but also prognosis.

What is the child's intelligence? Superior? Normal? Dull normal? Inferior? Feeble-minded? (High grade? Middle grade? Low grade?) Imbecile? Idiot?

Educational outlook: Could child probably complete grammar school? High school? College? Or should he have special class work? Vocational training?

There is of course danger that the demand for prediction may be pushed too far by child-placing agencies. It is also true that certain foster parents are unreasonably specific and exacting with respect to the special qualities and the outlook of the adoptive child. The probationary period, however, is an excellent safeguard which solves many difficulties of adjustment between child and foster parents. We do not wish to suggest, in urging clinical safeguards, that child adoption should be made absolutely scientific and should lose altogether its fine elements of faith and adventure and sacrifice.

It is possible in certain instances that adoption of a mentally deficient child may be consented to. I quote from a memorandum made in connection with the case of a girl who was examined at the age of twelve years. She was very attractive in appearance and made an impression of normality but proved to have a mental age of eight years and a school ability of less than third grade level. We were obliged to classify her as being a high-grade mental defective. The social agency in charge of this case asked us whether or not this girl is sufficiently promising to justify consent to adoption under all the circumstances. Our reply to the question was as follows:

Our impression after a long conversation with the mother is that adoption may be quite legitimate in as much as your agency has urged and accomplished considerable delay in approving such adoption and is in position to place all the hazards of such a step before the prospective parents. You have rendered a service in bringing about the delay and it may even be possible to prolong this delay until . . . is eighteen years of age. However, we can see no ground on which an issue can be made under all the circumstances. Mrs. . . . is apparently ready to take all the risks that would go with the step. Any other type of solution would not satisfy either Mr. or Mrs. . . . If their impulse for adoption is as sincere as it seems to be, and if they will consent to do all in their power to prevent marriage, the wise course may be to allow adoption. You are justified, however, in view of our reply, in making it clear that we have very grave and well founded doubts whether . . . can ever assume and meet the complex responsibility of making a home of her own.

A less clearly defined case presented itself at the age of two years and two months. The prospective foster mother who had boarded this child for some time brought her, not without pride, to the clinic for examination (and perhaps also for admiration). We were pleasantly impressed with the child. She was attractive in appearance, smiling, reactive, and responsive in her ways. She waved *bye-bye* and toddled trustfully into your out-spread arms and played eagerly with a ball. She was just the kind of child that would smite the heart of prospective adoptive parents, who on first sight even, might resolve to take her into the home, give her an education, and bring her up as a charming refined daughter. These parents would not be grievously disappointed, because the child is not definitely mentally deficient; but the whole evidence of the developmental examination showed that she consistently approximated the eighteen months level of development and we are very doubtful whether she will ever be able to complete a high school education. She may have some difficulty in completing the elementary grade schools. In ten fleeting years there may be pangs of disappointment when the limitations of this child are revealed.

Although it is a grave responsibility to prejudice in any way the opportunities of adoption, we ought within judicious limits to attempt to forestall all the pangs and aggravations which may come from ill-considered adoption. It is clear that probationary and clinical control of adoption must take into joint account the mutual interests of both child and parent.

Somewhat less exacting but no less important is the problem of child placement, whether the placement is administered by voluntary or public agencies. Child placement constitutes a permanent social problem of national significance. The magnitude of the problem is impressive. In 1917 it was estimated that there were over 200 organized child-placing agencies in this country annually finding homes for 50,000 children and that a nearly equal number of children were placed out by child-caring institutions. It is estimated that there are in this country 261,000 children deprived of parental care for reason of dependency, neglect, cruelty, or destitution. It takes very little imagination to sense the colossal size of the problem involved and also the importance of safeguarding the developmental rights of these children through clinical and supervisory procedures.

CHAPTER 37

DEVELOPMENTAL SUPERVISION

Carried to its logical limit developmental diagnosis leads to developmental supervision. If development were a self-limited predetermined process, this might not be true. But development is a continuous, dynamic, pliable series of phenomena, and we can only come to full terms with this series by pursuing it as it moves along. Even in frankly medical instances, where we deal with pathological deviations of development, it is advantageous to follow up the symptoms and to recur to them in successive "follow-up" examinations. Whether the child be normal or abnormal, the drama of development is never halted by a diagnosis; and we can comprehend the denouement only by keeping pace with the stages of unfoldment.

This is a truism; but it is one so fundamental that it justifies a discussion of the principles and the possibilities of Developmental Supervision, as distinct from Developmental Diagnosis in the restricted clinical sense of the latter term.

Developmental Supervision may be defined as a consecutive series of developmental diagnoses and inventories, in which a cumulative knowledge of the child is made the basis of safeguarding his development. Formulated in these terms, developmental supervision applies to normal as well as non-normal children and goes beyond the ordinary objectives of physical and medical examinations. Developmental supervision embraces the total physical and mental development of the child. It is concerned with more than the detection and removal of physical defect or disease. It finally involves constructive procedures for child guidance and parental guidance.

Developmental Supervision constitutes a logical step forward in the administration of consecutive medical and health service. Periodic medical examinations is a goal which is every year becoming more clearly defined and is, indeed, in a measure realized even now. An increasing number of dentists professionally engage in supervisory dental-hygiene work. By means of a calendar and an appointment clerk they keep a revolving succession of clients, children and adults, presenting themselves for dental inspection and prophylaxis,—a very simple but extremely significant arrangement. A few enterprising pediatrists are reaching their non-ill clients by a comparable, repeated birthday examination scheme. The National Health Council has launched the slogan (for those who can read or can hear the radio): "Get yourself examined on your birthday." Large industrial concerns and powerful insurance companies are undertaking far-reaching measures in the same direction. Meanwhile a large group of child welfare and child health organizations are educating the public to demand a consecutive type of medical service. The public hygiene movement is placing an increasing emphasis on personal, clinically-protected health.

The policy of systematic medical supervision has had its broadest and, in a sociological sense, its most significant application, in the field of public school hygiene and medical school inspection. In some communities this has meant an almost universal medical service for certain age groups of the population. In a few favored instances this service has been closely articulated with psychological, psychiatric, and educational procedures. Medical supervision of school children will always constitute an essential part of any health program; but its limitations are authoritatively pointed out in the following statement of Sir Arthur Newsholme, late principal medical officer in England: "The chief value of medical inspection of school children has been to demonstrate the extent to which children of school age are suffering from defects and disease which might have been prevented or minimized by attention to the pre-school period."

The more completely we commit ourselves to the policy of consecutive health oversight, the more certainly shall we concentrate
our emphasis on the pre-school period of development and on the
systematic supervision of that development. The ground work for
such supervision has been laid, and laid in a manner that will enable private practitioner, voluntary organizations, and public agencies alike to participate in the great task of making health protection
more nearly universal.

As recently as 1892 Dr. Budin established, in Paris, the first
Infant-Welfare Center. It was a simple but practical conception—
a consultation center for the examination of babies and the instruction of mothers in child care. Infant-welfare centers have since
spread the world over. They have multiplied at a phenomenal rate
during the last few years in England and America. Ambassador
Jusserand, speaking in 1910 at the first annual meeting of the
American Association for the Study and Prevention of Infant
Mortality, said: "When its far-reaching results shall have been
gauged, France will be as proud of Dr. Budin for his good work as
she is even of the discovery of the most startling inventions made
by any of her sons in the realm of science or industry."

The ambassador spoke with characteristic French insight; for
the child-consultation center, simple as it is, represents a social
device with unlimited possibilities of growth and elaboration.

In some respects this social device is of more significance even
than the public school. Why? Because it copes directly with the
most fundamental of all problems: the rearing of children. It makes
health its undivided concern. It reaches the parent as well as the
child. And it reaches the child before he has attained that stage
of relative completion and superannuation—the school age!

It may be that the consultation center in a new and enlarged
form will become as universal as elementary educational provisions.
This is an administrative problem which does not fall within the
scope of the present chapter. It is noteworthy, however, that the

Federal Conference on Minimum Standards as early as 1918 recommended a sufficient number of children's health centers to give health instruction under medical supervision for all infants and children not under the care of a private physician, and to give such instruction to mothers at least once a month throughout the first year of the child's life and at regular intervals throughout the pre-school age.

Our public school system penetrates the remotest rural corners and besets the crowded blocks of our cities; and this secures for all the children of the nation a fundamental equality of educational opportunity. To a similar degree the health and developmental opportunities of pre-school children must be equalized. It can only be equalized by a periodic type of health service which will be available to every new-born child and safeguard his general development through the whole pre-school period.

The further organization of such a developmental supervision cannot be forecast in any detail; it presents a permanent administrative problem which will depend upon experience and upon experimental demonstration for progressive solution. But even in the present formative state of pre-school hygiene this problem is sufficiently well defined to merit more systematic consideration. We suggest a few practical lines of approach. We shall formulate these suggestions in relation to infant-welfare and children's health-center work; but they will in principle apply to a similar supervision which might be instituted through private or group medical practice.

So far as possible health supervision should be personalized; it should be made cumulative and biographic. There should be a continuous record. Every examination should be brought into comparison with the previous one, and should be so recorded and graphed as to emphasize constantly the conception of growth. It is very easy, even when examinations are recurrent, to permit each examination to be a detached, independent event. Furthermore, when the child is examined topically by specialized clinics, one for nutrition, one for teeth, one for eyes, one for nose and throat, etc., the tendency toward depersonalization is increased. We can co-ordinate these diverse and multiple examinations only by the unifying conception of *development*, and the details of our approach to a contact with the parent should be designed to keep this very concept alive. It is in some ways a better concept than "Health"; it is less abstract; it definitely and organically ties the present with the past and the future.

Fortunately society and the medical profession do not have to create an interest in "Development." This interest is as ingrained, as naive, in the human race as is the interest in motion; indeed development is a form of motion. Only abnormal and impoverished minds are not sensitive to the phenomena of growth and change in living things. An interest in the oft-repeated miracle of development as displayed in early infancy is surely one of the things which the back tides of modernity have not eroded. This interest is part of the parental impulse. It is indestructible because it is necessary for the protection of the infant; it is most intense in the first year of infancy because it is then reinforced by a tenderness awakened by the help-lessness of the child; it is also reinforced by the dramatic speed with which the developmental scroll unrolls. In a sense the keen interest and even the keen perception for development diminish somewhat as the child grows older. Perhaps it is unnecessary to perpetuate the same high pitch of parental desire and expectancy which belongs to infancy. The child does and should become more independent as he matures; but the interest in his development ought not to decline.

It does decline; and a well-conceived, humanistic approach to the parent at each succeeding developmental examination will serve to project that interest and educate it in a manner which will yield rich results for our child-health programs. In last analysis the success of the pre-school phase of these programs will depend upon the sincerity with which parents coöperate. For this reason, the instinctively motivated interest in development is the most vital of all the assets with which health education has to deal. This asset cannot be capitalized unless we reckon with its profound psychology, and make *development* the central concern in the organization of health supervision.

When development is made the key of child-health supervision, our approach will be normative and regulative, just as it is in infant feeding, but on a wider scale which will include the mental as well as physical aspects of growth. Nutrition, physical defects, and disease will always be major considerations as they are now, but they will be constructively related to development and take into account wherever possible the welfare of the child's personality. Only in this way can mental health be brought within the scope of medical oversight. And there is a growing demand that mental hygiene be definitely incorporated into child-health procedures.

Can this be done with any success or is mental hygiene too nebulous and fugitive to be made an objective? In last analysis, mental health even in young children proves to be a reflex or a compound of everyday habits of living. It is bound up primarily with wholesome habits of eating, sleeping, resting, elimination, exercise, and play. These habits are definitely within the province of medical control and advice. They are powerfully influenced by the family morale and by the attitudes of parents and brothers and sisters. But even these domestic factors can be reached by methods of parental guidance.

When periodic health examinations broaden into developmental examinations, they will include a psychological inquiry into the health habits, the dispositions, capacities, and personality traits of the child, so that errors of development may be detected early and so that the parents may from the beginning assist the child to achieve mental as well as physical health.

A workable technique for administering this type of mental-hygiene service can undoubtedly be evolved. It is by no means certain that this service should be rendered by a specialized clinic even in large cities, except in the most complicated and abnormal cases. Much of the service can be rendered through the individual and group health instruction which is now becoming part of health center administration. Much of it may also be rendered through the home visitor, the public health nurses, and even the private duty nurse. Specially trained nurses and social workers, could also assist in making preliminary inventories of the child's habits and capacities, in connection with developmental examinations and home visitations. What we need is such a concrete formulation of normative and minimum standards of mental development that they can be effectively brought into play at periodic intervals. The physician himself needs a command of these standards in connection with periodic supervisory examinations. The nurse needs them in modified form to orient her in her numerous contacts with children. And parents need them much as they need diet cards and model menus to guide them in the task of proper child feeding.

In the technique of the nutrition clinic and supervisory nutrition work we have in rough outline the problems and methods involved in attaining a more comprehensive developmental supervision. We also have an earnest that the task, in spite of its bewildering complexity, is one which can be constructively undertaken.

Even in very young children, health depends upon what may be called a personal form of hygiene. In last analysis, therefore, pre-school health supervision must reckon with those intimate aspects of healthful living which will yield only to educational control by the parent. The guidance of the parents (and no less the training of prospective parents) ought to be correlated with the developmental supervision of pre-school children. The problem of parental education ought not to be formulated administratively as an isolated, independent problem of adult education. Basically it is a child hygiene problem which comes within the scope of medical and public health organization, and can best be attacked in concrete relation to supervisory child-health measures.

There is a basic interrelation between Developmental Diagnosis, Developmental Supervision, and Parental Guidance.

If the practical implications of this vital interrelation are realized, the medical profession will resume some of its ancient role of teacher, and make a new contribution to "education" as well as to public welfare.

CHAPTER 38

DEVELOPMENTAL DIAGNOSIS AND MEDICINE

The term "Developmental Diagnosis" has been used in this volume with special reference to the psychological aspects of development. It is not implied, however, that the term should be confined to these psychological aspects. On the contrary, it is very desirable that the term should be made to comprehend all the phenomena of development which properly come within the scope of medical diagnosis.

Ideally, psychological diagnosis should never be carried on independently and without reference to supporting and supplementary data. Developmental diagnosis should be made to include all those methods and criteria which have a normative or clinical relation to the appraisal of developmental conditions. It is one of the advantages of the term "Developmental" that it compels us to make no sharp distinction between mind and body. From a medical point of view and from the standpoint of scientific theory it is undesirable to perpetuate in any artificial or arbitrary manner this ancient distinction. The modern and clinical point of view is well formulated by Jelliffe and White in the preface to their textbook on Neurology and Psychiatry:

> The authors have kept in mind the concept of an individual as a biological unit, tending by development and conduct toward certain broadly defined goals and have considered the nervous system as only a part of that larger whole . . . .
>
> Man is not only a metabolic apparatus, accurately adjusted to a marvelous efficiency through the intricacies of the vegetative neurological mechanisms, nor do his sensori-motor functions make him solely a feeling, moving animal, seeking pleasure and avoiding pain, conquering time and space by the enhancement of his sensory possi-

bilities and the magnification of his motor powers; nor yet is he exclusively a psychical machine, which by means of a' masterly, symbolic handling of the vast horde of realities about him has given him almost unlimited powers. He is all three, and a neurologist of to-day who fails to interpret nervous disturbances in terms of all three of these levels, takes too narrow a view of the functions of that master spirit in evolution, the nervous system.

The above formulation of the new standpoint of neuro-psychiatry is in essential accordance with the behaviorist's reformulation of the problems of psychology. Whatever the ultimate outcome of the current behaviorist movement in the field of psychology, it is already clear that this movement will take psychology farther away from its philosophical fixation and bring it into closer relations with physiology and biology. The newer genetic psychology likewise will establish closer bonds with the biological sciences.

The term "Development" makes no false distinctions between the vegetative, the sensori-motor, and the psychic aspects of development. Indeed it invites the scientific and practical coördination of all usable criteria of development. The psychoneural diagnosis may well be more conclusive and fundamental because it brings us into immediate communication with the maturity and characteristics of the nervous system itself. An ideally complete developmental diagnosis, however, would bring psychoneural findings into interpretative relation with all anatomical and physiological symptoms of development. The proper interpretation of certain abnormal clinical cases depends upon a recognition of data from these fields. The future development of anthropology and of physiology and of bio-chemistry will undoubtedly furnish us with fundamental normative data for deriving more searching estimates of developmental status. We are already in possession of rough indices of anatomical maturity as revealed in the ossification of the carpal bones and the expressions "anatomical age" and "physiological age" have found a footing in literature. It is not impossible that further discoveries in the field of endocrinology will supply the physician with delicate techniques which will reveal the bio-chemical status of a developing individual.

For all these reasons it would appear that the scientific foundations of developmental diagnosis will be medical as well as psychological in the restricted sense of the term. Indeed it is impossible to imagine a fundamental program in this complicated field without recognizing the partial dependence of developmental diagnosis upon medical science and medical training.

In as much as psychiatry is an accepted and fundamental subdivision of medicine, it is pertinent to ask at once whether psychiatry could not be expanded and formulated in such a manner as to incorporate the principles and practice of developmental diagnosis. The broadness of the present-day conception of neuropsychiatry has already been noted. Psychiatry is becoming increasingly concerned with the genetic aspects of psycho-pathology. Although the emphasis of neuropsychiatry is directed to the interpretation of mental abnormality and disease, this interpretation involves inevitably a better understanding of normal developmental psychology. On purely logical grounds, therefore, it is clear that the organization of instruction in neuropsychiatry could be made to include systematic work in the genetic and normative psychology of normal children.

There are many reasons, however, why the whole subject of Developmental Diagnosis should find a fundamental articulation with Pediatrics. There are not only logical but practical reasons for such an orientation. Pediatrics is the broadest of all medical specialties. It has a responsible interest in the developmental welfare of infancy and childhood.

The pediatrician holds a most strategic position both in the field of public health and of private practice. His position is strategic because he deals with the crucial problem of nutrition and because he deals with the first and, therefore, the most fundamental period of human existence. His relation to childhood is such that he cannot limit his concern to obvious diseases and glaring defects. It is for this reason that the late Dr. Emmet Holt said, "Nowhere in the whole realm of preventive medicine is there such a field of usefulness as that which is open to the pediatrician."

Historically, the major duties of the pediatrician have been to recognize and combat disease; but the whole tendency of current pediatrics places a coördinate emphasis upon prevention and supervision. The supervision of nutrition in infancy is in many respects the central problem of pediatrics. This problem is so fundamental that it includes not only definitely sick children but the near-sick and the normal. This problem also is so fundamental that by implication and often by actual exigencies it includes the psychological and functional aspects of development. The protection of the nutritional health of the child becomes the natural basis for a broader and equally continuous type of developmental supervision.

INDEX